Newton
Take 3

**Written & Illustrated
by B. K. Hixson**

Newton
Take 3

Copyright © 2003
First Printing • June 2003
B. K. Hixson

Published by Loose in the Lab, Inc.
9462 South 560 West
Sandy, Utah 84070

www.looseinthelab.com

Library of Congress Cataloging-in-Publication Data:

Hixson, B. K.
    Newton Take 3/B. K. Hixson
    p.   cm.-(Loose in the Lab Science Series)

    Includes index
    ISBN 0-9660965-3-3
  1. Physics experiments-juvenile literature. [1. Phys
ics experiments 2. Experiments] I. B. K. Hixson II. Loose
in the Lab III. Title IV. Series
QP441.D54   2003
152.14

Printed in the United States of America
Heads up!

Dedication

Lesley E. Hanson
(my little sis)

It is not lost on anyone that you and Wile E. Coyote share the same middle initial and exhibit the same penchant for constant motion and near disaster. Your life of daring began in your Wheaties roadster, pictured above, doing wheelies and cutting cookies on the living room carpet. From there, it quickly matriculated into the Stroller Derby down the big hill in front of our house, much to Mom's panic and our mutual delight, only to be followed up with numerous trips down the big hill in the toboggan, until we lost that argument with the giant aspen at the end of one of our runs.

Given your fondness for flying, both in commercial jets as well as along roller coaster tracks, your penchant for skiing with complete disregard for other human life in the same National Forest, and your numerous automotive "indiscretions," it is only fitting that a book on speed, force, motion, and momentum be dedicated to you.

Hugs & Kisses,

Bryce

Acknowledgments

Getting a book out for public consumption is far from a one-man job. There are lots of thank-yous to be doodled out and, at the risk of leaving someone out, we attempt to do that on this page. In terms of my physics education, at the top of the list is Dick Roeter, my freshman physics professor who had as much fun in the lab twice a week as we did. I must also give a nod of appreciation to my lab partner who also wound up being one of my best friends, Glenn Brown. It was through his eyes and contorted mathematics that I came to understand that we truly each see the world through our own set of goggles but despite these apparent differences we all wind up in the same place. I will always have time to pop a cold one and enjoy the conversation.

As for my educational outlook, the hands-on perspective, and the use of humor in the classroom, Dr. Fox, my senior professor at Oregon State University, gets the credit for shaping my educational philosophy while simultaneously recognizing that even at the collegiate level, we were on to something a little different. He did his very best to encourage, nurture, and support me while I was getting basketloads of opposition for being willing to swim upstream. There were also several colleagues who helped to channel my enthusiasm during those early, formative years of teaching: Dick Bishop, Dick Hinton, Dee Strange, Connie Ridgway, and Linda Zimmermann. Thanks for your patience, friendship, and support.

Next up are all the folks who get to do the dirty work that makes the final publication look so polished but very rarely get the credit they deserve. Our resident graphics guru, Kris Barton, gets a nod for scanning and cleaning the artwork you find on these pages, as well as putting together the graphics that make up the cover. A warm Yankee yahoo to Eve Laubner, our editor, who passes her comments on, so that Kathleen Hixson and Eve Laubner (once again) can take turns simultaneously proofreading the text while mocking my writing skills.

Once we have a finished product, it has to be printed so that the good folks at Delta Education—Gary Facente, Louisa Walker, Selina Gerow, and the whole gang—can market and ship the books, collect the money, and send us a couple of nickels. It's a short thank-you for some very important jobs.

Mom and Dad, as always, get the end credits. Thanks for the education, encouragement, and love. And for Kathy and the kids—Porter, Shelby, Courtney, and Aubrey—hugs and kisses.

Repro Rights

There is very little about this book that is truly formal, but at the insistence of our wise and esteemed counsel, let us declare: *No part of this book may be reproduced or utilized in any form or by any means, electronic or mechanical, including photocopying, recording, or by any information storage and retrieval system, without permission in writing from the publisher.* That would be us.

More Legal Stuff

Official disclaimer for you aspiring scientists and lab groupies. This is a hands-on science book. By the very intent of the design, you will be directed to use common, nontoxic, household items in a safe and responsible manner to avoid injury to yourself and others who are present while you are pursuing your quest for knowledge and enlightenment in the world of physics. Just make sure that you have a fire blanket handy and a wall-mounted video camera to corroborate your story.

If, for some reason, perhaps even beyond your own control, you have an affinity for disaster, we wish you well. *But we, in no way take any responsibility for any injury that is incurred to any person using the information provided in this book or for any damage to personal property or effects that are directly or indirectly a result of the suggested activities contained herein.* Translation: You're on your own. Watch your fingers when you are playing with Newton's cradle and don't stick the gyro in your shorts while it is spinning.

Less Formal Legal Stuff

If you happen to be a home schooler or very enthusiastic school teacher please feel free to make copies of this book for your classroom or personal family use—one copy per student, up to 35 students. If you would like to use an experiment from this book for a presentation to your faculty or school district, we would be happy to oblige. Just give us a whistle and we will send you a release for the particular lab activity you wish to use. Please contact us at the address below. Thanks.

Special Requests
Loose in the Lab, Inc.
9462 South 560 West
Sandy, Utah 84070

Table of Contents

The National Content Standards (Grades K-4)
• *An object's motion can be described by tracing and measuring its position over time.*

• *The position and motion of objects can be changed by pushing or pulling. The size of the change is related to the strength of the push or pull.*

The National Content Standards (Grades K-4)
• *The motion of an object can be described by its position, direction of motion, and speed. The motion can be measured and represented on a graph.*

• *An object that is not being subjected to a force will continue to move at a constant speed and in a straight line.*

• *If more than one force acts on an object along a straight line, then the forces will reinforce or cancel one another, depending on their direction and magnitude. Unbalanced forces will cause changes in the speed or dirction of an object's motion.*

The 11 Big Ideas About Physics & Corresponding Labs

1. Simple Machines—wheels and axles, pulleys, levers, inclined planes, wedges, and screws—are all inventions that make it easier for us to do work.

2. Speed (v) is defined as the measured distance (d) an object travels in a fixed amount of time (t). This is described by the formula, v = d / t. Along these lines, Newton observed that force equals mass times acceleration, which makes up his Second Law.

3. Friction is the amount of force preventing two surfaces from moving past each other.

4. Newton's First Law: An object at rest or moving at a constant velocity will continue to do so unless acted on by an extenal force. This is also known as the Law of Inertia.

Even More Contents

5. Newton's Second Law: For every action, there is an equal and opposite reaction.

6. The center of gravity is a point where the forces acting on an object are all equal. This point may not necessarily be found in or on the object.

7. A buoyant force is created when a liquid exerts an upward force on an object that is immersed in it. This is due, in part, to the density of the object, which can be calculated as mass divided by volume.

8. Potential energy is defined as energy that has been stored. Kinetic energy describes energy that is being used to produce motion.

9. Circular motion encompasses a whole pile of ideas, like centripetal and centrifugal force, angular momentum, and rotational inertia, for starters.

10. Torque is a twisting force that applies energy in either a clockwise or counterclockwise direction.

11. Resonance is a characteristic of an object to mimic or copy the vibrational frequency of another object.

Who Are You? And ...

First of all, we may have an emergency at hand and we'll both want to cut to the chase and get the patient into the cardiac unit if necessary. So, before we go too much further, **define yourself**. Please check one and only one choice listed below and then immediately follow the directions that follow *in italics*. Thank you in advance for your cooperation.

I am holding this book because. . .

___ **A. I am a responsible, but panicked, parent.** My son / daughter / triplets (circle one) just informed me that his / her / their science fair project is due tomorrow. This is the only therapy I could afford on such short notice, which means that if I was not holding this book, my hands would be encircling the soon-to-be-worm-bait's neck.

Directions: Can't say this is the first or the last time we heard that one. Hang in there, we can do this.

1. Quickly read the Table of Contents with the worm bait. The Big Ideas define what each section is about. Obviously, the kid is not passionate about science, or you would not be in this situation. See if you can find an idea that causes some portion of an eyelid or facial muscle to twitch.

If that does not work, we recommend narrowing the list to the following labs because they are fast, use materials that can be acquired with limited notice, and the intrinsic level of interest is generally quite high.

Lab #2 • Angle of Ascent • page 26
Lab #7 • Calculated Leverage • page 44
Lab #13 • Marble Races • page 62
Lab #33 • Buddha's Temple • page 124
Lab #34 • Clay Boats • page 128
Lab #39 • Carry Me Back • page 149
Lab #50 • Resonant Balls • page 183

How to Use This Book

2. Take the materials list from the lab write-up and from page 209 of the Science Fair Project section and go shopping.

3. Assemble the materials and perform the lab at least once. Gather as much data as you can.

4. Go to page 186 and read the material. Then start on Step 1 of Preparing Your Science Fair Project. With any luck, you can dodge an academic disaster.

___ **B. I am worm bait.** My science fair project is due tomorrow, and there is not anything moldy in the fridge. I need a big Band-Aid, in a hurry.

Directions: Same as Option A. You can decide if and when you want to clue your folks in on your current dilemma.

___ **C. I am the parent of a student who informed me that he/ she has been assigned a science fair project due in six to eight weeks.** My son/daughter has expressed an interest in science books with humorous illustrations that attempt to explain classical mechanics and associated phenomena.

Who Are You ? And ...

Directions: Well, you came to the right place. Give your kid these directions and stand back.

1. The first step is to read through the Table of Contents and see if anything grabs your interest. Read through several experiments, see if the science teacher has any of the more difficult-to-acquire materials, and ask if they can be borrowed. Play with the experiments and see which one really tickles your fancy.

2. After you have found and conducted an experiment that you like, take a peek at the Science Fair Ideas and see if you would like to investigate one of those or create an idea of your own. The guidelines for those are listed in the Science Fair section. You have plenty of time so you can fiddle and fool with the original experiment and its derivations several times. Work until you have an original question you want to answer and then start the process. You are well on your way to an excellent grade.

___ D. I am a responsible student and have been assigned a science fair project due in six to eight weeks. I am interested in chemistry, and despite demonstrating maturity and wisdom well beyond the scope of my peers, I too still have a sense of humor. Enlighten and entertain me.

Directions: Cool. Being teachers, we have heard reports of this kind of thing happening but usually in an obscure and hard-to-locate town several states removed. Nonetheless, congratulations.

Same as Option C. You have plenty of time and should be able to score very well. We'll keep our eyes peeled when the Nobel Prizes are announced in a couple of decades.

How to Use This Book

___ **E. I am a parent who home schools my child/children.** We are always on the lookout for quality curriculum materials that are not only educationally sound but also kid- and teacher-friendly. I am not particularly strong in science, but I realize it is a very important topic. How is this book going to help me out?

Directions: In a lot of ways, we created this book specifically for home schoolers.

1. We have taken the National Content Standards, the guidelines that are used by all public and private schools nationwide to establish their curriculum base, and listed them in the Table of Contents. You now know where you stand with respect to the national standards.

2. We then break these standards down and list the major ideas that you should want your kid to know. We call these the Big Ideas. Some people call them objectives, others call them curriculum standards, educational benchmarks, or assessment norms. Same apple, different name. The bottom line is that when your child is done studying this unit on physics, you want them not only to understand and explain each of the eleven Big Ideas listed in this book, but also, to be able to defend and argue their position based on experiential evidence that they have collected.

3. Building on the Big Ideas, we have collected and rewritten 50 hands-on science labs. Each one has been specifically selected so that it supports the Big Idea that it is correlated to. This is critical. As the kids do the science experiment, they see, smell, touch, and hear the experiment. They will store that information in several places in their brains. When it comes time to comprehend the Big Idea, the concrete hands-on experiences provide the foundation for building the Idea, which is quite often abstract. Kids who merely read about torque, angular momentum, and acceleration, or who see pictures of pulleys, levers, and inclined planes but have never pinched their fingers using one are trying to build abstract ideas on abstract ideas and quite often miss the mark.

Who Are You ? And ...

For example: I can show you a recipe in a book for chocolate chip cookies and ask you to reiterate it. Or I can turn you loose in a kitchen, have you mix the ingredients, grease the pan, plop the dough on the cookie sheet, slide everything into the oven, and wait impatiently until they pop out eight minutes later. Chances are that the description given by the person who actually made the cookies is going to be much clearer because it is based on their true understanding of the process, **because it is based on experience.**

4. Once you have completed the experiment, there are a number of extension ideas under the Science Fair Extensions that allow you to spend as much or as little time on the ideas as you deem necessary.

5. A word about humor. Science is not usually known for being funny even though Bill Nye, The Science Guy, *Beaker from* Sesame Street, *and* Beakman's World *do their best to mingle the two. That's all fine and dandy, but we want you to know that we incorporate humor because it is scientifically (and educationally) sound to do so. Plus it's really at the root of our personalities. Here's what we know:*

When we laugh ...
a. Our pupils dilate, increasing the amount of light entering the eye.
b. Our heart rate increases, which pumps more blood to the brain.
c. Oxygen-rich blood to the brain means the brain is able to collect, process, and store more information. Big I.E.: increased comprehension.
d. Laughter relaxes muscles, which can be involuntarily tense if a student is uncomfortable or fearful of an academic topic.
e. Laughter stimulates the immune system, which will ultimately translate into overall health and fewer kids who say they are sick of science.
f. Socially, it provides an acceptable pause in the academic routine, which then gives the student time to regroup and prepare to address some of the more difficult ideas with a renewed spirit. They can study longer and focus on ideas more efficiently.
g. Laughter releases chemicals in the brain that are associated with pleasure and joy.
6. If you follow the book in the order it is written, you will be able to build ideas and concepts in a logical and sequential pattern. But that is by no means necessary. For a complete set of guidelines on our ideas on how to teach home-schooled kids science, check out our book, Why's the Cat on Fire? How to Excel at Teaching Science to Your Home-Schooled Kids.

How to Use This Book

___ F. **I am a public/private school teacher,** and this looks like an interesting book to add ideas to my classroom lesson plans.

Directions: It is, and please feel free to do so. However, while this is a great classroom resource for kids, may we also recommend several other titles: Simple Machines for Over Achievers *(Simple Machines)*, Let It Roll *(Speed, Acceleration, Velocity)*, What's the Rub?, *(Friction)*, Archimede's Tub *(Density and Buoyant Force)*, Newton for Three *(Newton's Three Laws of Motion)*, and Spin City *(Circular Motion, Torque, and Angular Momentum)*.

These books have teacher-preparation pages, student-response sheets or lab pages, lesson plans, bulletin board ideas, discovery center ideas, vocabulary sheets, unit pretests, unit exams, lab practical exams, and student grading sheets. Basically everything you need if you are a science nincompoop, and a couple of cool ideas if you are a seasoned veteran with an established curriculum. All of the ideas that are covered in this one book are covered much more thoroughly in the other six. They were specifically written for teachers.

___ G. **My son/daughter/grandson/niece/father-in-law** is interested in science, and this looks like fun.

Directions: Congratulations on your selection. Add a gift certificate to the local science supply store and a package of hot chocolate mix and you have the perfect rainy Saturday afternoon gig.

___ H. **My midnight automotive acquisition club is interested in expediting our collecting abilities via the clever and creative use of levers, reduced friction enhancers, and theft deterrent override theories. Can you help?**

Directions: Nope. Try Cell Block E at the Point of the Mountain.

Lab Safety

Contained herein are 50 science activities to help you better understand the nature and characteristics of classical mechanics and physics as we currently understand these things. However, because you are on your own in this journey, we thought it prudent to share some basic wisdom and experience in the safety department.

Read the Instructions

An interesting concept, especially if you are a teenager. Take a minute before you jump in and get going to read all of the instructions as well as warnings. If you do not understand something, stop and ask an adult for help.

Clean Up All Messes

Keep your lab area clean. It will make it easier to put everything away at the end and may also prevent contamination and the subsequent germination of a species of mutant tomato bug larva. You will also find that chemicals perform with more predictability if they are not poisoned with foreign molecules.

Organize

Translation: Put it back where you get it. If you need any more clarification, there is an opening at the landfill for you.

Dispose of Poisons Properly

This will not be much of a problem with the labs that are suggested in this book. However, if you happen to wander over into one of the many disciplines that incorporates the use of more advanced chemicals, then we would suggest that you use great caution with the materials and definitely dispose of any and all poisons properly.

Practice Good Fire Safety

If there is a fire in the room, notify an adult immediately. If an adult is not in the room and the fire is manageable, smother the outbreak with a fire blanket or use a fire extinguisher. When the fire is contained, immediately send someone to find an adult. If, for any reason, you happen to catch on fire, **REMEMBER: Stop, Drop, and Roll.** Never run; it adds oxygen to the fire, making it burn faster, and it also scares the bat guano out of the neighbors when they see the neighbor kids running down the block doing an imitation of a campfire marshmallow without the stick.

Protect Your Skin

It is a good idea to always wear protective gloves whenever you are working with chemicals. Again, this particular book does not suggest or incorporate hazardous chemicals in its lab activities. In fact, we are incorporating virtually no chemicals into these labs. If you do happen to spill a chemical on your skin, notify an adult immediately and then flush the area with water for 15 minutes. It's unlikely, but if irritation develops, have your parents or another responsible adult look at it. If it appears to be of concern, contact a physician. Take any information that you have about the chemical with you.

Lab Safety

Save Your Nose Hairs

Sounds like a cause celebre L.A. style, but it is really good advice. To smell a chemical to identify it, hold the open container six to ten inches down and away from your nose. Make a clockwise circular motion with your hand over the opening of the container, "wafting" some of the fumes toward your nose. This will allow you to safely smell some of the fumes without exposing yourself to a large dose of anything noxious. This technique may help prevent a nosebleed or your lungs from accidentally getting burned by chemicals.

Wear Goggles if Appropriate

If the lab asks you to heat or mix chemicals, be sure to wear protective eyewear. Also have an eyewash station or running water available. You never know when something is going to splatter, splash, or react unexpectedly. It is better to look like a nerd and be prepared than schedule a trip down to pick out a Seeing Eye dog. If you do happen to accidentally get chemicals in your eye, flush the area for 15 minutes. If any irritation or pain develops, immediately go see a doctor.

Lose the Comedy Routine

You should have plenty of time scheduled during your day to mess around, but science lab is not one of them. Horseplay breaks glassware, spills chemicals, and creates unnecessary messes—things that parents do not appreciate. Trust us on this one.

No Eating

Do not eat while performing a lab. Putting your food in the lab area contaminates your food and the experiment. This makes for bad science and worse indigestion. Avoid poisoning yourself and goobering up your labware by observing this rule.

Happy and safe experimenting!

Recommended Materials Suppliers

For every lesson in this book, we offer a list of materials. Many of these are very easy to acquire, and if you do not have them in your home already, you will be able to find them at the local grocery or hardware store. For more difficult-to-acquire items, we have selected, for your convenience, a small but respectable list of suppliers who will meet your needs in a timely and economical manner. Call for a catalog or quote on the item that you are looking for, and they will be happy to give you a hand.

Loose in the Lab
9462 South 560 West
Sandy, UT 84070
Phone 1-888-403-1189
Fax 1-801-568-9586
www.looseinthelab.com

Delta Education
80 NW Boulevard
Nashua, NH 03063
Phone 1-800-442-5444
Fax 1-800-282-9560
www.delta-education.com

Nasco
901 Jonesville Avenue
Fort Atkinson, WI 53538
Phone 1-414-563-2446
Fax 1-920-563-8296
www.nascofa.com

Ward's Scientific
5100 W Henrietta Road
Rochester, NY 14692
Phone 1-800-387-7822
Fax 1-716-334-6174
www.wardsci.com

Educational Innovations
151 River Road
Cos Cob, CT 06807
Phone 1-888-912-7474
Fax 1-203-629-2739
www.teachersource.com

Frey Scientific
100 Paragon Parkway
Mansfield, OH 44903
Phone 1-800-225-FREY
Fax 1-419-589-1546
www.freyscientific.com

Fisher Scientific
485 S. Frontage Road
Burr Ridge, IL 60521
Phone 1-800-955-1177
Fax 1-800-955-0740
www.fisheredu.com

Sargent Welch Scientific Co
911 Commerce Court
Buffalo Grove, IL
Phone 1-800-727-4368
Fax 1-800-676-2540
www.sargentwelch.com

The Ideas,
Lab Activities,
& Science Fair
Extensions

Big Idea 1

Simple Machines—wheels and axles, pulleys, levers, inclined planes, wedges, and screws—are all inventions that make it easier for us to do work.

Ramp It Up

The Experiment

We weren't there, but the first simple machine was probably an inclined plane.

Imagine that you are a cave kid. Also imagine that you want to move a very large rock into your cave for Mother's Day so that your mom can have a very fashionable, yet practical, granite table. No problem, it's the Stone Age—lots of rocks around. You roll a choice specimen over to your cave. The only problem is that the entrance to your cave has a three-foot porch, and you can't lift your new granite table into the cave. Basic physics to the rescue.

Materials

1   30-cm length of string
1   Coffee mug
1   Spring balance, 250 g
3   Wood blocks, 5 cm by 10 cm by 10 cm
1   Board, 10 cm by 45 cm
1   Ruler, 30 cm
1   Tabletop

Procedure

1. This lab will allow you to show that using an inclined plane to raise a heavy object is easier than lifting the object directly.

2. Tie one end of the string to the handle of the coffee mug and the other end to the hook on the end of the spring balance.

3. Gently lift the spring balance, with the coffee mug dangling below it, into the air and look at the scale. You will see a series of numbers and a thin marker. The marker will tell you the mass of the mug in grams. It should also tell you how many *Newtons* (a unit measuring force) it takes to lift the mug. This is the amount of force it takes to lift the mug (our imaginary rock table) directly up into the air. Record that force reading in the data table on the next page.

4. Place the coffee mug on a flat surface. Gently pull the mug across the surface and read the amount of force (in Newtons, *N*) it takes to pull the coffee mug using the spring balance.

   If you find that the marker in the spring balance moves, that is OK. Just try to get an average reading and enter that into the data table row marked *Flat on the Tabletop*.

5. Using the illustration at the top of the next page as a guide, set up an inclined plane.
   a. Place one wood block on the table.
   b. Position the board so that one end is resting on the block, and the other end is resting on the table.
   c. Place the coffee mug at the bottom of the ramp and gently pull the coffee mug up to the top of the ramp.
   d. Record the amount of force that it takes to pull the coffee mug up the ramp.
   e. Add a second wood block and repeat the test. Record your data on the appropriate line.
   f. Add a third wood block and repeat the test. Record this data, as well.

Ramp It Up

Data & Observations

Height of Ramp	Force (N)
Lifting Straight Up	
Flat on the Tabletop	
One block high	
Two blocks high	
Three blocks high	

How Come, Huh?

What you should have noticed is that the higher you tried to lift the mug, the more Newtons (force) it took to do the job.

In terms of mathematics, there is a simple formula that will allow you to calculate this.

IMA stands for Ideal Mechanical Advantage—a fancy term that means that using a machine makes the work easier for you. You have a mechanical advantage, or the advantage of using a machine. L stands for the length of the slope (how long the board measures), and H stands for the height of the slope. Here's the formula:

$$IMA = L/H$$

To calculate the IMA for each test, all you have to do is plug in the numbers:

IMA (1 block) = 45 cm/5 cm
IMA (1 block) = 9

Fill in the data table below.

# Blocks	Length of Slope	Height of Slope	IMA
1	45 cm	5 cm	9
2		10 cm	
3	45 cm		3

The higher the IMA number, the more the machine multiplies the force on the object. This makes it easier to move.

Science Fair Extensions

1. Design an experiment that proves that the length of the ramp does not change the results that you have found.

2. Using the formula to calculate the IMA, calculate the IMA numbers for four, five, and six blocks. Graph your data.

Angle of Ascent

The Experiment

This activity is a continuation of the previous one. If you have not done *Ramp It Up*, it is time to put it in reverse and come back to this lab in a couple of minutes.

In the last lab, you figured out that the higher you lifted the object, the more force it took to get the job done. Common sense tells you that much. In this lab, we are going explore how changing the angle of the ramp affects the amount of energy it takes to lift the object off the ground.

Materials

1   30-cm length of string
1   Coffee mug
1   Spring balance, 250 g
1   Tabletop
1   Board, 4 inches by 18 inches
1   Ruler, 30 cm
3   Wood blocks, 2 inches by 4 inches by 4 inches

Procedure

1. A ramp is an inclined plane, and it is a simple machine. This lab will allow you to collect data that shows that using a long, moderately inclined plane makes it easier to raise a heavy object than does a very steep, short inclined plane.

2. Tie one end of the string to the handle of the coffee mug and the other end to the hook on the end of the spring balance.

3. Using the illustration at the bottom of this page as a guide, set up an inclined plane.

    a. Place three wood blocks on the table.

    b. Position the board so that one end is resting on the blocks, and the other end is resting on the table.

    c. Place the coffee mug at the bottom of the ramp and gently pull the coffee mug up to the top of the ramp.

    d. On the next page, record the amount of force it took to pull the coffee mug up the ramp.

4. Using the ruler, measure 15 cm from the top end of the inclined plane and slide the board so that it rests on the blocks in that position. You have just made the ramp steeper.

Place the coffee mug at the bottom of the ramp and gently pull it up to the top of the ramp. Record the amount of force that it takes to pull the coffee mug up the ramp.

5. Using the ruler, meaure 30 cm from the top end of the inclined plane and slide the board so that it rests on the blocks in that position. You have just made the ramp really steep.

Place the coffee mug at the bottom of the ramp and gently pull it up to the top of the ramp. Record the amount of force that it took to pull the coffee mug up the ramp.

Angle of Ascent

Data & Observations

Length of Ramp	Force (g)
45 centimeters long	
30 centimeters long	
15 centimeters long	

How Come, Huh?

What you should have noticed is that the steeper the angle of the inclined plane, the more force it took to do the job. You know the formula behind this.

IMA stands for Ideal Mechanical Advantage—a term that means that you have a mechanical advantage, or the advantage of using a machine. Another definition of mechanical advantage is that it tells you the number of times a machine multiplies the effort force being applied to it.

For example, if you have an ideal mechanical advantage of 3, that would mean that the energy that you put into moving the object is multiplied by three. Your effort is tripled by the machine, which is why we use machines to help us in the first place. Moving a heavy rock becomes possible if we position the machine (a lever) properly under the rock. But now, back to the math.

L stands for the length of the slope (how long the board measures) and H stands for the height of the slope. Here's the formula:

$$IMA = L/H$$

To calculate the IMA for each test, all you have to do is plug in the numbers:

IMA (1 block) = 45 cm / 5 cm
IMA (1 block) = 9

Fill in the data table below.

# Blocks	Length of Slope	Height of Slope	IMA
3	45 cm	15 cm	3
3		15 cm	
3	15 cm		1

The higher the IMA number, the easier it is to move the object. So, just as you probably suspected, the steeper the ramp, the more energy it takes to move an object up that ramp.

Science Fair Extensions

3. If you are a math smarty-pants, you can sit down with the data table on this page and find a direct correlation between the angle of the inclined plane and the IMA. We will turn you loose on that one and see if you can figure it out.

4. Go on an inclined plane hunt around your home or school and see how and where inclined planes are used to give people an IMA in their world.

Double Incline Wedgie

The Experiment

For this lab, we are going to double up on our inclined planes. If you were to take two inclined planes and place them base to base, you would have a wedge. Another name for a wedge is a knife, and with that, you can add another simple machine to your list.

In addition to knives, wedges are used to split wood, drive golf balls out of sand traps, remove car tires from their rims, and hold doors open. (Wedgies, just for the record, are neither simple machines nor are they predicated on making life more pleasant.)

This experiment allows you to see how wedges are constructed and why they are useful when it comes to separating two objects.

Materials

1   Pair of scissors
1   Sheet of paper, 8 1/2 inches by 11 inches
1   Steak knife
2   Cubes of cheese, 1 inch by 1 inch each
1   Cutting board
    Adult Supervision

Procedure

1. First up, making wedges ... You will need a pair of scissors and a sheet of paper.

2. Fold the edge of the paper over onto itself, using the pattern above. Cut along the edge of the paper (where the dotted lines are located). Then, open the sheet up and cut down the middle, along the crease. When you are done, you will have two inclined planes.

3. Take the inclined planes that you just made, place them bottom to bottom, and hold them up. You can see now where the idea for a wedge came from.

4. You are going to be using a very sharp steak knife. If your folks or the adult in charge of herding you around feels that you need some supervision, pay attention, and get their help.

5. Place a cube of cheese on the cutting board. Flip the knife over so that the sharp side of the blade is facing toward you and away from the cube of cheese. Attempt to cut the cube of cheese with the flat side of the blade.

6. Grab a second cube of cheese and, using the thin side of the blade, attempt to cut the new cube of cheese. It should be much easier this time. Simple machines state their case again.

Double Incline Wedgie

How Come, Huh?

As you saw, the knife is composed of two inclined planes, fitted back to back. In the first attempt to cut the cheese, you are shoving the blunt edge of the knife against the cheese. The force of the blade pushes the cheese perpendicular to the direction that you want to cut. This takes a lot of energy and has the same effect as trying to lift a very heavy object straight up into the air: It is hard to do and requires a lot of energy.

When you push down on the cheese with the narrow portion of the wedge, you are forcing it to go up the plane of the knife. This is similar to using a ramp to move a heavy object to a higher position. It takes less energy because the machine gives you a mechlical advantage. So, starting narrow and getting wider, the wedge (knife) splits the cheese into two halves more easily.

Science Fair Extensions

5. Go on a wedge hunt around your house. List at least 5 wedges that you find.

A. _____

B. _____

C. _____

D. _____

E. _____

Spiral Inclines

The Experiment

If you take an inclined plane and twist it around a pole, you have either a bolt or a spiral staircase. If the pole comes to a point, you have a screw. These are three more simple machines that are adaptations of an inclined plane, and three more inventions that make life easier for people.

Materials

1   Sheet of paper
1   Pair of scissors
1   Felt marker
1   Roll of transparent tape
1   Pencil
1   Bolt, smooth
1   Screwdriver
1   Block, 2 inches by 4 inches by 6 inches
1   Screw

Procedure

1. More wedges. You will need a pair of scissors and a sheet of paper.

2. Fold the edge of the paper over onto itself using the pattern below. Cut along the edge of the paper, where the dotted lines are located. Then, open the sheet up and cut down the middle, along the crease. When you are done, you will have two inclined planes.

Spiral Inclines

3. Take one of the inclined planes that you just made, and using the felt marker, draw a thick line of ink across the hypotenuse (the top, diagonal edge).

4. Put a piece of tape on the tip of the triangle and tape the tip to the bottom of your pencil, using the illustration on the next page as a guide.

5. Slowly wrap the paper around the pencil. What you should notice is that the inclined plane is wrapping itself around the pencil and making a shelf or thread that starts at the bottom of the pencil and goes all the way to the top. If you look at the thick ink line you drew, it should be spiraling up the pencil. This is what a screw is—an inclined plane wrapped around a center post—a modified simple machine, like the wedge.

6. Placing the tip of your pen or pencil on the very bottom of the screw, slowly twist the shaft and follow the thread as far as you can. This is the same pattern that you created using the paper and the pencil—an inclined plane wrapped around a center core.

7. Place the end of the bolt on the piece of wood. Using a screwdriver, attempt to screw the bolt into the wood.

8. Replace the bolt with a screw and attempt to screw that into the wood. This time, the screw should penetrate the wood and start to work its way down into the material.

How Come, Huh?

A screw is an inclined plane that is wrapped around a center core. When you try to drive the bolt into the wood, it is just like climbing straight up a ladder. It takes a lot of energy.

When you place the screw on the wood and start twisting, the screw works its way down into the wood. It takes less energy because, instead of trying to shove the whole thing in at once (like climbing straight up the ladder), the wood is "climbing" up the inclined plane, so it takes less energy.

Science Fair Extensions

6. Look at the list of simple machines below. Circle the machines that include inclined planes.

Ramp	Wheel	Pulley	Tire iron
Doorstop	Gear	Teeter-totter	Shovel
Crowbar	Screw	Spiral staircase	Knife

Anatomy of a Lever

The Experiment

OK, enough of these inclined planes—climbing, splitting, and lifting. Time to shift over to another kind of simple machine, the lever. Crowbars are levers, a large stick or board can be used as a lever, and your arm is a lever. If you are using something long and skinny to pry, lift, or move a heavy object, chances are very good that you are using a lever. The word lever comes from the Latin root, *levare*, which means "to lift."

In this lab, you are going to be introduced to the different terms that apply to a lever, one, so that you know how to communicate effectively, and two, so that you will be able to tackle some of the mathematical problems that will be offered up as extensions to some of the labs.

Materials

1   Pencil

Procedure

Definitions with pictures ... keeps everyone happy.

A. <u>Lever</u>: The whole enchilada, or everything taken together, is called the lever. It is the thing (stick, shovel, tire iron, crowbar) that is working to lift the object.

B. <u>Resistance Force</u>: The thing that you are trying to lift has mass, it weighs a lot, and it is stuck. For some reason, it is hard to move and it provides a force that resists movement—hence the name, resistance force.

C. <u>Effort Force</u>: This is the force that you apply to the lever to get the object to move. You push down on the crowbar, tilt the shovel handle, or lift up on the cap of the pop bottle. This is the energy you apply to try to move the object.

D. <u>Fulcrum</u>: This is the point where the lever pivots. It is where the energy is transferred from the effort arm to the resistance arm. Now, if you only knew what those were ...

E. <u>Effort Arm</u>: This is the portion of the lever that is being pushed on. It is where the effort force is working. It could be the top handle of a shovel, the long end of a crowbar, or your side of a teeter-totter.

F. <u>Resistance Arm</u>: This is the other side of the fulcrum. This is the portion of the arm between the fulcrum and the object that is being lifted.

Use the illustration below to help you learn these different terms.

Anatomy of a Lever

Data & Observations

Look at the illustration below and identify each of the six parts of the system. Add letters to the drawing to identify the parts.

A. Lever   B. Resistance Force   C. Effort Force

D. Fulcrum   E. Effort Arm   F. Resistance Arm

Look at this new illustration and identify each of the six parts of the system. Add letters to the drawing to identify the parts.

A. Lever   B. Resistance Force   C. Effort Force
D. Fulcrum   E. Effort Arm   F. Resistance Arm

Science Fair Extensions

7. Find, draw, and label 5 different levers that you find around your school or home.

Flexible Fulcrums

The Experiment

You should know the parts of the lever before you tackle this lab activity. To calculate the mechanical advantage of any lever, you simply have to take two measurements: the length of the effort arm and the length of the resistance arm. Divide the first length by the second, and the higher the IMA, the easier it will be to lift the object with the lever.

Materials

2   5-oz. wax cups
1   Roll of masking tape
1   Ruler, 30 cm
1   Pencil
3   Superballs, small
1   Box of paperclips

Procedure

1. Place a loop of tape, sticky side out, on the bottom of each wax cup. Then attach the cups to opposite ends of the ruler, as pictured here.

2. Place the pencil under the ruler at the 10-cm mark, and adjust the cups until the instrument balances. The pencil should be perpendicular to the ruler, forming a funny looking plus sign when you look at the whole contraption from the top.

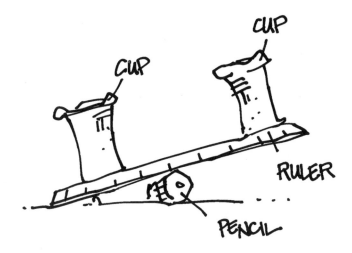

3. Place the Superball in one of the cups and add paperclips, one at a time until the balance tips. Record the number of paperclips it took to balance the object in the space provided in the *10 cm* column.

4. Move the pencil so that it is resting under the 15-cm mark. Then, either add or remove paperclips so that the balance balances again. Record that number in the *15 cm* column below. Repeat the process after moving the pencil to the 20-cm mark.

5. Repeat the procedure using one, two, and then three Superballs in the cup.

Data & Observations

Using the data table below, record the number of paperclips required to tip the lever and lift the ball(s) in the cup.

# *Superballs*	*10 cm*	*15 cm*	*20 cm*
1. _____	____	____	____
2. _____	____	____	____
3. _____	____	____	____

Flexible Fulcrums

How Come, Huh?

Back to our original definitions. When you placed the pencil under the ruler, you were creating a simple machine—a lever. The object that you put in the cup to weigh was called the load—also, the resistance force. To determine the weight needed to lift the resistance force that you placed in the cup, you added paperclips—not only our unit of measure but also called the effort force.

The effort force pushed down on the effort arm to lift the load. The critical part of this experiment now becomes the location of the center point, or the fulcrum.

By moving the pencil closer to the object weighed, you were actually making it easier for the object to be lifted by the cup full of paperclips. The lever was giving you a mechanical advantage by multiplying the effort that you put into lifting the balls. This is evidenced by the fact that all of the numbers in that column were lower than the numbers in the *15 cm* column.

By moving the pencil (fulcrum) farther away from the object weighed, you were actually making it harder for the object to be lifted by the cup that was full of paperclips. This is evidenced by the fact that all of the numbers in that column were higher than the numbers in the *10 cm* column.

Data & Observations

Using the illustration at the top of the previous page, identify each part of the lever and write the corresponding name next to that part.

A. Lever   B. Resistance Force   C. Effort Force
D. Fulcrum   E. Effort Arm   F. Resistance Arm

Science Fair Extensions

8. Using the idea of a lever, design and build a scale that measures the weight of an object. Be sure to incorporate a method to calibrate (zero out) your scale as well as accurately measure the weight of the object placed on the scale.

9. Design and build a scale that specifically measures either gas or liquids. Show how the scale can be calibrated, and determine what limitations your scale has, if any.

10. Go on a lever hunt around your house. List at least 5 levers that you find.

A. _____

B. _____

C. _____

D. _____

E. _____

11. Design and build a teeter-totter with a moveable fulcrum. Figure out where you have to place the fulcrum in order to be able to lift your dad into the air by yourself.

12. Compare levers and pulleys. List 3 situations that are ideal ones for using each of these types of simple machines.

Calculated Leverage

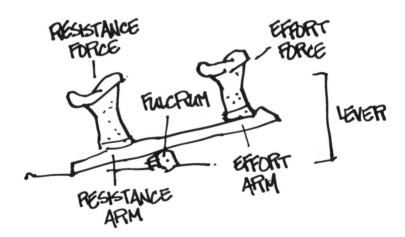

The Experiment

You should know the parts of the lever before you tackle this lab activity. To calculate the mechanical advantage of any lever, you simply have to take two measurements: the length of the effort arm and the length of the resistance arm. Divide the first length by the second, and the higher the IMA, the easier it will be to lift the object with the lever. Lab time!

Materials

2 5 oz. wax cups
1 Roll of masking tape
1 Ruler, 30 cm
1 Pencil
1 Box of paperclips
1 Rock, large, 3-inch diameter

Procedure

1. Place a loop of tape, sticky side out, on the bottom of each wax cup. Then attach the cups to the opposite ends of the ruler as pictured on the next page.

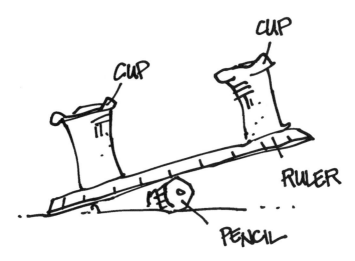

2. Place the pencil under the ruler at the 5-cm mark. The pencil should be perpendicular to the ruler, forming a funny looking plus sign when you look at the setup from the top.

3. Place the rock in the cup at the 0-cm end of the ruler. Add paperclips until the rock lifts off the tabletop. Record the number of paperclips, measure the length of the effort arm and the resistance arm, and calculate the IMA.

Data & Observations

Using the data table below, record the number of paperclips required to tip the lever and lift the rock in the cup.

Fulcrum	# Paperclips	L_e	L_r	IMA
5 cm		5 cm		
10 cm			20 cm	
15 cm				1
20 cm		20 cm		
25 cm				

Calculated Leverage

How Come, Huh?

Not to beat a dead horse, but IMA stands for Ideal Mechanical Advantage. The point of using a simple machine is to give you an advantage when you are doing work. The machine takes the force that you apply to it and multiplies that force to make doing the task easier.

In this case with levers, L_e stands for the length of the effort arm—this is how long the lever measures from the fulcrum to the force. L_r stands for the length of the resistance arm—that's the part that is left over. Here's the formula:

$$IMA = L_e / L_r$$

To calculate the IMA for each test, all you have to do is plug in the numbers:

IMA (15-cm fulcrum) = 15 cm / 15 cm
IMA (1 block) = 1

The larger the IMA number, the more the machine multiples the force that you apply to it, and the easier it is to lift the rock. This is supported by the number of paperclips that needed to be added to the second cup to lift the rock. The higher the IMA, the lower the number of paperclips. It is a direct correlation.

Science Fair Extensions

13. Repeat this experiment using a meter stick instead of a 30-cm ruler and see if this rule holds up for really long levers, too.

14. Someone once said, "If you had a lever that was long enough, you could lift the world by yourself." Is that true? Where would your fulcrum be located? Would it depend on the kind of material or would wood work as well as metal? Who was this idiot, anyway?

Classifying Levers

The Experiment

There are three kinds of levers: first-, second-, and third-class. Each kind of lever is defined by the location of the fulcrum, the load, and the force moving the load. You are going to review the three kinds of levers, and then use your body to experience each type.

Materials

1   Body, complete

Procedure

1. *First-Class Lever*

This is the kind of lever that you have been experimenting with if you are going in the order found in the book. The fulcrum is located between the load and the force lifting the load. A seesaw is a good example of this kind of lever.

2. *Second-Class Lever*

To create this kind of lever, the fulcrum is at one end, the resistance is in the middle, and the effort to lift the object is on the other end. A wheelbarrow is an excellent example of this kind of lever.

3. *Third-Class Lever*

Finally, a third-class lever finds the fulcrum at the end of the lever, the effort is in the middle, and the resistance is at the end. A hockey player shooting a puck would be a good example of a third-class lever.

Classifying Levers

Data & Observations

Using the illustrations below, identify the levers that are located in your body as first-, second-, or third-class levers.

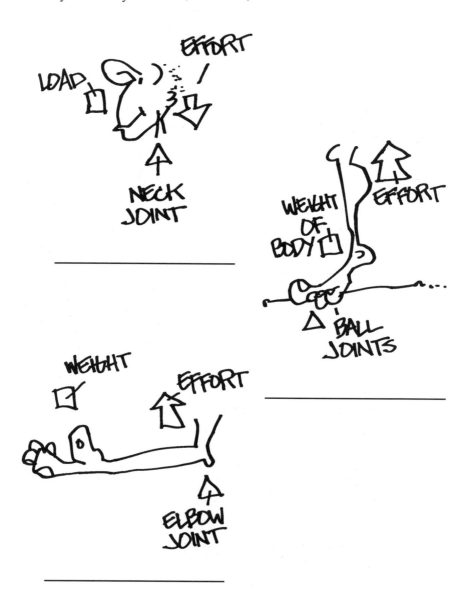

_____

_____

_____

How Come, Huh?

By definition, the movement of your head up and down, pivoting on the vertabrae of your spinal column, would be considered a first-class lever. Your head naturally bends forward when no effort is applied to it. Just watch the old geezers in church if you are not sure about this concept.

Raising up on your tiptoes is a second-class lever. The fulcrum is your toes, the effort force is found in your heel as you lift your body upward, and the resistance is located between the effort and the fulcrum.

By sheer elimination, the bicep curls would be our third-class lever. The weight in your hand is the resistance pulling down on the arm. Your elbow is now your fulcrum, with your bicep serving as the effort force lifting the weight in your hand.

Science Fair Extensions

15. Find a model of a skeleton, either cardboard or bone, and take a look at how each of the bones moves. There are many levers in our bodies. Identify as many as you can, and tell if they are first-, second-, or third-class levers and why you think so.

16. Take a look at the example of three levers on the previous page. Write a simple phrase that will help you remember the difference between first-, second-, and third-class levers by noting the location of the fulcrum, effort, and resistance.

17. Time for another scavenger hunt. Head out into your house—the garage especially—and find as many levers as possible. Be sure to include scissors, rakes, shovels, spades, wheelbarrows, rolling garbage cans, pruning shears, spades, and trowels, for starters. We are sure that you will find more. Identify these items as first-, second-, or third-class levers.

18. Design a machine using two or more simple machines.

Wheel & Axle

The Experiment

Wheels appear all over the place, and you'll notice them in some of the oddest locations, once you figure out how they are disguised. For example, your doorknob is a wheel, and so is the handle on your water faucet. Not convinced? Try opening the door or turning on the water without those two knobs to give you a mechanical advantage. Not easy ... trust us.

A wheel and an axle form another kind of a simple machine. They are actually two wheels, one larger than the other, that work together to make turning an object easier.

Materials

1   Drill bit
1   Piece of wood, 2 inches by 4 inches by 6 inches
1   Hand drill
1   Wooden airplane with propellor

Procedure

1. Place the end of the drill bit on the surface of the 2-by-4 and twist the bit with your fingers, trying your very best to create a hole.

2. After you have attempted to make a hole, replace the drill bit with a hand drill. Place the end of the drill on the wood and start to turn the handle. You should find that making a hole with the advantage of the simple machine is much easier.

3. Assemble your wooden airplane. The plane is powered by a rubberband that stores energy and then releases it to spin a propellor. Try winding the rubberband without the aid of the propellor, using only your fingers.

4. After you have tried this for awhile, re-attach the propellor and spin it with your finger to store energy. The propellor is the larger wheel, and the rubberband is the axle in this model.

How Come, Huh?

In each case, the wheel and axle multiply the force that you apply to the machine and make it easier to turn the smaller of the two wheels. To determine how much easier the object is to move, you can also calculate the IMA, or Ideal Mechanical Advantage.

The IMA for a wheel and axle are calculated using the following formula, where IMA equals the Ideal Mechanical Advantage, r_w equals the radius of the wheel, and r_a equals the radius of the axle. Here is the formula:

$$IMA = r_w / r_a$$

The logical conclusion that can be drawn from the formula is that the greater the difference between the wheel and axle, the easier it is for the axle to be turned. But why believe us? Head for the *Science Fair Extensions* section and solve some problems.

Wheel & Axle

Science Fair Extensions

19. Listed below are a number of wheel and axle combinations. Using a metric ruler, measure in centimeters the radius of the larger wheel and then the radius of the smaller wheel. Calculate the IMA for each wheel and axle combination.

$$IMA = r_w / r_a$$

Item	r_w	r_a	r_w / r_a	IMA
Doorknob				_____
Knob (r_w)	_____			
Stem (r_a)		_____		
Hand Drill				_____
Handle (r_w)	_____			
Drill (r_a)		_____		
Car Steering Wheel				_____
Wheel (r_w)	_____			
Shaft (r_a)		_____		
Bicycle Pedal				_____
Pedal (r_w)	_____			
Center Post (r_a)		_____		
Bicycle Handle Bars				_____
Handle (r_w)	_____			
Stem (r_a)		_____		
Wrench & Nut				_____
Wrench Handle (r_w) _____				
Nut (r_a)		_____		

20. Draw four different wheel-and-axle combinations. Identify the wheel. Then find the radius of the wheel as well as the axle in each group. Determine the IMA for each combination.

Impromptu Pulley

The Experiment

Two of your friends are holding broom handles about six inches apart. They are convinced that they can keep the broom handles separated, but you seem to think that you can squeeze the two handles together with a single hand—despite the fact your two friends are very large and very strong. So, who's going to win the contest of brute strength? You with the aid of a simple machine, or your two muscular friends? (Physics always wins.)

Materials

2   Broom handles
2   Assistants
1   Rope, 6 feet long
1   Clock with a sweep-second hand

Procedure

1. While your two assistants are holding the broom handles about six inches apart, tie one end of the rope to the broom handle nearest you. The picture below should help.

2. Loop the rope around the far broomstick and give it a gentle tug while your assistants try to keep the sticks separated. Record the amount of time it takes to close the gap between the sticks.

3. Repeat the experiment, adding loops around the two sticks. Use the illustration at the right as a guide. Try each combination of loops around the sticks and fill in the data table below.

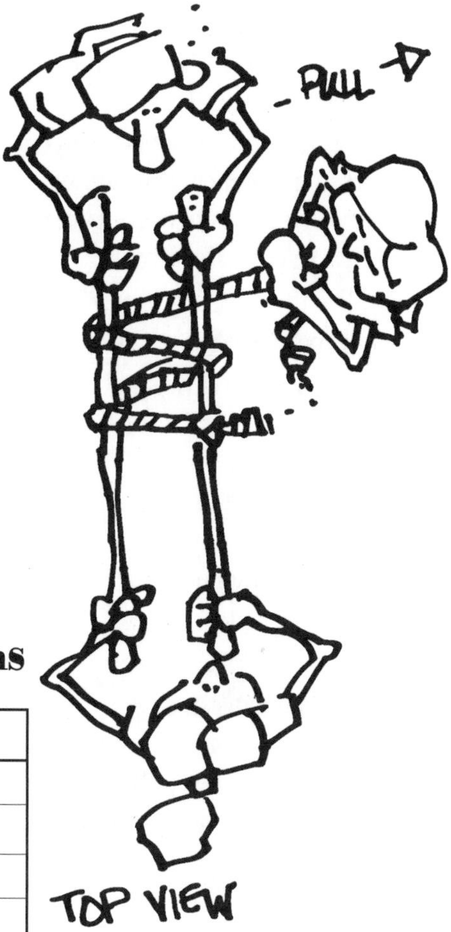

Data & Observations

# Loops	Time (sec.)
2	
3	
4	
5	

TOP VIEW

How Come, Huh?
Wrapping the rope around the broomstick is similar to looping it through a pulley. The force pulling on the rope is equal to the resistance. When you add a second loop, you multiply the force that is applied and increase the mechancial advantage to the person pulling on the rope. This is a great lead-in to the next lab.

Pulleys

The Experiment

Pulleys can be classified three ways: fixed, moveable, and as a block and tackle system. You will experiment with two of the three in this lab activity.

Pulleys are wheels, which also makes them simple machines. They are used to lift objects that are very heavy (like car engines) and objects that need to be lifted to places that are very high (like flagpoles). They can be fixed, mobile, or in combination.

Materials

1   Roll of string
1   Pair of scissors
1   Pulley
1   Ring stand
1   Paperclip
1   Spring balance
3   Weights

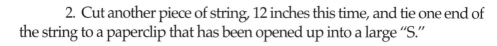

Procedure

1. Cut an 8-inch length of string and attach the pulley to the ring stand ,as shown in the picture above. This is a fixed pulley.

2. Cut another piece of string, 12 inches this time, and tie one end of the string to a paperclip that has been opened up into a large "S."

3. Thread the string along the groove on the top of the pulley so that the weight, the paperclip, hangs down. Tie a loop in the other end of the string and attach it to the spring balance.

4. Lift the weight by pulling down on the spring balance. The amount of force that is needed to lift the weight is shown as *Newtons* on the scale. Record that number in the *Fixed* row of the data table in the *Data & Observations* section on page 58.

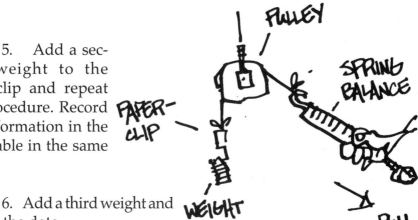

5. Add a second weight to the paperclip and repeat the procedure. Record the information in the data table in the same row.

6. Add a third weight and record the data.

7. Remove the string that holds the pulley from the ring stand.

8. Remove the weights from the paperclip "S" that was holding them, and attach the paperclip to the ring stand.

9. Hang a single weight from the pulley and balance it on the string while you hold the other end.

10. Attach the spring balance to the other end of the string. This is a moveable pulley that you have constructed. Take readings of *Newtons* for one, two, and three weights, and enter that data in the data table.

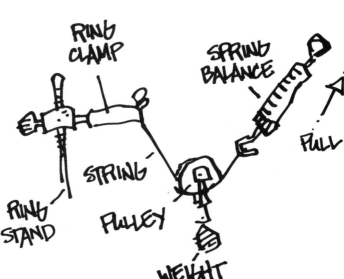

Pulleys

Data & Observations

Pulley Type	Reading on Spring Balance (N)		
	1 Weight	2 Weights	3 Weights
Fixed			
Moveable			

How Come, Huh?

The mechanical advantage (MA) of a pulley is determined by the number of ropes pulling up on the mass. With a single fixed pulley, the MA is 1 because you have a single rope attached to the pulley, pulling up on the weight.

With a moveable pulley, the MA is 2 because you have two ropes pulling up on the weight. The rope attached to the ring stand is pulling up on the pulley and the weight as well as the other rope that is being pulled on by you as you lift. The data you collect with the spring balance should support this idea.

Science Fair Extensions

21. Figure out how to incorporate 4 pulleys into a block and tackle system, and calculate the MA for that arrangement.

22. Go on a pulley hunt and list 5 pulleys in your neighborhood.

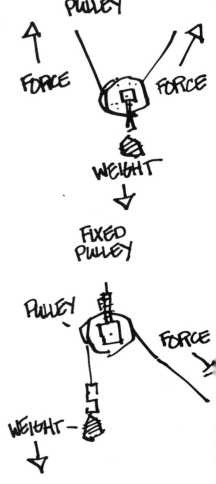

Big Idea 2

Speed (v) is defined as the measured distance (d) an object travels in a fixed amount of time (t). This is described by the formula, v = d/t. Along these lines, Newton observed that force equals mass times acceleration, which makes up his Second Law.

Inclined Plane Races

The Experiment

The speed that an object travels can be determined by taking two measurements, distance and time. In this particular lab, you are going to measure the time that it takes for a marble to travel down a 1-meter track. Knowing the time and the distance, you will then calculate the average speed of the marble when it is started from different heights.

Materials

10 Pennies
1 PVC marble track, 1 meter long
1 Marble, large
1 Stopwatch or sweep-second hand clock
1 Assistant

Procedure

1. Place 2 pennies under the end of the PVC track to elevate it just a bit. Hold the marble near the elevated end, and when the assistant is ready and says, "Go!," release the marble and let it roll down the tube. In your data table, record the amount of time it takes to appear at the other end.

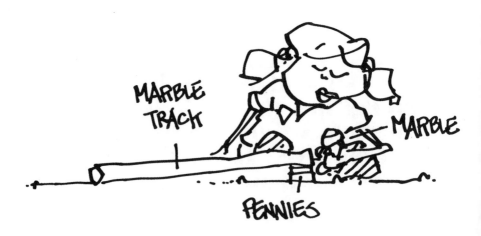

MARBLE TRACK

MARBLE

PENNIES

2. Repeat this experiment two more times to get an average reading.

3. Repeat steps 1 and 2 from heights of 4, 6, 8, and 10 pennies. Be sure to measure each trial three times to get an average reading, and then calculate the speed for each trial. Use the formula, *speed (v) = distance (1 meter)/time (seconds)*.

Data & Observations

Height	Trial #1	Trial #2	Trial #3	Avg.	Speed
2					
4					
6					
8					
10					

How Come, Huh?

The higher you stacked the pennies, the more potential energy the marble had when you put it on the track. When the marble was released, gravity started pulling down on it, and it began to roll. The potential energy was converted into kinetic energy. A higher start equals more potential (stored) energy, which equals more speed.

Science Fair Extensions

23. Figure out a way to cut the PVC track in half lengthwise so that you can see the marble as it rolls down the track. Measure increments of 10 centimeters and mark them with a black marker on the track. Measure and collect data so that you can calculate the speed of the marble for every 10 cm of track.

Marble Races

The Experiment

The speed that an object travels can be determined by taking two measurements, distance and time. In this particular lab, you are going to measure the time that it takes for marbles with different masses to travel down a 30-centimeter track. Knowing the time and the distance, you will then calculate the average speed of the marbles when they are started from the same height.

Materials

5 Pennies
1 Ruler, 30 cm, with groove
1 Styrofoam ball, 0.5-inch diameter
1 Stopwatch or sweep-second hand clock
1 Assistant
1 Marble, large, glass
1 Marble, steel
1 Sphere, wooden, 0.5-inch diameter

Procedure

1. Place 5 pennies under one end of the ruler to elevate it.

2. Hold the styrofoam marble near the elevated end, and when your assistant is ready and says, "Go!," release the marble and let it roll down the groove. Record the amount of time it takes to travel the entire length of the ruler.

3. Repeat this experiment two more times to get an average reading.

4. Repeat steps 2 and 3 using the other three kinds of spheres. Be sure to measure each trial three times to get an average reading and then calculate the speed for each marble. Use the formula, *speed (v) = distance (1 meter)/time (seconds)*.

Data & Observations

Material	Trial #1	Trial #2	Trial #3	Avg.	Speed
Styrofoam					
Wood					
Glass					
Steel					

How Come, Huh?

The amount of energy that is stored in an object is directly affected by the mass of that object—heavier objects store more energy than light ones. Drop a big rock on your toe from the same height as a small pebble and see if you agree. Each sphere was lifted to the same height. However, the heavier sphere required more energy to get to that height and, therefore, stored more energy.

When the spheres were released, gravity started pulling on them, and the heavier spheres ultimately rolled faster than the lighter ones because they had more energy stored in them.

Weighted Wheels

The Experiment

Not all wheels are created equal. In fact, the way that a wheel is weighted makes all the difference in the world as to how fast it starts to roll and how long it continues to roll. In this lab, we are going to continue to measure speed, but we are going to add another twist to our experiment, adjusting the location of the weight in the wheel.

Materials

1   Thick book
1   Board, 1 meter long, 6 inches wide
3   Styrofoam discs, 1 inch thick, 10-inch diameter
3   Marbles, steel
1   Stopwatch or sweep-second hand clock
1   Assistant

Procedure

1. Place the thick book under one end of the board to elevate it. You've just created your racetrack.

2. Use the guides at the right and on the next page to prepare your three wheels. The first wheel has the marble inserted in the very center of the disc. Place the disc on its side and gently push the marble into the styrofoam until it is flush with the surface of the disc.

3. The second wheel has the marble inserted at the very edge of the wheel. Again, make sure it's flush with the rim so that it does not bump as it rolls down the ramp.

WEIGHT

WHEEL 3

4.   The third wheel is going to be somewhere between a weighted center and a weighted rim. You are going to place the weight about halfway between the center and the rim of the disc—again, flush with the edge.

5.   Place Wheel #1, with the weight in the center, at the top of the ramp. When your assistant is ready, he or she will say, "Go!" At that point, have your assistant start the stopwatch. Record the amount of time that it takes Wheel #1 to complete the 1-meter course.

6. Repeat this experiment two more times to get an average reading. Enter this data in the data table at the top of the next page.

7. Repeat steps 5 and 6 using the other two wheels. Be sure that the weight in each is positioned correctly. Measure each trial three times to get an average reading and then calculate the speed for each wheel. Use the formula, *speed (v) = distance (1 meter)/time (seconds).*

Weighted Wheels

Data & Observations

Wheel	Trial #1	Trial #2	Trial #3	Avg.	Speed
1					
2					
3					

How Come, Huh?

The location of the weight is what influences the speed at which the wheel travels. This has to be the case because the diameter of the wheel, the weight, and the width are all identical. The only thing that could influence the outcome would be the distribution of the weight.

Starting with Wheel #1, the mass is located in the center of the object. The force of gravity is pulling down on the marble and it begins to rotate almost immediately.

With Wheel #2, the weight is way out there on the rim of the wheel. That means that gravity is going to have to reach up and pull down on the weight. To get the whole wheel moving, the weight is going to have to fall as the wheel rolls, which gives this wheel design more inertia. More inertia means that it takes a while for the whole banana to get rolling.

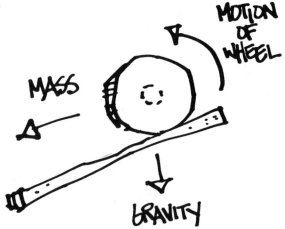

Finally, Wheel #3 has the weight halfway between the center of the disc and the rim. As you would expect, the results are halfway between Wheels #1 and #2. It takes a while to get rolling—but not as long as it takes for the wheel that has the weight on the rim to roll.

Science Fair Extensions

24. Figure out how to place Wheel #2 on the inclined plane and make it roll uphill instead of downhill. If you need some help, think about the effect of gravity on the weight.

25. Experiment with wheels that are solid versus wheels that have spokes. Determine which rolls faster and why.

26. Substitute spheres for wheels. Locate spheres made of glass, wood, metal, and plastic. Find both solid and hollow spheres, and spheres of different diameters. Test all of these spheres for acceleration, speed, and velocity, and write a simple law based on the data that you have collected.

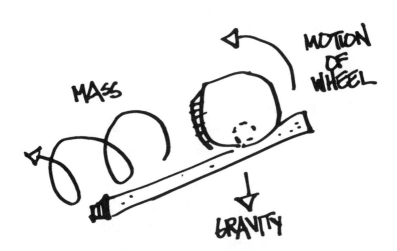

Balloon Races

The Experiment

Speed is defined as the distance an object moves during a given period of time. For the mathematically inclined, we offer the following equation: speed (v) equals distance (d) divided by time (t), or $v = d/t$.

In this lab, you are going to measure the speed of a balloon rocket racing down a string, first with a single engine and then with two engines. You will know the distance, which is 5 meters. All you have to do is measure the amount of time that it takes to travel that distance, and then perform some simple division.

Materials

1   Partner
1   Piece of string (5 meters)
1   Straw
2   Balloons
4   4-inch strips of masking tape
1   Stopwatch or sweep-second hand clock
1   Assistant

Procedure

1. You will be working with a partner through all of these steps. The first step is to thread the string through the straw.

2. Inflate the balloon, but do not tie it off. You will need the air to escape in order to provide the necessary thrust for your rocket. Using two pieces of masking tape, attach the balloon to the straw. Use the illustration on the opposite page as a guide.

3.	Ask your partner to walk to the other end of the room with the string. You should have the balloon in one hand and one end of the string in the other. Your partner should hold the other end of the string.

4.	When both of you are ready, the balloon holder needs to lift the balloons to belly-button level for launch, and the partner needs to hold the other end of the string at belly-button level but slightly lower than yours. You will say, "Three, two, one, launch!," and when you come to the word *launch*, let go of your balloon. The timer will record the amount of time it takes to complete the course.

5.	After you have completed your flight, work with your partner to fill in the data table. Record the amount of time it takes for your balloon to travel to the end of the string three times. Average those times and enter that information in the data table on the next page.

6.	Add a second balloon and race it down your string three more times. Once all of the data has been entered, create a **bar graph** showing the information. After that is completed, *infer*, or figure out, how fast you think a rocket with three and four "engines" would travel by drawing bars to represent what you *think* the data would look like.

Balloon Races

Data & Observations

Engines	Trial #1	Trial #2	Trial #3	Avg.	Speed
1					
2					
3					
4					

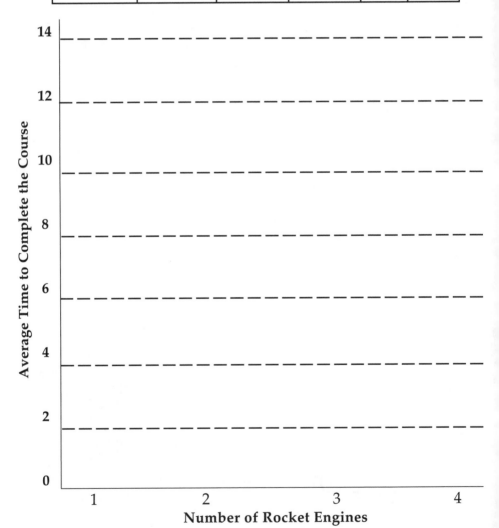

How Come, Huh?

As you released the neck of the balloon, air began escaping out the back. That was the action. For every action, there is an equal and opposite reaction. In this case, the air pushed against the front and sides of the balloon, producing a net forward force. The balloon propelled along the string. To get a bit of visual insight into exactly what we are talking about, check out the illustrations below.

Science Fair Extensions

27. Change the track that the balloon rocket travels down and use different materials. Try twine, fishing line, steel wire, and so forth.

NET FORCE IS ZERO

28. Determine if the shape of the engine—round vs. oblong—makes a difference in the speed that a rocket travels.

29. See if your results replicate when going up at a 45-degree angle.

30. Build a Cub Scout Space Derby racer and use it to collect data.

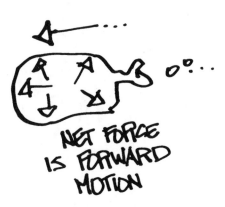

NET FORCE IS FORWARD MOTION

Big Idea 3

Friction is the amount of force preventing two surfaces from moving past each other.

What's the Rub?

The Experiment

As anyone who has tooled around the physics lab for any kind of time at all will tell you, not all surfaces are created equal. This is one of those inalienable principles of physics—one that you will get to experiment with today.

Today, we are less concerned with equality and more concerned with the friction that is created when two surfaces pass by each other. In this lab, the constant will be the friction created by a tabletop. The variable will be four different surfaces that you drag across the tabletop to measure the amount of friction that is created.

Materials

1   Paperclip
1   24-inch length of string
1   Eye screw
1   Wood block, 2 inches by 4 inches by 6 inches
1   Spring balance
1   Eye hook
1   Roll of tape
1   Sheet of construction paper
1   Sheet of wax paper
1   Sheet of tissue paper
1   Sheet of sandpaper

Procedure

1. Open the paperclip up to form an "S" shape. Tie one end of the string around the bottom of the paperclip, as is shown here. This will be the hook that attaches to the eye screw in the wood block.

What's the Rub?

2. Tie a loop in the other end of the string so that you may insert the hook on the spring balance.

3. Screw the eye hook into the end of the wood block and hook the paperclip into the eye screw. Stretch the string out and start to pull the wood block across the table. As you pull the two surfaces, the wood block and the tabletop will begin to interact. Pull the wood block across the tabletop as evenly and smoothly as possible. Read the amount of force, in *Newtons,* that it takes to pull the block across the tabletop. Record that information in your data table.

4. Repeat this experiment two more times and then take the average of the three readings.

5. Place the wood block at the end of the table again—only this time cut and tape a piece of wax paper for the bottom side of the wood block. With the wax paper in place, pull the block across the tabletop and record the amount of force that it takes to overcome the friction between the two surfaces. Take three readings and average them like you did for the first surface.

6. Repeat this experiment three more times, replacing the wax paper with construction paper, tissue paper, and sandpaper. Take three readings for each material and record your observations in the data table below.

Data & Observations

Surface	#1	#2	#3	Average
Wood				
Wax Paper				
Construction Paper				
Tissue Paper				
Sandpaper				

How Come, Huh?

If you could shrink down and become very small—small enough to fit comfortably between the wood block and the tabletop—you would see two very rough surfaces. As the wood block starts to move, pieces of the surface of the wood block catch on pieces of the tabletop, and they get tangled up. This happens bazillions of times between the wood block and the tabletop, and it makes it harder for the wood block to slide along the surface. The "stickiness" between the two surfaces is called friction.

Different surfaces act differently, depending on the abundance and size of the little hooks that are sticking down, trying to grab the tabletop. The more the surfaces grab one another, the more force it takes to slide the block, and the more friction there is. The easier it is to slide the block, the less friction there is between the two surfaces.

Science Fair Extensions

31. Use a concrete sidewalk instead of a tabletop and repeat all five tests, measuring the amount of friction between the surfaces.

...What a Drag

The Experiment

Air provides a considerable amount of friction. Just ask any meteorite that makes it all the way through the atmosphere and plunks into the Earth ... that is, if it makes it to the surface without burning up in the atmosphere.

Air is matter, air takes up space, and any object that wishes to navigate the atmosphere of our planet must figure out a way to move through, over, under, or around the quintazillions of air molecules in its way.

This experiment will allow you to see and experiment with the effect of surface area on air friction.

Materials

2   Pennies
2   Index cards, 3 inches by 5 inches
1   Roll of tape
    Air
2   Hands
1   Clock with sweep-second hand
2   Coffee filters

Procedure

1.   Tape one penny to the middle of an index card. This is Card 1.

2.   Tape the other penny on the edge of a card, directly across from the middle.   This is Card 2.

3.   Hold Card 1 in the palm of your hand.   Hold your arm straight out from you.   Use the illustration above as a guide. Hold Card 2 the same way.   Count to three and drop your arms quickly so that the cards fall toward the ground at the same time.

4. Repeat the experiment, dropping one card at a time. Drop each card three times and in the data table, record the amount of time it takes for each card to hit the floor. Find the average for each card.

5. Take one of the two coffee filters and crumple it up as small as possible. Leave the other filter in its original shape.

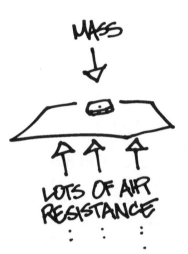

6. Hold the crinkled coffee filter in the palm of one hand and the perfectly shaped, uncrinkled coffee filter in the other palm. Drop them the same way you dropped the cards in the previous steps. Note how fast each piece of paper falls to the ground.

7. Repeat the experiment, dropping one coffee filter at a time. Drop each filter three times and record in the data table the amount of time it takes for each filter to hit the floor. Find the average for each.

Data & Observations

Item	Trial #1	Trial #2	Trial #3	Average
Card 1				
Card 2				
Coffee Filter 1				
Coffee Filter 2				

...What a Drag

How Come, Huh?

Air friction. Next time you are zipping down the road, ask your parents if you can shove your hand out the window. Stick your hand out flat to the wind, and it will feel like the air is going to rip it right off your arm. Slice the air with a skinny hand, and your portable airfoil zips through the air with little-to-no resistance.

This is because air is matter and it takes up space. If a large, flat surface pushes against the air molecules, it takes lots of energy to move all of those molecules out of the way. If you reduce the surface, you reduce the number of air molecules you are running into. Reduce the amount of air friction, and it is easier to move.

When you taped the penny to the center of the card, you were insuring that the card would fall flat, with the greatest amount of surface area and consequently the greatest amount of air friction pushing against it. The card with the penny at the edge, on the other hand, tipped toward the penny and fell through the air, with a very thin edge pushing against the air. Same thing with the coffee filters. The crumpled coffee filter has much less resistance than the open, wider coffee filter.

Science Fair Extensions

32. Use parachutes to demonstrate how air friction affects the speed at which an object falls.

33. Compare air foils to parachutes. Explain the difference between the two.

34. Find out how parachutes are used in drag cars.

Reducing Resistance

The Experiment

Friction is created when two surfaces come in contact with each other. As the two surfaces pass, they grab and pull each other in the direction that is opposite to the way that they each want to move, and this resistance is called friction. This friction can cause one of the objects to slow down, get hot, or even be torn up. Just ask your knees after they

have taken a long slide over a carpet, and they will tell you that there is a lot of grabbing, heating, and tearing going on.

To reduce this friction, there are a couple of things that you can do. One, you can reduce the amount of surface exposed. We did this in the last experiment. Or, you can add something to act as a buffer between the two surfaces—a lubricant that makes it easier for the two surfaces to slide past each other.

Materials

1	Bottle of hand lotion	2	Hands
1	Clock with sweep-second hand	1	Liquid crystal thermometer
1	Paperclip		
1	Piece of cotton string, 12 inches	1	Spring balance
1	Wood block with eye screw	1	Table
1	Bottle of talcum powder	1	Air hockey table
1	Air hockey puck	2	Paddles
1	Partner		

Reducing Resistance

Procedure A

1. Hold you hands open and together, just as though you were saying a prayer before a big math test. Place a liquid crystal thermometer between your hands and note the temperature. Record that temperature in the data table at the bottom of the page.

2. Watching the clock, rub your hands together as fast and as hard as you can for 20 seconds. You should notice a significant increase in the temperature that you feel.

3. When the 20-second mark has been reached, place the liquid crystal thermometer between your hands again, hold it there for 5 seconds, and record the new temperature that you see. Record that number in the second row of the data table.

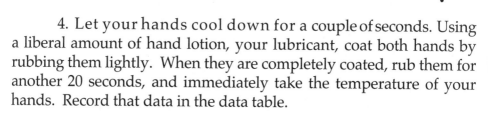

4. Let your hands cool down for a couple of seconds. Using a liberal amount of hand lotion, your lubricant, coat both hands by rubbing them lightly. When they are completely coated, rub them for another 20 seconds, and immediately take the temperature of your hands. Record that data in the data table.

Data & Observations A

Test	Temperature	Difference
Holding hands still		////////
Rubbing without lubricant		
Rubbing with lubricant		

Procedure B

1. Open a paperclip up so that it forms an "S." Tie it to one end of the cotton string and tie a loop in the other end. Attach the spring balance to the loop.

2. Slide the paperclip into the eye screw on the wood block. Place the wood block on the surface of the table at one end. Gently and evenly pull the wood block across the surface of the table; then read the amount of force that it takes to pull the block. Do this three times, so that you get a good average.

3. Open up the bottle of talcum powder—your lubricant—and sprinkle it on the bottom of the wood block and along the pathway on which you'll pull the block. Place the block at the far end of the table and pull it across, reading the amount of force that it takes to do so. Be sure to do this three times, also, and determine the average.

4. Compare the amount of force that it takes to pull the block with and without the lubricant. Record all data.

Data & Observations B

Test	#1	#2	#3	Average
Block w/lubricant				
Block w/o lubricant				

Reducing Resistance

Procedure C

1.   Place the air hockey puck on the table. With you and your partner at each end, as if you are in the heat of competition, start whacking the puck back and forth. After you have each hit the puck three or four times, turn the air blower on.

2.   With air coming up through the holes in the table, whack the puck back and forth three or four more times and compare the difference between the two conditions.

How Come, Huh?

A. When you were rubbing your hands together, they got very hot. If you could use a very powerful microscope to look at the surface of your hands, you would see why. There are tons of ridges, bumps, valleys, grooves—all kinds of places to hook, grab, pull, and generally create resistance.

As these two surfaces pass by each other, they not only grab each other and try to keep the other side from moving, but they also convert some energy to heat—which you should have measured with the liquid crystal thermometer.

When you placed the lubricant on your hands, two things happened. First of all, a lot of those grooves, bumps, and valleys got filled in with lotion. The two surfaces were smoother. Second, the lotion was full of water. Water absorbs heat.

So, when you rubbed your hands the second time, the surfaces were smoother and the lotion absorbed some of the heat that was produced.

B. The talcum powder was a little different. If you could see the talcum powder under a microscope, it would look like bazillions of tiny, white ball bearings.

When you pulled the wood block the first time, it was wood against wood. The second time, there were all these tiny ball bearings between the wood surfaces, so there was less surface area and, therefore, less friction.

C. Finally, the air hockey game was so successful because it almost completely reduced the friction between the plastic puck and the metal surface. The air supported the puck so that it would float, almost frictionlessly, over the metal.

Science Fair Extensions

35. Look at the role of lubricants, particularly graphite, in Pinewood Derby competitions. Compare the speed of cars with and without graphite on the axle shafts.

36. Try using corn oil as a lubricant between your hands, and note what you feel.

Table Surfing

The Experiment

In the previous experiment, we suggested that the talcum powder would look like countless tiny ball bearings, if you were able to actually see them. Ball bearings are used in machines to reduce friction all the time. You will find them in bicycle wheels, gear casings, in power tools, and in any place that it's important for two surfaces, usually metal, to slide past each other.

In this lab, you will see the dramatic effect of reducing the contact between two surfaces. In this case, the surfaces include tables that you will surf from one end of the lunchroom to the other.

Materials

2	Tables	1	Bag of marbles
4	Assistants	1	Metric ruler
	Adult Supervision		

Procedure

1. With the permission of an adult, flip a table upside down and stand on it. With one assistant at each leg, have them pull you from one end of the lunchroom to the other. It should not be very easy, especially if you are the starting tackle for the football team.

2. Step off the tabletop and carefully place eight marbles under the surface. Try to space them out as evenly as you can. Have your friends hold each of the four legs again while you gently step onto the table, supported by only the eight marbles.

3. This is the tricky part. You need only one person to push you down the floor. If you have not figured out how to do this yet, you will very quickly. The other three assistants have the dubious job of trying to place marbles in front of the moving table fast enough so that it flows freely, while at the same time collecting the marbles that come out the back side.

The objective is to take advantage of this reduced surface area to travel as quickly to the end of the room as is possible. Be sure to go the same speed as with your original test.

Data & Observations

Measure the surface area of the table, and then measure the surface area of the eight marbles that are touching the table.

How Come, Huh?

The surface area of the table should be somewhere around 12 square feet, or roughly 5400 cubic centimeters. The surface area of the eight marbles is 1 cubic centimeter, if you are being very generous. This quick math tells us that it should be 5000 times easier to push the table with ball bearings than it is to push the table without them.

Science Fair Extensions

37. 5000 times easier? Prove it.

Big Idea 4

Newton's First Law: An object at rest or moving at a constant velocity will continue to do so unless acted on by an extenal force. This is also known as the Law of Inertia.

Weight vs. Mass

The Experiment

On Earth, there is no real difference between the two terms, *weight* and *mass*. However, for purposes of definition, physicists view them differently.

Mass is the measure of the amount of matter in an object. Weight is the force of attraction between that object and the particular planet or moon that it is currently resting on. For example, you plunk your bones on the bathroom scale here on Earth. The scale reads 75 pounds. That is your mass, in pounds, on Earth. It is also your weight.

Now, if you were to take a spaceship to the Moon and step on a Moon man's bathroom scale, the reading would be quite different. The Moon has one-sixth the gravitational attraction (pull) of the Earth. So, the force attracting you to the surface of the Moon would be one-sixth as great. Your weight on the Moon? A very skinny 12 pounds. However, you still have the same mass (amount of matter in your body) as you did on Earth, so your mass on the Moon would be 75 pounds, but your weight (the force attracting you to the surface of the Moon) would be 12 pounds.

Even funnier still is your weight in space. When you get out a certain distance from the Earth, the force of gravity is zero. The term that is used by astronauts is that you are *weightless*. You still have all 75 pounds of your mass with you, but because there is not any attraction between you and the spaceship, your weight is zero.

So, for purposes of measuring here on Earth, the terms *weight* and *mass* can be used interchangeably. However, if you start taking physics classes on other planets, you will have to expand your terminology a bit.

Weight vs. Mass

Materials

1   String, 12 inches long
1   Paperclip
1   Spring balance
4   Fishing weights

Procedure

1. Open the paperclip up to form an "S" shape. Tie one end of the string around the bottom of the paperclip, as in the picture at the right. This will be the hook that attaches to the fishing weights that you are going to use in the experiment.

2. Tie a loop in the other end of the string so that you may hang it off the hook that you find on the spring balance.

3. Add one fishing weight to the spring balance and let it hang. The fishing weights should have weights stamped on them in grams. When you look on the side of the spring balance, you will see two sets of numbers. One is in grams and the other is in Newtons (a measure of force). Record both numbers in the data table on the next page.

4. Add a second, third, and fourth fishing weight to the spring balance. Record the mass in grams and the weight in Newtons each time you add a weight.

Data & Observations

# Fishing Weights	Mass (g)	Weight (N)
0		
1		
2		
3		
4		

How Come, Huh?

The main thing to remember is that mass is a description of an amount of matter—the amount of stuff you have. Weight is a measure of how hard that pile of stuff is being attracted to the planet or Moon that it is on. So, mass is an amount of matter, and weight is an amount of force pulling that matter toward the planet.

Different planets and moons have different masses, and therefore dramatically different gravitational pulls. One hundred pounds of stuff will weigh 100 pounds on the Earth, but only 16 pounds on the Moon, and nothing on the trip *to* the Moon—but it will always have a mass of 100 pounds.

Science Fair Extensions

38. Do a little research and find out what the gravitational attraction is for every planet. Using that information, prepare a chart to show how much you would weigh on each planet in our solar system.

39. When you play air hockey, the puck is said to be on a frictionless surface. That is why it slides so easily. What is the difference between a frictionless surface and a weightless environment? Demonstrate the difference between the two using an air hockey table.

Rubberband Scales

The Experiment

Inertia is a term that is used to describe how much force it takes to get a stationary object moving. The amount of mass in an object and the amount of inertia are in direct proportion to each other.

In this lab, we are going to create a new tool, a rubberband scale, and use an unusual unit of measure, the paperclip. As soon as we bring them to life, we are going to start to build our understanding of inertia and mass.

Materials

1   Sheet of cover paper
1   Pair of scissors
1   Roll of tape
1   Rubberband
1   5 oz. wax cup
1   12-inch length of string
1   Box of paperclips
1   Pencil

Procedure

1. Fold the cover paper lengthwise. Unfold and cut along the crease.

2. Position the rubberband at the top of the page and tape the top edge of it to the cover page. Use the illustration at the right as a guide.

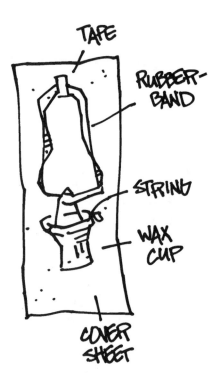

3. Punch two small holes opposite each other into the top of the wax cup, near the lip. Thread the string through one of the holes, and tie it off.

4. Thread the string through the bottom of the rubberband and into the other hole in the cup. Tie the string off.

5. You should now have a rubberband taped to the top of a long, skinny piece of paper, with a paper cup "bucket" hanging off the bottom of the rubberband. Use the illustration shown here to verify that all of the directions have been followed.

6. Hold the paper upright and mark the location of the bottom of the rubberband. This is your 0 paperclip mark.

7. Add 5 paperclips to the wax cup and see how far the rubberband has stretched. Mark that point with a pencil.

8. Continue to add paperclips in increments of 5 all the way until you have 100 paperclips listed on your scale.

9. Using your scale, weigh various objects by putting them in the cup and determining the force in number of paperclips it would take to lift each object.

How Come, Huh?

All objects have mass, and this mass gives them inertia proportional to their mass. The more mass and inertia, the more the rubberband was stretched.

Science Fair Extensions

40. Replace the rubberband with a wire spring and create another instrument that can measure.

Currency Exchange

The Experiment

Stack five washers on a hard, smooth surface. Without touching the stack of washers in any way, take a sixth washer and place it under the stack.

Surprisingly, when you count the stack, there are only five washers in the pile. Use Newton's First Law to help you out.

Materials

6   Washers
1   Smooth surface
1   Finger
1   Table with smooth top

Procedure

1. Stack five of the washers, one on top of the other, so that you form a tower of washers. Do this on a smooth, slick surface, such as a hardwood table or a kitchen countertop.

2. Aim the remaining washer at the bottom of the stack of washers and give it a good hard flick with your finger so that it heads straight for the bottom washer on a direct collision course.

3. As the washer travels toward the pile, it has kinetic energy. When this washer strikes the washer on the bottom of the pile, it transfers its energy to that washer, which begins its journey across the tabletop, while the energy donor rests comfortably under the pile. It happens every time.

How Come, Huh?

1. According to Sir Isaac Newton, an object at rest remains at rest, unless a force acts on it. It has inertia, so it's not moving. In the case of our stack of washers, they are happy to hang out on the table.

2. We know that energy can be transferred from one object to another in a variety of ways. It can push, pull, twist, or collide. In this case, the sixth washer is the washer with the energy. As it goes sliding along the tabletop, it hits the bottom washer in the pile and transfers all of its energy to that washer when it collides with it.

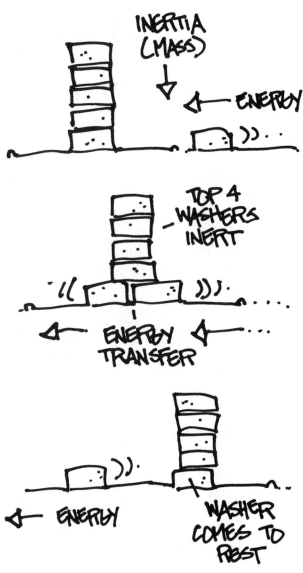

3. When two objects collide, it is possible for the moving object to give all of its energy to the stationary object and stop dead in its tracks—while the object that was once stationary absorbs the energy and starts moving. This happens all the time in the game of pool, and occasionally in politics. Turn the page for the big picture.

Currency Exchange

The lone washer was given energy by your finger; the other 5 washers were fat, happy, and inert—content to just sit and hang out. When the washer that was launched from your finger struck the bottom washer, it transferred all of its energy to that washer and stopped dead in its tracks, under the pile. Meanwhile, the washer that was on the bottom of the stack now has all of this new energy, so it zips off down the tabletop until friction gets the best of the deal and stops the washer.

Science Fair Extensions

41.   Try flicking two washers at the same time into a stack of four washers. If you want to make this really interesting, whip three washers at three washers and see what happens.

42.   Talk someone into letting you play a game of pool. After you have a chance to play for awhile, compare that game with this experiment.

43.   Try the old "whip the tablecloth out from under the dishes" trick. Get permission and use old, heavy dishes. Make sure the table-cloth does not have a hem.

Catching Washers

The Experiment

Arrange three washers in a straight line on your right forearm. Your challenge is to figure out a way to grab all five of the washers using only your right hand.

Oh, two other things: One, you can't drop any of the washers, and two, as you probably already suspect, Isaac's First Law can help you out with this challenge as well. To that lab!

Materials

3   Washers, 1.5-inch diameter
1   Set of quick reflexes

Procedure

1.   Place the three washers on your arm, as shown here. Do your best to arrange them in a straight line. You will have much more success if you do.

MOTION OF ARM

2.   This is the part that requires a little bit of practice. As quickly as you can, move your hand forward. As you drop your elbow, the washers will remain suspended in the air for a very brief moment due to the inertia they possess. This gives you time to bring your hand forward and catch all three of the washers before they disappear to the floor below.

Catching Washers

How Come, Huh?

The washers have mass. This means that they also have inertia—the tendency to resist moving until enough force is applied to overcome the amount of mass. They will remain in place for a brief moment if their support (your arm) is removed.

The washers are also lined up in a straight line. This is consistent with the way that your arm and your hand move forward when you drop your elbow straight down.

So when you put it all together, this is what you have: As you dropped your elbow, the washers were temporarily suspended in the air. The cool thing is that, because of the way that your body has been designed, your hand moved in a perfectly straight line as your elbow and arm dropped toward the floor in an arc. This straight-line movement allowed you to nab all of the washers simply by dropping your arm— although a little bit of hand-eye coordination is helpful.

Science Fair Extensions

44. When we were kids in junior high school, we used to make a game of catching quarters. We would have a contest to see who could line up the most quarters on their arm and still catch them all. Try the same thing with washers, and even if you lose, you will probably still be able to eat lunch.

45. Make a list of 10 things that you can balance and catch.

Ring & Dowel

The Experiment

Snap the small plastic dowel off the inside of the ring. Balance the ring on the mouth of the pop bottle and place the plastic dowel directly on top of the ring. The whole setup should look something like the illustration at the right.

Your task, the proverbial challenge as it may be, is to remove the ring from the top of the bottle in such a manner that the plastic dowel falls directly and succinctly into the pop bottle. Call it a hole in one, a shot down the middle, or threading the proverbial physics needle ... we don't care. Just get the dowel in the bottle.

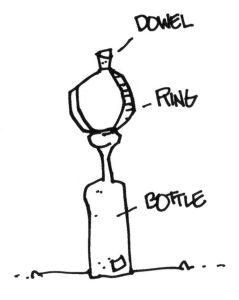

Materials

1   1/2-inch piece of plastic dowel
1   Soda pop bottle, empty, clean
1   5-inch diameter plastic ring, 0.5 inch thick
1   Pile of gullible friends

Procedure

1.   Set the plastic ring on the bottle opening. Balance the dowel on the very top of the ring, directly over the opening of the hole. Use the illustration at the upper-right as a guide.

2.   In honor of Sir Isaac Newton and his First Law, you are going to play a game that demonstrates inertia with your friends. The object of the game is to remove the ring and have the dowel fall directly into the bottle. Demonstrate this in slow motion.

Ring & Dowel

3. Replace the ring and dowel. Theatrically, whap the outside of the ring several times, causing the dowel to pop up in the air. Your obvious lack of success should be very noticeable to your friends. After three or four unsuccessful attempts, stop and up the ante. Bet your friends something small, like a candy bar, or maybe have them do your chores for an evening if you can successfully knock the dowel into the bottle.

4. When you go to knock the ring out of the way this time, you will want to pass by the outside edge and whap the ring in the middle. This flattens the ring while you move it out of the way, and it allows the dowel to fall directly into the opening of the bottle. Everyone groans—and you get a clean room.

How Come, Huh?

When the ring is hit on the outside edge, the force from your finger causes the ring to compress upward. The upward movement of the plastic is transferred to the dowel, which shoots up into the air. It is possible that the dowel would

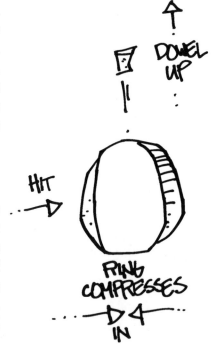

DOWEL UP

HIT

RING COMPRESSES IN

then fall directly into the pop bottle, but in 15 years of doing this demonstration, we are 0 for 24,718. But, it could happen. It is mathematically possible.

The more predictable method of solving this puzzle is to pass by the outside of the ring and whack the inside of the ring. This stretches the ring outward, which produces an interesting result from the dowel's point of view. It is experiencing Newton's First Law.

One minute, the dowel is resting comfortably on its perch above the bottle. The next minute, it is suspended in midair with absolutely nothing underneath it. The ring is removed without disturbing the dowel, much like pulling a tablecloth out from under a pile of dishes. It happens so quickly that none of the energy is transferred from the tablecloth to the dishes, or in this case, the ring to the dowel.

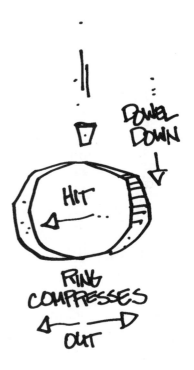

The end result is that the ring is gone, the dowel is in midair thanks to its inertia, and the bottle is directly below, perfectly lined up for a hole in one. Gravity takes over, tugs the dowel straight down, and with no other forces to disrupt its path, it falls directly into the bottle—most of the time.

Science Fair Extensions

46. Supersize this expeirment. Use a 5-gallon water bottle, a giant ring made from a plastic barrel or drum, and a huge wooden dowel. Same concept, same outcome ... just easier to see.

Dizzy Chickens

The Experiment

Two chicken eggs, both white ... Figure out which one is raw and which one is hard-boiled without having to crack either one open.

Materials

1	Hard-boiled chicken egg
1	Raw chicken egg
1	Smooth, hard surface
1	Finger
1	Pencil
1	Sink

Procedure

1. Spin one of the eggs in a clockwise motion, gently touch your finger to the top of the egg for a second, and then quickly release it. If the egg stops dead in its spin, it is hard-boiled. But if the egg starts spinning again once it is released, it is raw.

When you think that you have determined if the egg is raw or hard-boiled, write your educated guess on the shell, using a pencil.

2. Repeat the experiment with the second egg. The results that you get should be opposite those for the first egg. Identify your guess on the shell of this egg, also. Crack both eggs over a sink and see if your guesses were correct.

How Come, Huh?

Once an egg has been boiled, the previously-liquid proteins, which make up what we call the yolk and the white inside the egg, coagulate, and they become solid all the way through. There are no fluids present. The hard-boiled egg is solid throughout, so it acts like a single unit. When you spin the shell, the contents, which are solid, follow along by default. However, if you place your finger on the top of the hard-boiled egg, you stop both the inside and the outside of the egg. The force of your finger stopping the shell is enough to keep the entire egg stopped.

A raw egg has a liquid center, made up of the yolk and white, that is not connected to the hard shell of the egg. When you spin the shell, it takes a second for the energy to be transferred to the yolk and get it spinning. When you put your finger on the shell and stop it, the liquid contents of the egg continue to spin. They are moving and have inertia. The amount of friction between the inside of the egg and shell is not enough to stop it right away. When you take your finger off the shell, the liquid inside the shell, which is still spinning, exerts a force on the eggshell and starts it spinning again.

HARD-BOILED, CENTER & SHELL STOP

RAW, SHELL STOPS LIQUID CENTER STILL MOVING

Science Fair Extensions

47. Substitute plastic eggs for the real thing. Fill both with water and stick one in the freezer. Take both eggs and see if you can use the same technique to tell which one is still liquid inside and which one is frozen solid.

48. Build an inclined track that will hold an egg. Roll eggs, with both liquid and solid centers, down the track. Determine if there is any difference between a solid and liquid center in terms of how far and how fast the eggs travel.

Big Idea 5

Newton's Second Law: For every action, there is an equal and opposite reaction.

Collision City

The Experiment

Collisions are a way of life for us. When you sit down on a chair, it is a controlled collision. When you run into a door and cause it to swing open, another collision. Drop your books on the table, collision. Toss a ball at a competitor racing across the prison ball field and nail him in the thigh, collision.

Isaac Newton observed collisions and concluded that for every action, there is an equal and opposite reaction. This is known in the fair city of New York as the "You whap me and I'm gonna whap you" principle. Newton simply called it his Second Law of Motion.

In this lab, you are going to drop a variety of objects and measure the amount of elasticity they have when they collide with the floor. From this data, you can conclude how much energy was lost in the collision.

Materials

1 Meterstick
1 Superball
1 Racquetball
1 Tennis ball
1 Sponge ("Nerf") ball
1 Ball of clay
1 Fresh egg

Procedure

1. You have six different objects to drop. Hold each object so that the bottom of the sphere is at the top of the meterstick. Make sure each one falls one full meter. Hold the meterstick so the 100-cm mark is on the floor.

Collision City

2. Release the sphere, let it hit the floor, and then catch it at the top of its rebound. Measure the height that it rebounded by looking at the bottom of the sphere, not the top.

3. Repeat the experiment three times and determine the average height that the sphere rebounded.

4. Repeat this procedure for the remainder of the spheres until you have dropped and measured the first five. When you get to the sixth sphere, you are going to have to ask for your parents' permission. Assuming that they give you the go-ahead, you need to drop a raw egg only once—simply for the database. Every result, as you can imagine, will be the same.

Data & Observations

Item Dropped	Trial 1	Trial 2	Trial 3	Average
Superball				
Racquetball				
Tennis ball				
Sponge ball				
Ball of clay				
Fresh egg				

To determine the amount, or percentage, of energy lost in a collision, all you have to do is plug your numbers into a simple mathematical equation. Energy Lost (e-) equals the average height rebounded (h_1) divided by the total height dropped (h_2). It looks like this:

$$e\text{-} = h_1 / h_2$$

Using this formula, calculate the percentage of energy lost for each ball, and then rank the balls from most elastic (the highest number) to least elastic (the most energy lost).

Ball	Height Rebounded	Original Height	%	Rank
Superball				
Racquetball				
Tennis ball				
Sponge ball				
Ball of clay				
Fresh egg				

How Come, Huh?

As you can see from your data, every ball is different. Some of the energy, a very small amount, is lost to air friction—the air molecules push on the ball as it falls to the ground and then rebounds back again. Most of the energy lost was dissipated by the material in the ball itself. The ball hits the ground, it squishes, giving energy to the floor; the floor pushes back on the ball, and depending on how well the ball responds, the ball bounces back up off the ground ... unless, of course, you are an egg. The amount that the ball bounces back is called its elasticity.

Newton's Cradle

The Experiment

Isaac Newton was a very famous scientist who lived in Europe in the 1600s. He not only came up with three laws to describe the motion of objects, but he also invented the branch of mathematics called calculus, to help him explain the movement and behaviors of objects that he observed during his course of studies.

Materials

1   Newton's Cradle

Procedure

1.   As you first look at the cradle, you will see five to seven metal balls, depending on your version of the model, hanging from two supporting threads. All of the balls are at rest.

2.   Grab the end ball and pull it back. By doing this, you are giving the ball energy, or more specifically, potential energy. Release the ball and observe what happens to the other balls in the cradle.

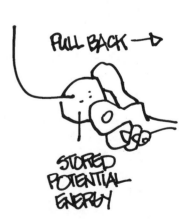

3.   This time, pull two balls back and release them together. Observe what happens when they hit the remaining balls and transfer their energy.

4. Repeat this experiment, pulling three, four, and then finally all five of the metal balls back as a group, and releasing them as a group, too.

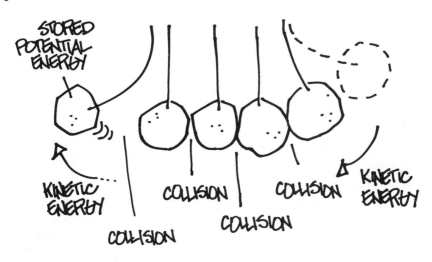

How Come, Huh?

As you lifted the end ball up, you gave it potential energy. When you released the ball, it started to move as gravity pulled on it, and it fell toward the stack. When the end ball hit the next ball in the stack, it transferred all of its energy through the collision. The second ball did not have far to travel until it hit the third ball or the fourth. Finally, when the fourth ball hit the end ball, it was free to move, so it swung out away from the group, storing the kinetic energy as potential energy. When that ball got to the peak of its swing, it stored all of the kinetic energy as potential energy, but only for a second. It then returned back to the other balls and started the transfer of energy through collisions going the other way.

Science Fair Extensions

49. Demonstrate the same principle, using a pool table, balls, and pool cue.

Racquetball Launcher

The Experiment

Your task is to take a small Superball and, dropping it from waist height, get it to bounce from the floor and hit the ceiling. A couple of rules to follow before you do the Sherlock Holmes ...

1. The ball may only be dropped, not thrown, shot, or accelerated toward the floor in any way other than using plain old gravitational attraction from a free release.

2. You may not kick the ball, have it land on a mousetrap, or smack it with a baseball bat once it hits the floor. (It must rebound to the ceiling using only the energy that was given to it as it was dropped to the ground from waist height.)

3. You may use other objects to transfer energy to the small Superball, but they must be dropped at the same time and from the same height.

Materials

1   Playground ball, 10-inch diameter
1   Superball, small
1   Hard surface
1   Pair of hands
1   Meterstick

Procedure

1. Drop the large playground ball, holding it four feet above the floor. Measure how far it bounces back up. Some of the energy in the ball is lost to the floor as friction and heat, but for the most part, it bounces back to you. This is called a partially elastic collision. Do this three times to get an average height.

2. Now drop the little Superball from the same place and see how high it bounces back up. Some of the energy in the ball is lost to the floor with the little ball as well. Better ... but still partially elastic. Do this three times.

3. This is the tricky part. Place the Superball on top of the large ball, as is shown in the illustration above, and drop both balls together from the same height. See what happens. Repeat this three times.

Data & Observations

Object	Trial #1	Trial #2	Trial #3	Average
Playground ball				
Superball				
Balls together				

Racquetball Launcher

How Come, Huh?

When two objects collide, they transfer energy. If the two objects that are colliding are both elastic, like the Superballs, the transfer of energy tends to be more complete.

The amount of energy in each ball is partly determined by the weight of the ball. Newton's Second Law at work: $F = ma$, or force equals the mass times the acceleration. In simple terms, the big ball has more energy than the little ball.

When the balls were dropped onto the floor individually, some of their energy was lost to the floor as friction and heat. When you dropped the two balls together, the big ball hit a fraction of a second sooner than the Superball. It smacked the floor and started to rebound up into the air, when it immediately collided with the Superball still coming down. The big ball had lots of energy and transferred almost all of it to the little ball. The scientific term for this is *conservation of momentum* and *conservation of energy*, and it is the reason the little ball went zinging up the way it did. The little ball had all the energy that the big ball had had, but only one-fourth the weight.

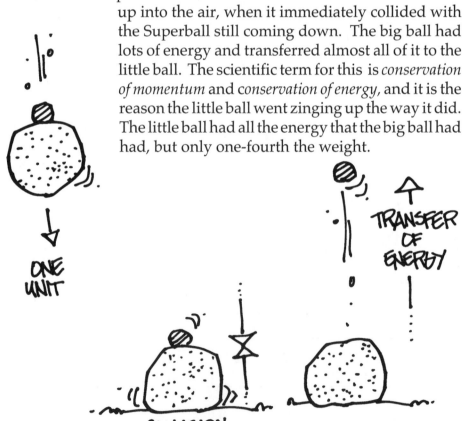

ONE UNIT

TRANSFER OF ENERGY

COLLISION

The formula brings it home: $M_1V_1=M_2V_2$. M stands for mass and V is for velocity. The mass and velocity of the two balls dropped must equal the mass and velocity of just the small ball shooting up into the air. In order for this to be the case, the velocity must increase to make up for the loss of mass. It does this by leaving the big ball behind.

Science Fair Extensions

50. Use different balls for the bottom ball. Try a big, red playground ball, a volleyball, a football, or anything that you can think of that will bounce. List the balls that you used from the one that makes the little ball bounce the highest to the one that makes it bounce the lowest. Get that scale out and weigh the balls to see if they are being true to Mr. Newton's Second Law.

51. Repeat the experiment but use a pool ball and a metal or glass marble. See if you get the same results.

52. Try wooden blocks that are cut to different sizes. Compare the density of the wooden blocks with the metal/glass/ceramic material that the spheres were made from.

53. Make air hockey pucks of different sizes and from different kinds of wood. Collide the pucks on the air hockey table and see if the Law of Conservation of Momentum holds up.

Astroblaster

The Experiment

An Astroblaster is a physics toy that demonstrates all kinds of ideas. First, it reinforces the ideas from the previous lab, (conservation of momentum.) It also demonstrates Newton's Law of Action and Reaction as well as force equals mass times acceleration.

Beyond all that, it is a great way to wind up chasing a little red ball all over your classroom, house, or down the street, if you are silly enough to drop this off the roof of your garage, like we were.

Materials

1   Astroblaster
1   Hard surface

Procedure

1. Your Astroblaster should be comprised of four balls stacked on a stick—each ball getting progressively smaller as you go up the stick. Take the small, red ball off the top of the Astroblaster and hold it waist high. Drop it on a hard surface and see how far it rebounds up into the air.

2. Place the ball back on the top of the pile. Hold the Astroblaster by the top of the stick at your waist height and drop it directly to the ground. Observe what happens to the little ball on the top of the pile.

3. Repeat the experiment if you can find your ball.

How Come, Huh?

As the Astroblaster fell toward the ground, all four balls and the stick fell as a unit. When the biggest ball hit the ground first, it collided with the floor and started to rebound. It immediately collided with the next-largest ball, transferring all of its energy to it. The second ball hit the third ball, which immediately smacked into the smallest ball.

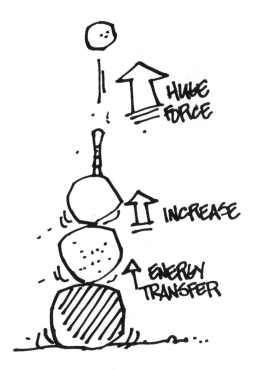

The upshot of all this whacking is that all the energy from the bottom three balls was transferred to the smallest ball. Using our famous conservation of momentum equation, $M_1V_1=M_2V_2$ where M stands for mass and V stands for velocity, we know that the mass and velocity of the four balls dropped must equal the mass and velocity of just the small ball shooting up into the air. In order for this to be the case, the velocity must increase to make up for the loss of mass. The big ball is left behind. This is why the little ball takes off like it does.

Science Fair Extensions

54. On the packaging that comes with the commercial version of the Astroblaster, it claims that this is a model for supernovas. Do some research to find out why the inventors of this toy think that the little ball is like a gamma ray. Explain how in the world you could possibly simulate a supernova on your driveway.

Big Idea 6

The center of gravity is a point where the forces acting on an object are all equal. This point may not necessarily be found in or on the object.

Literary Bridge

The Experiment

We are going to introduce you to the concepts of balance and center of gravity by having you construct a bridge between two tables, using books.

When you are done, you will have a bit of an idea of how the center of gravity can allow you to create structures that you would otherwise think would be impossible to build. You will also understand how the ancient Romans built their arches—history and science all in one lesson.

Materials

20	Books
2	Tables
2	Steady hands

Literary Bridge

Procedure

1. Scoot the two tables together so that they are about 18 inches apart. Use the illustration above as a guide.

2. Place two books, one on each table, directly opposite each other. Place another book on top of each of the first books but, instead of putting them directly over the top of the first books and lining them up so that they are neat, hang them over the edge about an inch.

3. Place another book on top of each of the stacks you just placed on the table. Hang these books over an inch. Build your bridge.

4. Carefully add a fourth and fifth book to the piles on the respective tables. At some point, the two stacks should come very close to connecting. When this happens, place a single book across the opening and complete your literary bridge.

How Come, Huh?

The center of gravity can also be called the center of mass. If you were to find the very center of a symmetrical object, like a book, you would also be at the center of gravity. For example, if you were to measure half the length, half the width, and half the height, you would find the center of gravity for a single book. Illustration please ...

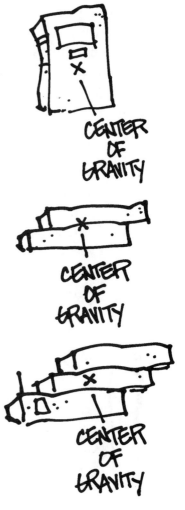

When you plop a second book on top of the first—slightly cockeyed at that—you create a new object with a different center of mass. It is now located between the two books and is shifted toward the top book. Check the illustration for more clarity.

As you continue to add books, the center of gravity continues to shift. When you pile the last book on top of the pile, it will fall to the floor if it is stacked by itself, but because it will now be part of a unit, its center of gravity is much lower in the stack and is still over the table.

Science Fair Extensions

55. Do a little research and find out how the Romans built their famous stone arches that were self-supporting. Does this concept use center of gravity or some other idea?

56. Explain how high-wire walkers use center of gravity to their advantage to help keep them from falling off the wires.

Balancing Stick

The Experiment

Find a large, plastic stick that looks like a craft stick with a groove cut in either side of it. Your task is to get this thing that we call a balancing stick to balance vertically on your fingertip … just like in the cartoon at the right.

Materials

1   Plastic balancing stick
        or
1   Craft stick with notches
1   Piece of bell wire, 18 inches long
6   Large washers
1   Finger

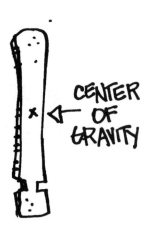

CENTER OF GRAVITY

Procedure

1.   When you place the balancing stick on the end of your finger, it will almost immediately start to fall and be very difficult to balance. The reason for this is that the center of gravity is directly above your finger in the center of the stick, and that center of gravity wants to fall toward your finger.

2.   Bend the bell wire in half and wrap it around the notches that are found near the bottom of the stick. The groove in the plastic balancing stick is designed so that you can wrap a loop of copper wire around it.

3. Bend the ends of the wire into a "U" shape and hang 3 washers off each end of the wire. With the added weight, balance the end of the stick on your finger. You should have better luck because the lower the center of gravity, the easier it is to balance an object. Lower the center of gravity below the focal point, and you are actually creating a downward force to counteract the pull of gravity.

Circus performers who walk on the high wire carry large, flexible poles. The ends of these poles actually droop below the level of the wire. This lowers the center of gravity for the wire walker and actually makes it much easier for him or her to balance.

4. Needless to say, if other kids are trying to balance the stick with no assistance and you are walking around the room with the stick not only balanced but also staying in place as you walk, you will be accused of cheating, playing unfair, and generally behaving in an improper manner. This is all true ... and makes the whole deal a lot of fun.

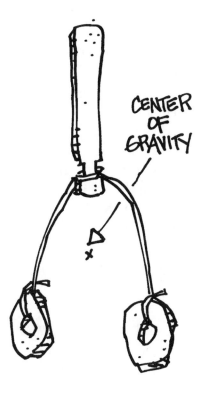

CENTER OF GRAVITY

Balancing Stick

How Come, Huh?

Trying to balance the stick before you add the washers is almost impossible. The entire weight of the stick is above your finger and that weight, pulled by gravity, tends to make the stick fall over.

By wrapping the wire and placing the washers where you did, two things happened. One, you lowered the center of gravity to a point under your finger, and two, this means that there is weight pulling down on the stick when there wasn't any before. This weight created a pair of downward forces that was strong enough to prevent the stick from falling over. The more weight that you add, the more stable the stick becomes. Don't believe us? Try it.

Science Fair Extensions

57. Experiment with the amount of weight you hang off the wire and the stability of the stick. Does the stick become easier or harder to balance as you add more weight?

58. Try getting the stick to hang horizontally from your fingertip. When you are done, the stick should be sticking straight out from the tip of your finger, but it should not fall to the ground.

Clay Ball Sticks

The Experiment

You have a lump of clay and a large piece of wood doweling. Your task is to figure out where to place the lump of clay on the stick—on top, in the middle, near the bottom, or maybe somewhere else—so that the stick can be balanced in the palm of your hand for the greatest amount of time.

Materials

1   Bar of clay
1   Dowel, 11 inches long and 0.5 inch in diameter
1   Hand
1   Watch with sweep-second hand

Procedure

1.   Locate the clay and flatten it into a pancake. Wrap the pancake around one end of the dowel and shape it into a ball around the stick. Smoosh the clay just a little so that the ball stays attached to the stick.

2.   Balance the stick in the position shown in the illustration at the right, and record, in seconds, how long you can keep it from falling over. Do this three times and calculate an average amount of time.

Clay Ball Sticks

3. Flip the stick upside down so that it looks like the picture shown here. See how long you can balance the stick with the weight of clay now at the bottom of the stick. Take three measurements and average the time.

4. Finally, move the ball of clay to the center of the stick and see how long you can balance the stick with the clay in that position. Take three readings, average your times, enter your data in the data table, assume a thoughtful position, and determine where you would place a clay ball to give the stick the most stability.

Data & Observations

Clay Ball	Trial #1	Trial #2	Trial #3	Avg.
Top				
Bottom				
Middle				

The stick is most stable when the clay ball is located _____

_____.

How Come, Huh?

The more mass an object possesses, the more inertia it has and the more force it takes to get it moving: Newton's First Law.

In this case, the mass of the clay ball and stick does not change, but the center of mass does. In the top illustration, the mass is farther away from the hand than in the lower illustration. Because gravity is pulling on the object, or applying a torque and causing it to fall, the scientific term for this idea is called the *moment of inertia.*

The greater the moment of inertia, the more force it takes to get the object moving. The lower the moment of inertia, the easier it is to get the object moving. In this case, the farther the clay is from the palm of your hand, the greater the moment of inertia, the longer it takes for gravity to get the ball moving, and the more time you have to adapt and adjust for the movement of the stick.

Science Fair Extensions

59. Use sticks of different lengths and thicknesses and see if there is any difference in your ability to balance them. When you are done with that, prove that the heavier the ball of clay on the top of the stick, the easier it is to balance the stick in an upright position.

60. Bet your big brother that you can balance the stick longer than he can. Hand him the stick so that he balances it with the ball of clay near his palm. After he tries, flip the stick over and win.

Buddha's Temple

The Experiment

1.   Take one of seven nails and wiggle it into the hole in the center of a square plastic base so that it is sticking straight up out of the center.

2.   Figure out a way to balance the remaining six nails on top of the nail that you have just wiggled into the base. Before you get too tricky, these are the rules that you need to follow:

a.   You must leave the plastic base flat on the table—no tipping, balancing, or otherwise moving the chunk of plastic.

b.   You may not use rubberbands, glue, tape, spit, or any other adhesive to hold the nails in place on the head of the center nail.

c.   The nails cannot touch the plastic base of the square when they are on top of the center nail. In other words, no teepees, metallic bonfires, or nail cones.

Materials

1   Square plastic base
7   #8 nails

Procedure

1.   Place one nail in front of you so that it is horizontal.

2. Place two nails *on top of* the horizontal nail, pointing away from you, and snug them up to the bottom nail shaft so that their heads are touching.

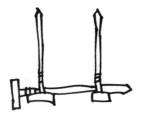

3. Place two more nails on top of the horizontal nail, just inside the two nails you placed in step 2, but these nails should be pointing down toward you. Snug the heads of these nails up to the shaft of the nail, also. You should now be looking at something of an abstract "H."

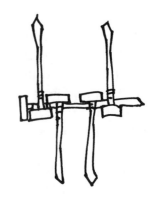

4. Place the final nail in the groove that is created by the four nails on top of the horizontal nail. Be sure to reverse the direction of the top nail and make it point in a direction exactly opposite the very bottom nail.

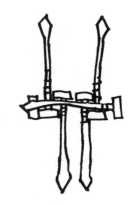

5. Gently pinch the ends of the design and pick it up. Balance the center of the bottom nail on the head of the nail in the plastic base. Use the illustration at the bottom of the page to see how you should set the six nails on the head of the nail in the base.

6. When the nails are balanced, gently let go of the bundle, and the nails will come to rest exactly on top of the head of the nail. They function as a unit, so if you gently tap one of the nails hanging down, the whole thing will rock.

Buddha's Temple

How Come, Huh?

The center point in this experiment is the top of the head of the nail inserted in the plastic base. As gravity pulls down on the four nails hanging off either side of the bottom nail, those nails trap the top nail. Because the weight (force) is equal on both sides, 2 nails hanging one way and 2 nails hanging the opposite way, you have a system that is in balance.

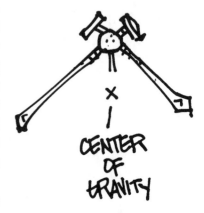

The other factor is that the weight of the nails hanging below the center point changes the center of gravity. It is now below the head of the nail in the plastic base. This is the same trick that tightrope walkers use. They hold a long pole that droops below the wire that they are walking on, and the center of gravity is lower, giving the walker more time to adjust and compensate for ripples in the program.

Science Fair Extensions

61. Add nails in multiples of two and see how many you can get on the center nail. As long as you add them in pairs with equal and opposing forces, you will have success. The record, at least as far as we know, is fifty-four #16 nails stacked in multiple layers. If you can beat that, send us an email with a photograph.

62. Try using different sizes of nails. Most hardware stores stock a variety that go from very small up to railroad spikes that are one foot in length or more.

63. Use other items like toilet plungers or garden rakes, and see if you can replicate the pattern on a grand scale.

Big Idea 7

A buoyant force is created when a liquid exerts an upward force on an object that is immersed in it. This is due, in part, to the density of the object, which can be calculated as mass divided by volume.

Clay Boats

The Experiment

Solid materials like wood, cork, and plastic, float when they are placed in water—not too surprising. That's because their density is less than that of water.

The question before us and the challenge for this lab would be to take a lump of clay, which is much denser than water, and get it to float. To study and understand this idea, we are going to incorporate the ideas of a Greek mathematician, Archimedes, who lived in the third century B.C.

Materials

1   Drinking glass, 12 oz.
    Water
1   Lump of clay
1   1 mL pipette
1   Box of paperclips

Procedure

1.   Fill the drinking glass three-quarters full with water and set it in front of you.

2.   Roll the lump of clay into a ball. Hold it over the water and gently release it. Observe what happens to the lump.

3.   Not too much of a surprise ... it sinks. That's because the clay is denser than the water, so it heads straight to the bottom of the cup and displaces (pushes up) an equal volume of water.

4. Shape the clay so that it forms half a sphere. Use the illustration on the previous page to help you complete this task. Place the clay gently in the water and observe what happens this time.

You should see a much different result. The clay, without changing its mass or relative density, now floats in the water.

5. Now comes the fun part. You are going to test the ability of the clay boat that you created to support weight before it sinks. The way that you are going to do this is to create boats of different volumes, squishing the clay and making the inside volume larger by making the walls of the boat thinner.

6. Let's start with a boat that has thick walls. Roll the clay into a ball. Stick your thumb into the clay, make an indentation, and shape the indentation into a boat that you know will float.

7. Using a 1-milliliter pipette, fill the center of the boat with 3 milliliters of water. The water level should come just to the top edge of the boat. If it does not, make the boat either bigger or smaller so that it holds exactly 3 mL of water.

8. Place your boat in the glass of water so that it floats.

9. Gently add paperclips, one at a time, until your boat sinks. In the data table on the next page, record the number of paperclips it took to sink your boat. Then, retrieve your boat from the bottom of the glass.

10. Make the boat a little larger this time so that it now holds 6 mL of water. Place the boat in the water and gently add paperclips until the boat sinks again.

Clay Boats

11. Repeat this procedure with boats that have volumes of 9 mL and 12 mL. On a separate sheet of paper, graph your data to see if there is a predictable pattern that evolves from the information that you have collected.

Data & Observations

Volume of Boat	# Paperclips
3 mL	
6 mL	
9 mL	
12 mL	

How Come, Huh?

Back to our friend Archimedes ... Archimedes discovered that the buoyant force, the upward push on an object in a fluid, is equal to the volume of the liquid that is displaced (pushed out of the way) by that object.

What this means is that, when we put the clay ball in the water, it started shoving the water molecules aside as soon as it entered the water. The water also immediately started pushing up on the clay ball, but because the amount of water displaced by the ball was less than the weight of the ball, the ball sank. There was not enough buoyant force to hold it up.

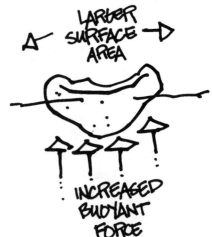

When you shaped the ball into a weird-looking boat, you increased the surface area of the clay pushing down on the water. The bigger something is, the more water it is going to push out of the way (displace). If the amount of water that is displaced is greater than the weight of the object, the object will float.

Science Fair Extensions

64. Repeat this experiment using fluids of different densities and see if the principle holds true. Try cooking oil, vinegar, corn syrup, and glycerine.

65. Use a graduated cylinder to calculate the amount of buoyant force created by your clay ball. If 1 mL of water equals 1 gram, prove that the buoyant force and the weight of the boat were equal when the boat sank.

66. Does the shape of the boat make any difference, or is it just the internal volume that is important when it comes to displacing the water in the glass?

Density Column

The Experiment

Density is a word that describes how tightly packed the atoms inside a material are. For example, if you were to take two rocks, pumice and granite, you would find that they are made out of exactly the same mix of minerals. They are identical, except that the granite was formed when a big blob of molten rock cooled very slowly underground, and the pumice was formed when the exact same molten mass of rock was spit out of a volcano. If you placed both rocks in water, the granite would sink and the pumice would float. The granite is denser than—packed tighter together than—the pumice.

Another way to explore this idea is using liquids. All liquids have different densities. If you could shrink down to the size of an atom, you could swim around inside a glass of water and then in a glass of corn syrup, and you could compare which one is more crowded. Chances are, the corn syrup would win that contest. The lab you are about to do will allow you compare the different densities of five liquids.

Materials

1   Toobe or 500 mL graduated cylinder
1   100 mL graduated beaker or cylinder
5   Wax cups, 5 oz. each
    50 mL water
    50 mL rubbing alcohol
    50 mL glycerine
    50 mL corn syrup

    50 mL vegetable oil
1   Bottle of blue food coloring
1   Bottle of green food coloring
1   Bottle of red food coloring
3   Craft sticks
1   Pen
1   Roll of masking tape

Procedure

1.   Add 50 mL of water to wax cup #1 and label it: *Cup 1 – Water.* Add 50 mL of the four remaining liquids to four cups and label them respectively: *Cup 2 – Rubbing Alcohol, Cup 3 – Glycerine, Cup 4 – Corn Syrup,* and *Cup 5 – Vegetable Oil.*

2.   Add the following food colors to the respective liquids: Cup 1 – Water – Blue Food Coloring, Cup 2 – Rubbing Alcohol – Green Food Coloring, and Cup 3 – Glycerine – Red Food Coloring. Using craft sticks, mix the food coloring into the liquids until they are uniform.

3.   Using your fingers, eyes, and any other instruments that you were born with, touch, look at, examine, and compare the five liquids. Put them in order from thickest (densest) to thinnest (least dense) and record your predictions of density in the spaces provided on the next page.

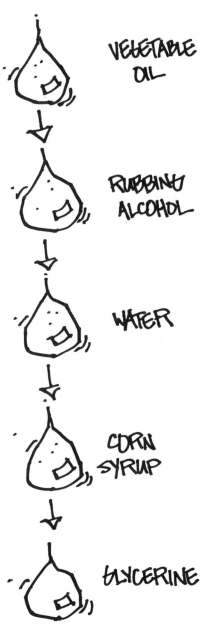

VEGETABLE OIL

RUBBING ALCOHOL

WATER

CORN SYRUP

GLYCERINE

Density Column

4. Based on your observations and predictions, add the thickest liquid to the bottom of the Toobe. Then tilt the Toobe at a 45-degree angle and SLOWLY add what you believe to be the next-thickest liquid. If this liquid is less dense than the first liquid, it will remain on top of the first liquid. If it is denser, it will displace the liquid and sink under it.

5. Add the remaining liquids in a similar fashion, following the order that you predicted. When you have added the fifth and last liquid, record your findings in the *Data & Observations* section. For each liquid that you predicted correctly, place a check mark next to your entry.

6. Now comes the fun part. Place your hand over the open end of the Toobe and shake the liquids up and down, mixing them together. Some of the liquids are very similar in their densities and will mix. Let things sit for a day; then observe how they settle out. Compare the order of the liquids in the Toobe before it was mixed with the order of those in the Toobe that you sloshed all over the place.

Data & Observations

Predict the order of density for the five liquids in this experiment. Use your senses to determine that order.

Thickest	Cup #	Liquid
1		
2		
3		
4		
5		

Record your findings after you have stacked the liquids into the Toobe.

Thickest	Cup #	Liquid
1		
2		
3		
4		
5		

How Come, Huh?

As we mentioned in the opening, density is a term that describes how tightly packed together a material is. In the cases of the glycerine and corn syrup, you have long, heavy chains of hundreds of atoms floating very close to one another in solution. When you compare that to water, which has a measly three atoms, it is no wonder that the water is less dense than the glycerine.

Scientists describe density with this equation: density (d) equals (=) the mass of the liquid (m) divided by the volume of the liquid (v), or $d = m/v$.

Density Column

Science Fair Extensions

67. Make your own density column using liquids of your choice. If you have access to a double pan balance, you can weigh identical volumes of liquids and make very accurate predictions about which liquids will float in which positions in the Toobe.

68. Locate a source for dry ice. Try the grocery store or look under "Ice" in the Yellow Pages. Dry ice is solid carbon dioxide and sublimates from a solid to a gas without becoming a liquid. It is also very nasty stuff. If given the chance to come in contact with skin, it will kill cells almost immediately. **Have an adult help you with this material.**

If you place the dry ice in an aquarium, in a large plastic tub, or in a sink that has been plugged, it will fill the tub with a gas that is heavier, or denser, than air.

To prove this, blow soap bubbles over the tub and allow them to float down into the container. When the bubbles, full of air from your lungs, come in contact with the carbon dioxide, they stop falling and will rest directly on the layer of heavier, denser gas. Cool. Try rocking the container (unless it is a sink), and you will see the bubbles rolling back and forth as the heavy gas sloshes around inside the container.

69. Create an experiment that allows solid objects to sort by density when they are shaken in a Toobe.

70. Use the equation, $d=m/v$, and measure the weights of each of the 50 mL liquids used in this experiment. See if the densities, as calculated, are true to the observations that you made.

Eggzasperating Puzzle

The Experiment

Three containers, three clear liquids, three eggs—all we need now are the Three Stooges, but alas, they have all retired to the Big Lab in the Sky, so we'll have to wing it.

Like the previous lab, this lab also addresses density. You are going to take three identical containers, fill them with three liquids, and place a fresh egg in each container. Despite apparent similarities in these conditions, the egg in the first container sinks right to the bottom. The egg in the second container is not interested in sinking at all, and instead, floats right on top of the liquid. The third egg, truly an individual, decides to neither sink nor float, but simply hovers in the middle. Density weirdness is alive and well.

Materials

3   Eggs, fresh
3   Drinking glasses, 12 oz. each
1   Pound of salt
1   Spoon
    Water

Eggzasperating Puzzle

Procedure

1. Fill Drinking Glass #1 full of water. That's it, not too glamorous.

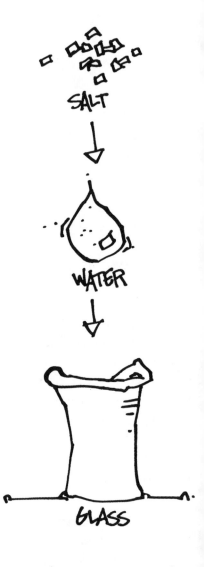

2. Fill Drinking Glass #2 until it is half-filled with water, and add four heaping spoons of salt. Hold your hand over the open end of the glass and shake the container until all of the salt dissolves or until your arm gets tired.

Fill the container the rest of the way with water and continue to shake, dissolving the remaining salt. If you use warm water, you will find that the dissolving of the salt goes a little faster.

3. Fill Glass #3 until it is half-filled with water. Then add four heaping spoons of salt. Once again, hold your hand over the open end of the glass and shake the container until all of the salt dissolves.

Place the spoon inside the glass and slowly pour water into the container on top of the layer of salt water. As the water level rises, lift the spoon up, also, to minimize the mixing of the fresh water with the salt water. Fill the container all the way to the top.

4. Finally, add an egg to each container. The best way to do this is to place the egg in the spoon and lower the spoon into the liquid, rolling the egg out of the spoon gently.

Data & Observations

In the spaces provided below, draw the location of each egg after you placed it in the respective containers. Identify the liquid contents of each container.

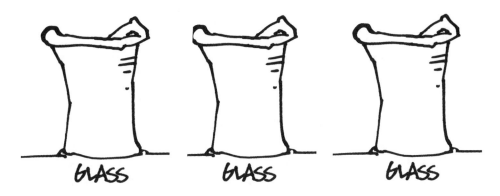

GLASS   GLASS   GLASS

How Come, Huh?

Again, our old buddy Archimedes comes to the rescue. His law states that the buoyant force of a liquid on an object is equal to the weight of the liquid that is displaced by that object.

In other words, when the egg was placed in the liquid, it pushed aside, or displaced, a cer-

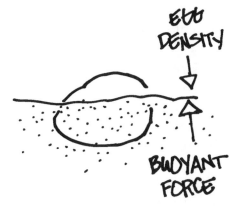

EGG DENSITY

BUOYANT FORCE

tain volume of fresh water. It also pushed aside the *same, identical volume of salt water* when it was placed in that beaker. The only difference is that salt water is denser than fresh water. 100 mL of salt water is going to weigh more than 100 mL of fresh water. So, when the egg displaced the salt water, there was more weight displaced, and as a consequence, the buoyant force on the egg was greater ... so great, in fact, that the silly egg now floats rather than sinks.

Eggzasperating Puzzle

Here's what happened in each case. Glass #1 contained fresh water. The weight of the egg was greater than the buoyant force of the water, so the egg sank. In Glass #2, the salt increased the buoyant force of the water significantly ... so much so that the weight of the egg was supported by the liquid. Glass #3 is your sneaker. The weight of the egg was too great for the buoyant force of the fresh water in the top half of the glass. When the egg sank far enough to encounter the salt water layer, it stopped sinking because the buoyant force at that point in the solution was great enough to support it.

Science Fair Extensions

71. You can repeat the experiment and get a little more sophisticated by incorporating additional containers. Vary the ratios of the salt water to fresh water. Set the lab up before your friends come over to see it, and you can have five different containers with eggs floating all the way from the top to the bottom, and four different places in between. Drives 'em crazy.

72. Place two different cans of soda pop in a tub of water. One can is regular soda pop and the other is diet. One will float, and one will sink—answers please. Experiment with different brands of soda and diet soda pop. Try regular cola, root beer, lemon-lime, and the diet versions of the same drinks. Graph your results.

Sewer Maggots

The Experiment

Gases can be dissolved into liquids, and that particular fact is experienced by some folks on a near daily basis. Carbon dioxide is the gas that is dissolved into soda pop liquid to give it the bubbly, fizzy appearance that you see when you pop the top off a bottle or can.

This lab also doubles as a lab on density. As the carbon dioxide adheres to the sides of raisins that are placed in a soft drink, they become buoyant and rise to the surface of the container. If they lose their carbon dioxide floats at any time along the way, they become heavy and fall to the bottom again.

And finally, if you really want to have some fun, you can make up a story about sewer maggots, and totally gross out your friends. Inquiring minds want to know, and we will tell all.

Materials

1   Can of Mountain Dew
1   Toobe or other container
1   Box of raisins in a plastic tub
1   Cup of warm water

Procedure

1. Open the can of Mountain Dew and pour it into the Toobe. Mountain Dew, by design, is a yellowish liquid that could easily be presented as a sample of recently acquired sewer water. This is not to say that it tastes or in any other way resembles sewer water, lest the legal counsel for Pepsi Co. sees a potential legal suit on the horizon.

Sewer Maggots

2. Announce to your friends that you have a sample of sewer water, and that you want to introduce them to the insect community via a little critter called a sewer maggot. The sewer maggot, you explain, is used to purify the water. When sewer maggots are added to the sewer water, they can be seen diving up and down, gulping the various nutrients available. Drop about 10 to 15 raisins, which have been soaking in warm water for about a half an hour, into the Mountain Dew. They will start to bob up and down.

3. What you will notice, upon closer examination, is that the gas in the Mountain Dew (the carbon dioxide bubbles) sticks to the sides of the raisins. The bubbles become part of the outsides of the raisins and, as a result, change the overall density of the raisins. They start to float to the top of the container. When they get to the top, watch very carefully as the bubbles pop or escape from the raisins.

4. If you want to play this out a little bit more, you can explain that the sewer maggots swim around in the "pee" water and make it potable—a fancy word that means that you can drink it. To prove this to your friends, take the container of "pee" water and sip it—a little sweet, but good.

5. If they are not on the verge of tossing chunks yet, you can put them there by also telling them that maggots or larvae are a rich source of protein and considered delicacies in some areas of the world. Again, to prove this to them, catch a sewer maggot and pop it into your mouth.

How Come, Huh?

This is more physics than it is chemistry: The bubbles of carbon dioxide stick to the sides of the raisins. When they do this, they decrease the average density of the raisin—the gas makes them less dense than the soda pop—and they float to the top of the Toobe.

When the raisins get to the top, they start to roll, and some of the gas is released. This makes the overall weight of the raisin heavier, and it starts to fall to the bottom of the container.

Another way of looking at this is in terms of Archimede's principle. The buoyant force on the raisins is equal to the weight of the Mountain Dew that is displaced by the raisins. When the bubbles attached themselves to the raisins, the raisin-bubble combos displaced more soda pop than before. The buoyant force therefore increases and pushes the raisin to the top of the glass—another solved mystery for the record books.

Science Fair Extensions

73. The fizz that is present in all soda pop is called carbonation. The reason it has this name is that carbon dioxide—carbonic gas—is dissolved into the pop. Try the previous experiment with soda pop that has been sitting out for several hours and has had a chance to de-gas.

Big Idea 8

Potential energy is defined as energy that has been stored. Kinetic energy describes energy that is being used to produce motion.

Ping-Pong Poppers

The Experiment

There is a great physics toy that is manufactured in great quantity in China and imported to the USA by boatloads. It consists of a plastic sphere that is cut in half. When the sphere is inverted and placed on a hard surface, the potential energy that was stored inside the disc is released as kinetic energy when the disc pops into the air. Great way to learn about stored energy, energy transfer, and spontaneous laughter during lab.

This is the challenge: You must place an energy disc on a table so it hops into the air about 3 feet. A couple of caveats and exceptions:

    a. You may not place the disc on anything other than a hard surface: no mousetraps, explosives, sleeping crickets, or anything else that would cause the plastic to jump into the air.

    b. You may not drop the disc onto a hard surface in combination with anything else. It must simply start on the table and hop into the air of its own accord.

    c. You may not strike the table or hard surface from underneath.

Materials

1   Popper
1   Hard surface
1   Ping-Pong ball
1   Superball
1   Pair of goggles

Ping-Pong Poppers

Procedure

1. Flip the disc inside out and set it on a hard surface with the thick rim of the sphere resting on the table.

2. Wait a couple of seconds and observe what happens when the potential energy in the popper is released.

3. Goggle up and flip the disc inside out. Set it on a hard surface, only this time, set the disc upside down so that it creates a little bowl.

4. Quickly place the Ping-Pong ball inside the bowl and observe what happens when the potential energy is released. Did we mention that you should duck?

5. Finally, repeat step 4, inverting the popper and placing it upside down so that it forms a bowl. This time, though, place the Superball in the popper and compare the height that it shoots into the air with the height reached by the Ping-Pong ball.

PING-PONG BALL

INVERTED POPPER

How Come, Huh?

The plastic disc has a "memory" or a shape that it is most comfortable in. When you flipped the disc inside out, it took energy from your muscles for you to do this. When you added this energy to the disc, it was stored in the plastic as potential energy, or *p.e.* This is energy that is sitting there, waiting to be used, but in the meantime it will be happy to just hang out.

If you watched the inverted disc carefully, you could see it slowly moving back toward its original, preferred shape. It was using the potential energy you gave it to return to its original shape. As it got closer and closer to that shape, the changes came faster and faster until at the very end, the disc snapped right back into its original shape very quickly.

This final snap created a force against the table—an action. The table, having both read up on Newton's Second Law of Action and Reaction and not wanting to be perceived as a wimp, smacked the disc back—a reaction: a bit impetuous, perhaps, but a reaction. Newton observed it this way: "For every action there is an equal and opposite reaction." The disc smacks the table, and the table smacks the disc back. Basically, nursery school physics. The thing to remember is that the mass of the disc and the amount of energy stored in the disc is very small compared to the mass of the table. When the disc smacks the table, the table simply returns the same amount of energy. This force, fairly significant as far as the disc is concerned, sends it sailing into the air.

The plastic disc still has a "memory" or a shape that it is most comfortable in. When you added this energy to the disc, it was stored in the plastic as potential energy. Nothing has changed too much from the previous experiment, except that the disc is upside down but still wants to return to its original shape.

When the disc finally does return to its original shape, it transfers the energy that you stored in it to the ball, instead of the table. A combination of Newton's

Ping-Pong Poppers

Second Law, $F=ma$, and his Third Law, or, "The more force on an object, the more it accelerates, but the more massive it is, the more it resists acceleration," and, "For every action there is an equal and opposite reaction."

The disc smacks the ball: action. The ball shoots into the air: reaction. The fact that the ball is so light figures into the $F=ma$ equation. Force equals the mass times the acceleration. Or, if we wiggle the equation around a bit: $a=F/m$, the acceleration of the ball equals the force of the popper smacking the ball, divided by the mass of the ball. In this case, the ball is very light, so the bottom number is small and the ball shoots way up into the air—as you probably observed.

The rest of the story is that the ball shoots as high as it can until the pull of gravity overcomes the force that was applied by the popper, or it hits the ceiling. When that happens, the ball falls to the Earth and generally rolls under the refrigerator. At least it works that way in our house.

Science Fair Extensions

74. Take your popper home and try it on lots of different surfaces. Collect as much data as you can to determine a rule for how poppers behave.

75. Create an experiment that measures the height to which the balls are shot into the air more accurately. Use balls of similar sizes but of at least four different weights, and graph your data to see if there is a predictable pattern.

76. Apply the same concept to levers as catapults. Shoot the balls into the air by dropping different amounts of weight. Make a correlation between the weight and the height of the shot.

Carry Me Back

The Experiment

Energy is being used, transferred, and stored all the time. It changes from physical energy to electrical energy to light energy and back, if the circumstances are right. In the lab that you are going to do today, you are going to take kinetic energy and store it as potential energy (temporarily), and then watch as it is used as kinetic energy again. Just like a pan of popcorn with the lid off or a room full of ADD kids—lots of energy everywhere.

Materials

1   Lid, plastic "snap-on" type
1   Nail
1   Hammer
1   Can, small
1   Rubberband
1   Bolt with hex nut
2   Paperclips

Procedure

1. Take one of the plastic snap-on lids, and using the nail, poke a small hole in the center of it. Remove the nail. Using the nail and the hammer, make another small hole in the metal end of the can. Remove the nail.

2.   Push one end of the rubberband through the hole and put a paperclip on the end of the rubberband. Pull the rubberband back through the hole until the paperclip anchors it. Use the illustration at the right as a guide.

Carry Me Back

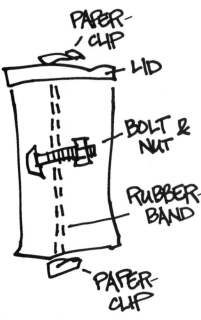

PAPER-CLIP
LID
BOLT & NUT
RUBBER-BAND
PAPER-CLIP

3. Thread the hex nut onto the end of the bolt. Tie the bolt-and-hex-nut combo in the middle of the rubberband with an overhand knot.

4. Stretch the rubberband and push the free end through the hole in the bottom of the can. Once it is through, put the paperclip on this end of the rubberband so it can't be pulled back through the hole, just like the other end.

5. Push the lid onto the end of the can so that you have a rubberband holding a bolt and hex nut, suspended between two ends of a can. Use the illustration at the left to help you construct the final machine.

6. Place the can on a smooth, hard floor and roll it away from you as fast you can, while still keeping it moving in a straight line. Observe what happens.

How Come, Huh?

Odd, huh? Here's what happened. As you rolled the can across the floor, your arm gave kinetic energy to the can. The can, newly endowed with this power, started to roll. However, not all of the can was rolling together.

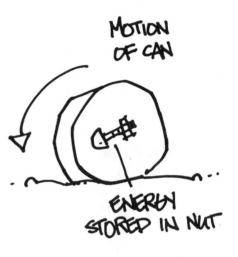

MOTION OF CAN

ENERGY STORED IN NUT

The bolt inside the can has considerable mass compared to the can. If you started at the front of this book, you also know that this means that it had inertia and it took energy to get the bolt rolling. While the energy to get the bolt moving was being transferred from the can down the rubberband to the bolt, the rubberband started twisting and stealing (storing) some of this energy.

As the can continued to roll, the energy that you gave it was being used up by the can, to overcome the friction between the can and the floor, and it was also being stored in the rubberband and bolt. When the amount of energy stored in the nut and bolt (resisting the movement of the can) was greater than the amount of energy propelling the can forward, the forces became equal. The can wobbled and stopped. With no more forward motion to twist the rubberband, it started to unwind and the energy stored in the rubberband was released. When this happened, the can started to roll backward as the rubberband unwound, transferring its energy to the sides of the can and causing it to roll backward. Pretty cool.

Science Fair Extensions

77. Supersize this experiment.

78. Roll the can down a long slope and see if it stops eventually, even though gravity is still pulling down on the can.

Pendulums

The Experiment

You have a pendulum made out of string, a paperclip, and a couple of washers. The pendulum works just fine, but you want it to swing a little bit faster. Do you: 1) add more weight to your pendulum, 2) lengthen the string, 3) shorten the string, or 4) pull the pendulum back farther so that it has more energy? Answers, please. We are all breathless in anticipation.

Materials

1	String, 24 inches long
1	Paperclip
1	Metric ruler
3	Washers, 1.5-inch diam.
1	Hand
	Gravity

Procedure

1.   Now we are going to study pendulums. There are two things that may affect how long it takes a pendulum to swing back and forth—the length of the pendulum and the weight of the pendulum. We are going to experiment with both. First we need to have a few rules:

a. You will always time the swings for 30 seconds.

b. You will always release the pendulum from the same place—not farther back one time and closer another.

c. You will count once each time the pendulum passes your belly button.

2.   To make your pendulum, you will need to bend the paperclip out into an "S" shape. Tie one end onto the string and add a washer to the other end.

3. With the assistance of your teacher or parents, fill in the chart below. To get you started, the first experiment is like this. You will put one washer on the paperclip and hold the string at 12 inches. Let it swing for 30 seconds and record the number of swings in the box under *1* and next to *12 inches*.

4. Now add a second washer and count for another 30 seconds; record your answer under *2* washers in the *12 inches* row.

5. Finally, add a third washer and repeat your procedure.

6. Repeat this experimental sequence using pendulums that have strings that are 18 inches and 24 inches long. Record your data in the spaces provided below.

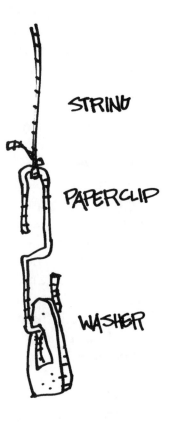

STRING

PAPERCLIP

WASHER

Data & Observations

Length of String	Number of Washers		
	1	2	3
12 inches			
18 inches			
24 inches			

Pendulums

How Come, Huh?

As you can see from your data, the only thing that really matters in this experiment is the length of the string. The mass and the distance that you pull the string back have no effect on the speed at which the pendulum swings.

Imagine riding your bike down a hill, into a dip, and back up on to the other side. If the dip is little (short string), your trip is very quick. If the dip is large (long string), your trip is going to take awhile. The mass of the weight and the amount of potential energy have no influence.

In terms of kinetic and potential energy, the pendulum gets its initial energy from your hand, and it stores this energy at the top of the swing. As the pendulum swings, it uses the stored energy to move on the way down. Once it passes the center point, it starts to store energy again until it gets to a point where it stops, is full of potential energy, gravity starts to pull on it, and kinetic energy kicks in again.

Science Fair Extensions

79. We're pretty sure that it is the length of the string, but what if it is the string itself? Try other materials and see if the data changes.

80. Let your pendulum swing until it stops completely. Compare the number of swings as the mass changes.

Big Idea 9

Circular motion encompasses a whole pile of ideas, like centripetal and centrifugal force, angular momentum, and rotational inertia, for starters.

Tops

The Experiment

If you spin a black-and-white Holstein cow around and around in a farmer's field, will you begin to see a cow of many colors? No, but you might see stars if the cow regains balance and takes after you. Besides, cows are too big to spin. Let's use black-and-white patterns on a disc, instead. In addition to spinning different patterns of black and white, you can also experiment with combinations of colors to get them to mix and produce secondary and tertiary colors, as well. Crayons up!

Setting the Trap ...

Tell your friends that light not only has the ability to be split into the colors of the rainbow, but you can also take those same seven colors and mix them back together to make white light.

CRAYON

Materials

3	Index cards, no lines
1	Empty quart can
	or other object with round end
1	Set of black-and-white patterns
1	Pair of scissors
1	Hole punch
1	Set of crayons or colored pencils
1	Drill, electric

PAPER DISC

TOP

Procedure

1. Place the can on the index cards and draw as many circles as you possibly can on each card; then cut them out. Make a hole in the very center of each disc, using the hole punch.

2. Create the first four color combinations listed in the data table below. For each disc, color half the disc one color and the other half the other color. Place the disc on the drill and give it a spin. Record the resulting color. If there are more than two starting colors, divide the disc equally.

Data & Observations

Disc	Colors	Resultant Color(s)
1	Blue/Red	
2	Blue/Yellow	
3	Red/Yellow	
4	Green/Yellow/Orange	
5		
6		
7		
8		

Tops

3. Once you have tried the first four combinations, then experiment with other color combinations of your own design. Be sure to fill in the data table on the previous page with your experiments and observations.

4. Finally, attach the black-and-white disc to the drill and give it a spin. It you look carefully, you will be able to see colors.

How Come, Huh?

When the top is spinning, it has angular momentum, which is described by the equation, $H=MR^2W$. M is the mass of the spinning object, R is the radius of the top squared, and W is the velocity of the spin. What this equation tells us is that, as long as the top has enough energy to spin, it maintains a predictable pattern and resists the pull of gravity. Not to beat a dead horse, but this probably requires a little more explanation …

This spinning energy opposes or fights against the pull of gravity. Why? The spinning motion also creates a centrifugal force, the same force that keeps water from falling out of a spinning bucket. So a spinning top can be placed on a fingertip, string, or any other stand, and it will continue to stay in place as long as it is spinning and producing angular momentum and centrifugal force.

Why you see colors on the black-and-white-pattern discs is still somewhat of a mystery, but scientists believe it has to do with the cones that are located in the back of your eyeballs.

There are three kinds of cones that collect each of the colors, red, green, and blue. They also seem to process the information at different speeds. This is called *latency time*. For example, red cones are the quickest to collect light information. They also dump the information to the brain the quickest. This is called the *persistence of response* time. Blue cones, on the other hand, are the slowest to collect and the slowest to send the information on. This helps to begin to explain why our brains think they see colors.

As the disc spins, your eye sees alternating flashes of black and white. As the flashes of white light (made up of all the colors of the rainbow) hit your cones, the cones do not collect the colors at the same rate, nor do they send that color information on to the brain at the same rate. It is kind of like the difference between eating buttered, salted popcorn by the handful versus eating a piece of popcorn, then salting your tongue, and then smearing a patty of butter across your tongue. You have the same basic components, but much different perception by your brain.

This same response time is responsible for the mixing of colors when the color wheels spin. Your eyes will take the colors and send the information to your brain, where it mixes the colors.

Science Fair Extensions

81. The results you see are also affected by the direction in which the pattern is spinning. If you have a variable-speed drill, it probably has a reverse button. Try the pattern in the opposite direction.

82. The thickness of the lines also makes a big difference in the colors that you do or do not see. Experiment with the line thickness and the ability to see colors using a basic disc pattern.

83. Jump on a playground-sized version of a merry-go-round and launch balls by releasing them from the center as it zips around.

Gyroscopes

The Experiment

A gyroscope is a spinning wheel, usually mounted in a moveable frame. Two common examples of gyros are bicycle wheels and spinning tops. Both stand up straight when they are spinning, and both tend to fall toward the Earth when they are stopped. Gravity-defying gizmos ... that's what gyros are.

Materials

1   Gyro with stand
1   Cotton string, 18 inches long
1   Fellow scientist

Procedure

1. First a little gyroscope anatomy. Review the drawing below so that you are familiar with its different parts.

2. Place the stationary gyroscope in its stand, with the axle straight up and down. Let go and see what happens to the gyro.

3. Wind the string around the axle, give it a tug, and when the gyro is spinning, try to balance it on the stand. Observe what happens to the gyro as it spins.

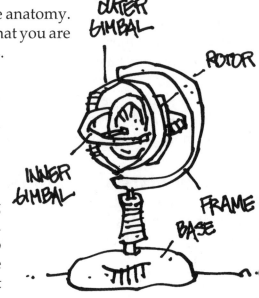

4. Get the gyro spinning as fast as you can, and balance it on the tip of your finger. With your other hand, gently push down on the top end of the axle and observe what happens.

5. Once again, get the gyroscope spinning quickly and balance it on the piece of string that you and your partner have stretched between you. Place the gyroscope on the string so that it is parallel to the ground. Observe what happens.

How Come, Huh?

When the gyroscope is spinning, it has angular momentum, which is described by the equation, $H=MR^2W$. M is the mass of the spinning object, R is the radius of the wheel squared, and W is the velocity of the spin. What this equation tells us, in a nutshell, is that a large, heavy wheel that is spinning very fast has a bucketload of energy that we call angular momentum.

This energy opposes or fights against the pull of gravity. Why? The spinning motion also creates a centrifugal force, the same force that keeps water from falling out of a spinning bucket. So a spinning gyroscope can be placed on a fingertip, string, or any other stand, and it will continue to stay in place as long as it is spinning and producing angular momentum and centrifugal force.

Science Fair Extensions

84. A gyroscope can be made out of a bicycle wheel and an office chair that spins. Have at it.

Whirling Can

The Experiment

Flip a soup can that has been filled halfway with water upside down, but don't have any of the water fall out. For the immediately clever—no, you cannot freeze the water or cover the can with any kind of top or covering like plastic wrap or wax paper.

Materials

1   #303 soup can, empty,
        one end cut out
1   Hammer
1   #16 Nail
1   String, 36 inches long
    Water

Procedure

1.   Using the hammer and nail, make two small holes near the top of the can, directly opposite each other.

2.   Thread the string through the holes and tie it off. It should look something like the illustration shown here.

3. Fill the can halfway with water and, working outside or in a large area away from your friends, start to gently swing the can of water back and forth. Swing the can higher and higher until you can make the can whirl in a complete circle. Once you get the can swinging in a circle, keep it moving around and around and observe what happens to the water inside.

How Come, Huh?

Gravity is a force that pulls objects toward the center of the Earth. It is a powerful force, but it can be overcome by other kinds of forces. When objects spin in a circle, they create a centripetal force that radiates out from the center of the spin. This force pushes objects inward, toward the center of the spin. It is opposed by inertia, which resists the centripetal force and keeps the object in the same place.

If an object is spinning and being pushed away from the center of the spin by inertia, it will continue to move away from the center until it is stopped by another force, usually centripetal force. The centripetal force of the object at any point along the circular path is equal to the tension in the string and the component of the object's weight pointing to the center of the circle. So, if the velocity of the can is great enough, the water won't fall out. This velocity is called the critical speed, and it takes into account the length of the string and the total mass spinning around the center. The string is what is keeping the can in orbit around your head.

Think about what would happen if you let the string go. The can would start moving in a straight line. But, because the string holds the can in orbit, the inertia of the water keeps it in the bottom of the can, and the centripetal force keeps the can accelerating around your finger.

Whirling Can

Science Fair Extensions

85. Experiment with larger and larger cans of water. See if there is a limit to this experiment and what that limit may be.

86. Try this experiment, varying the length of the string that is holding the can. Figure out how that affects the experiment, if at all.

87. Replace the water with sand, rocks, pebbles, pancake mix, or carbon dioxide gas. What results do you get, and does it make a difference if the object that you are spinning is a solid, liquid, or gas?

88. There are a number of rides that you can find at your local county or state fair that use the idea of centripetal force to create an entertaining (to some folks) experience. In particular, there is a ride in our part of the country called The Rotor. You climb into a giant, circular top and stand next to the wall. As the rotor starts to spin, your inertia pushes you against the wall. When the machine builds up a sufficient speed, the floor drops out and you are completely suspended against the wall. Fun ... until you puke.

Draw a picture, or better yet, head to the fair, and experiment with the forces that are created by this machine. Compare them with this experiment. They are identical ... we think.

89. Find other rides, in particular, those that use circular motion to their advantage, and ride them. Draw the forces that keep you in your seat as you fly upside down.

Tornado Tubes

The Experiment

Two bottles are connected in the middle with a piece of plastic, called a Tornado Tube. The top bottle is full of water and the bottom one is full of air. What is the fastest way to get the air up into the top bottle and the water down into the bottom bottle?

Materials

1   Tornado Tube
2   Pop bottles, 2 liter or 1 liter each
1   Clock with sweep-second hand
    Water

Procedure

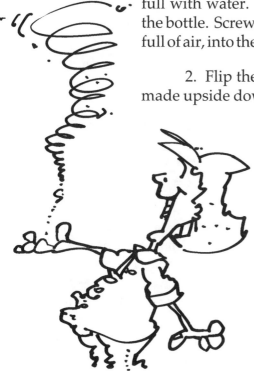

1.   Fill one of the pop bottles two-thirds full with water. Screw the Tornado Tube onto the bottle. Screw the second pop bottle, which is full of air, into the other half of the Tornado Tube.

2.   Flip the connection that you have just made upside down and, in the data table on the next page, record the amount of time that it takes for the water to move from the top bottle to the bottom one.

3.   Flip it over again, grab the top bottle, and make large circles with your upper hand until the water starts swirling in the shape of a vortex. Record the time it takes the water to empty into the bottom bottle again.

Tornado Tubes

Data & Observations

Trial	Time to Empty
1	
2	

How Come, Huh?

When you turn the bottles over without spinning them (trial #1), the water pretty much stays in the top bottle. That's because the air in the bottom bottle blocks the water in the top bottle. In order to get the water into the bottom bottle, you have to exchange it with air from the bottom bottle.

When you spin the bottles (trial #2), you create a force that pushes the water to the outside. Water molecules tend to hang onto one another—a characteristic called cohesion. So, if you get water molecules going in a particular direction, they tend to drag their buddies along with them.

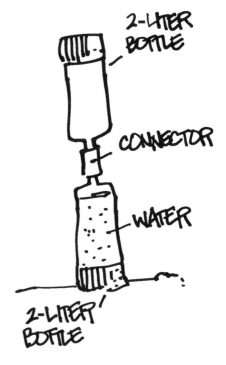

This leaves a gap in the center that the air can use to move from the bottom bottle to the top bottle. As this happens, water moves down the sides into the bottom bottle. The water continues spinning like a tornado because once something is in motion, it tends to stay in motion. If you want to impress friends and family, this is called rotational inertia.

When liquids are exposed to a circular force, they start to form a vortex, or tornado. The center of the tornado consists of empty space filled with air, and the sides of the tornado are composed of the water molecules. One of the characteristics of a tornado is that air rushes up inside the vortex—along with small dogs, fenceposts, and old ladies on bicycles.

Science Fair Extensions

90. Use different-sized pop bottles, and see if the size of the tornado is any different.

91. Prove that you can get the tornado to swirl clockwise and then counterclockwise. See if it is possible to reverse the flow halfway through the experiment.

Gyro Rings

The Experiment

You have a ring with 5 very colorful washers trapped on it. Your task is to get the washers spinning around the ring and then keep them spinning for at least 3 minutes (and more when you get good at solving the puzzle).

Materials

1   Gyro ring
1   Pair of hands
    Lots of practice

Procedure

1. Hold the gyro ring in either hand. You will notice that the colored washers hang at the bottom of the ring. Keeping your other hand open, whack all of the washers with a quick downward movement. Hit them so that they start to spin around the ring.

2. When you can hit all of the washers and get them spinning fairly quickly, immediately start to rotate the ring in a smooth motion toward you. It may take a couple of tries, but what will eventually happen is the washers will continue to spin as the ring passes through them.

With a little bit of practice, you will be able to move the ring through the washers at a speed that allows them to remain spinning as long as you move the ring at a fairly constant speed.

How Come, Huh?

You must first figure out a way to get the washers spinning around the ring. One very good way to do this is to add energy to the washers to get them moving. A whack with the hand does the trick.

When a washer is spinning around the ring, it is in constant contact with the ring as it spins. This constant contact is due to the friction between the inside of the washer and the ring. If the ring moves, it transfers some of that energy to the washer. It is a lot like when a gear transfers energy to the drive shaft of a car as it spins.

To keep the washers spinning, you must constantly add energy to the ring. In this case, you can roll the ring toward you in a smooth motion.

Here's what happens: Think of each washer as a spinning top. The *precession*, or wobble, of each spinning washer causes one edge of the inner surface of each washer to rub against the steel ring. Due to friction, the point of contact between a washer and the ring acts like a gear. This "gear" transfers energy from the upward motion of the ring to the rotating motion of the washers.

If you speed up the ring, the speed of the washers also speeds up. This is a lot like spinning the wheel of a bicycle by hand. The more energy you give it, the faster it spins. Take the energy away and the wheel eventually stops.

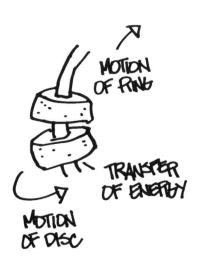

MOTION OF RING

TRANSFER OF ENERGY

MOTION OF DISC

Gyro Rings

The Earth's rotation and tilted axis undergo a wobble like that seen in a top or gyroscope. This slow wobble, called precession, takes 26,000 years to complete one cycle and causes the tilt of the Earth's axis to change the direction in which it is pointing. As a result, a January ski vacation to Utah 13,000 years from now will be extremely disappointing unless you like skiing on bare rock in 80-degree weather.

Science Fair Extensions

92. Rather than give the washers a whack, some folks who make a living selling these things in mall science and nature stores have perfected a way of starting the washers by simply flipping them with their thumbs.

93. Once you get good at keeping all of the washers spinning, the next skill that you want to master will be flipping the whole gyro into the air and catching it while keeping the washers spinning. Try under-the-leg, behind-the-back, and around-the-neck moves too. Not too scientific, but a great way to entertain distant relatives and visiting dignitaries.

Big Idea 10

Torque is a twisting force that applies energy in either a clockwise or counterclockwise direction.

Flipover Tops

The Experiment

You have a funny-looking top, called a flipover top. It looks like a wooden apple with a really big stem. The question at hand today is, figure out if this top, which rotates down onto its stem as it spins, works if it spins clockwise and counterclockwise, or works only in one direction.

Materials

1 Flipover top
1 Hard surface
1 Ambidextrous set of hands

Procedure

1. Find a hard surface and give the top a good, fast clockwise spin. Observe what happens.

2. Using this same hard surface, give the top a good, fast counterclockwise spin. Observe what happens now.

3. Honestly, we can't think of a third idea that will really help you, but we couldn't resist the temptation to write something on this line anyway .... Shouldn't you be answering the question?

How Come, Huh?

The center of mass for this top is not in the exact center of the round part of the top. It is located slightly above the middle of the sphere. This is because the stem sticks up, and that adjusts the center of mass toward the stem. What this means is that, when you spin the top, the forces that are acting on the top are unequal. As the top spins, a torque is placed on the sphere, causing the stem to get lower and lower toward the surface that it is on. Eventually, the top will wind up spinning on its stem when all of the forces become balanced.

Science Fair Extensions

94. Find a large salad bowl in your kitchen, ask for permission to use it for science experiments, and spin the top inside the bowl. Start the top on the side as well as on the bottom, and see what happens.

95. Spin the top on an inclined plane, a ramp, and see if the effects of gravity and the inclined plane affect the way that the top behaves.

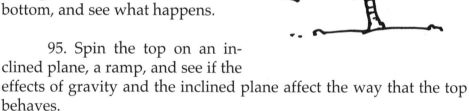

96. Create a series of boards with different amounts of friction. Use wax paper, sandpaper, aluminum foil—anything that you can find. Attach the paper surface to a piece of cardboard and arrange the boards from high friction to low. Try the top on each surface and time how long it takes for the top to flip over. Does friction help or hinder the top in its quest for equilibrium?

Spinning a Penny

The Experiment

When you flip a penny into the air a hundred times, statistics tells us that it will probably land heads half the time and tails half the time. When you spin a penny a hundred times, you get an entirely different result. What comes up more often, heads or tails, and why? Lab time!

Materials

1   *New*, Lincoln-head penny
1   Hard surface
     Very good record-keeping

Procedure

Spin the penny 100 times, recording the number of heads and the number of tails that you get each time. Use the data table that we have provided in the space below.

Data & Observations

Use the data table below to record a mark each time that you flip the penny. Bundle your marks in groups of 5 and then enter the total as a number. Once you are done, ask your classmates what totals they got. Then, working with your teacher, average the data and record it in the proper space.

	Tally	Total	Average
Heads			
Tails			

Class Average	Heads	Tails

How Come, Huh?

As with all well-thought-out science experiments, you will need a data table to record each result. Once the data is in, compare it with the information that your classmates produced. They should be coming up with roughly the same sets of numbers.

If you examine the penny carefully, you will notice that the side that has Lincoln's head on it sticks out a little farther; it has just a little bit more metal on it than the other side. This extra mass on one side has an effect on a rotating object. It creates a force, called torque.

This torque, mild as it may be in this situation, affects the end result. You can see from the illustration at the right that it pushes the penny toward the heads side—something that should be supported by your data.

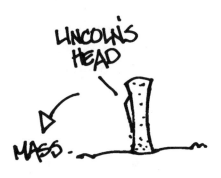

Science Fair Extensions

97. Construct discs to spin and then figure out a way to weight them on one side. Increase the amount of weight on one side and make predictions based on the data you collect as to how many more times each disc will fall to the heavier side.

Torque Bar

The Experiment

Balance a piece of plastic that we can call a torque bar by placing it on the end of your finger, as pictured below. Put the end of the triangle shape on your forefinger and gently release it.

It will take a little more than patience to figure this one out, so loosen your belt and settle in for another brain tickler. When you get torqued enough, you'll figure it out.

Materials

1   Torque bar
1   Belt
1   Finger

Procedure

1. Apply a force to the plastic bar that causes it to be pushed into your finger. If you have that belt loose, now may be a good time to figure out where it fits into this experiment.

2. You may also want to alter the center of gravity by adding some weight to the torque bar. We'd hit you over the head with the way to do this, but it's inappropriate for a teacher to **belt** his/her student.

3. Interestingly enough, the notch in the torque bar is just about the right size to allow a belt to slide down into it ... hmmmm, wonder why we would go to all the trouble to say something like that? So much for being subtle.

BELT GROOVE

4. When you finally get frustrated enough, take the belt and drape it over your index finger. Find the point where the amount of weight on both sides feels equal, and slide the belt into the groove on the torque bar.

5. Place the torque bar back on your finger and you should have no problem getting the piece of plastic to balance. It works every time. If you have a little trouble, adjust your belt a little bit so that it is completely centered in the groove.

How Come, Huh?

Torque is the name given to a force that produces a twisting motion on an object. When you open a door or screw a lightbulb into a socket, you are applying a torque, a twisting motion, to that object to get it to move.

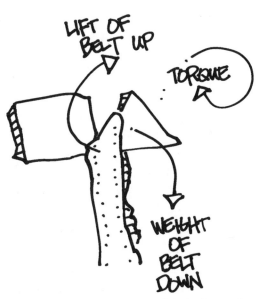

LIFT OF BELT UP

TORQUE

WEIGHT OF BELT DOWN

In this experiment, the center of gravity for the torque bar without the belt is in the middle of the bar, well past the end of your finger, so gravity grabs the torque bar and yanks it to the ground every time. When you place the belt in the groove on the torque bar, two things happen. First, gravity continues to yank on one side of the belt and pull it downward. At the same time, this pushes up on the other side of the belt and jams it into the torque bar. You can see that if one side is being pulled down by gravity and the other side is being pushed up, we have a torque holding the plastic in place.

Torque Bar

Science Fair Extensions

98. Try other materials: a different belt, a piece of string with lead weights attached, a strip of paper with washers taped to both ends, or a jumprope with a cat duct taped to each end (just kidding ... cats hate duct tape, so use Super Glue ....)

OFFICIAL DISCLAIMER FOR ALL CAT LOVERS: We are kidding about the cats, really. Kids, don't try this at home. It will simply produce letters from irate catophiles.

Big Idea 11

Resonance is a characteristic of an object to mimic or copy the vibrational frequency of another object.

Resonant Rings

The Experiment

You have a board with four different paper rings of different sizes attached to it. As you add varying amounts of energy to the board by shaking it, you will see that the different rings respond differently.

This demonstrates the characteristic of resonance in materials and how the size and rigidity of the paper affect the speed of the resonant waves.

Materials

1   Sheet of construction paper, 14 inches by 20 inches
1   Roll of masking tape
1   Board, 6 inches by 12 inches
1   Stapler

Procedure

1. Cut four 1-inch-wide strips from the construction paper. The longest strip should be about 20 inches long, and each successive strip should be about 3 inches shorter than the previous one.

2. Roll the strips into rings by taping the two ends of each strip together. Then staple the rings to the wood board as shown in the illustration on the next page.

3. Place the wood board on the table and move it back and forth in front of you, using a regular rhythm.

4. Start at a very low frequency and slowly increase the frequency of your shaking. Notice that different rings vibrate strongly, or resonate, at different frequencies.

5. The largest ring will be the first to vibrate, followed by the second-largest, and on down to the ring with the smallest diameter. The smallest ring starts to vibrate at the highest frequencies. Keep shaking the cardboard faster and faster, and notice that the largest ring will begin to vibrate strongly again.

6. Each ring will vibrate at more than one frequency, but the shape of each ring will be different for each resonant frequency. The rings will also have different resonant frequencies if you shake the board up and down instead of back and forth.

Resonant Rings

How Come, Huh?

The frequencies at which the rings vibrate most easily (resonant frequencies) are determined by several factors, including the rings' inertia (mass) and their stiffness. Stiffer objects have higher resonant frequencies because it takes more energy to overcome their resistance to movement. Larger rings have lower frequencies because it takes less energy to get them moving back and forth.

The biggest ring has the largest mass and the least stiffness, so it has the lowest resonant frequencies. Put another way, the largest ring takes more time than the smaller rings to respond to an accelerating force. During earthquakes, two buildings of different sizes may respond very differently to the Earth's vibrations, depending on how well each building's resonant frequencies match the "forcing" frequencies of the earthquake. Of course, a building's stiffness—which is determined by the manner of construction and the materials used—is just as important as the building's size.

Science Fair Extensions

99. You can make the vibration frequency audible and more obvious by cutting a 1-inch section of plastic drinking straw, inserting a BB into it, taping paper over the ends of the straw, and taping the straw to a cardboard sheet parallel to the end. As you shake the sheet, the BB will tap against the ends of the straw at the same frequency as your vibration.

Resonant Balls

The Experiment

This experiment provides the opportunity for you to learn about harmonic, or resonant, sound vibrations by actually seeing them.

It comes from a book published by the good folks at the Exploratorium in San Francisco. The book is called *The Spinning Blackboard,* and it is full of science snacks that have been tested by teachers and kids (so you know that the experiments will work).

In this lab, four wooden dowels of varying lengths are each topped with an identical weight. These four dowels are then rocked back and forth together, and when the vibration caused by you matches the resonant frequency of one of the dowels, that dowel vibrates back and forth—and it resonates.

Materials

1 Board, (2 x 4),
    approximately 2 feet long
1 Electric drill
1 Vice
3 1/4-inch wooden dowels,
    1 1/2 feet long,
    2 feet long, and
    2 1/2 feet long
1 3/4-inch dowel,
    2 feet long
4 Superballs, large
   Adult Supervision

SUPERBALL

DOWEL

Procedure

1. Drill four holes, approximately 4 inches apart, down the center of the 2 x 4 (board). The first three holes should be smaller than 1/4 inch, and the fourth hole should be just a bit smaller than 3/8 inch.

Resonant Balls

2. Gently wiggle, shovel, and cajole the dowels into the holes so that they are held firmly in place.

3. Using the drill, carefully make a 1/4-inch hole halfway through three of the Superballs, and a 3/8-inch hole halfway through the fourth. Use a vice to keep the balls from moving around.

4. Place one Superball on the end of each dowel.

5. Grab the board at each end and slide it back and forth sideways across the tabletop. As you vary the rate at which you move the board, different dowels will swing back and forth at different rates. Some will move with great amplitude; others may hardly move at all.

6. Move the board at different speeds and compare how each of the dowels moves. Write a general rule that correlates length with the resonant frequency of the dowel.

How Come, Huh?

When you find the resonant frequency of any object, the amplitude of the vibration—the size of it, and how much it moves back and forth—becomes very large.

Some common examples of this can be found on the playground. When you push someone in a swing and you match your push to the back-and-forth motion of the swing, the amplitude of the swing gets larger and larger. The same thing happens when you get a good string of attacks going on the tetherball court: You hit the ball and it goes faster and faster and higher and higher, and you use your knowledge of physics to whip your opponent.

Resonance has been responsible for the destruction of buildings during earthquakes and bridges during windstorms. When an army marches across a bridge, soldiers break cadence and walk in irregular strides so that the resonant period of the bridge does not start moving the bridge up and down.

Science Fair Extensions

100. Repeat the experiment without the balls and see if takes more energy or less to find the resonant frequencies.

101. Find out how engineers "dampen" resonant waves in large structures like bridges. Find out what happened to the Verrazano Narrows bridge in Washington when this was ignored.

Science Fair Projects
•
A Step-by-Step Guide: From Idea To Presentation

Science Fair Projects

Ah, the impending science fair project—a good science fair project has the following five characteristics:

1. The student must come up with an *original* question.

2. That *original* question must be suited to an experiment in order to provide an answer.

3. The *original* idea is outlined with just one variable isolated.

4. The *original* experiment is performed and documented using the scientific method.

5. A presentation of the *original* idea in the form of a lab write-up and display board is completed.

Science Fair Projects

As simple as science report versus science fair project sounds, it gets screwed up millions of times a year by sweet, unsuspecting students who are counseled by sweet, unknowing, and probably just-as-confused parents.

To give you a sense of contrast, we have provided a list of legitimate science fair projects and then reports that do not qualify. We will also add some comments in italics that should help clarify why they do or do not qualify in the science fair project department.

Science Fair Projects

1. Temperature and the amount of time it takes mealworms to change to beetles.

Great start. We have chosen a single variable that is easy to measure: temperature. From this point forward, the student can read, explore, and formulate an original question that is the foundation for the project.

A colleague of mine actually did a similar type of experiment for his master's degree. His topic: The rate of development of fly larvae in cow poop as a function of temperature. No kidding. He found out that the warmer the temperature of the poop, the faster the larva developed into flies.

2. The effect of different concentrations of soapy water on seed germination.

Again, wonderful. Measuring the concentration of soapy water. This leads naturally into original questions and a good project.

3. Crystal size and the amount of sugar in the solution.

This could lead into other factors, such as exploring the temperature of the solution, the size of the solution container, and other variables that may affect crystal growth. Opens a lot of doors.

vs. Science Reports

4. Helicopter rotor size and the speed at which it falls.

Size also means surface area, which is very easy to measure. The student who did this not only found the mathematical threshold with relationship to air friction, but she had a ton of fun.

5. The ideal ratio of baking soda to vinegar to make a fire extinguisher.

Another great start. Easy to measure and track. Leads to a logical question that can either be supported or refuted with the data.

Each of these topics *measures* one thing such as the amount of sugar, the concentration of soapy water, or the ideal size. If you start with an idea that allows you to measure something, then you can change it, ask questions, explore, and ultimately make a *prediction*, also called a *hypothesis*, and experiment to find out if you are correct. Here are some well-meaning but misguided entries:

Science Reports, <u>not Projects</u>
1. Dinosaurs!

OK, great. Everyone loves dinosaurs, but where is the experiment? Did you find a new dinosaur? Is Jurassic Park alive and well, and we are headed there to breed, drug, or in some way test them? Probably not. This was a report on T. rex. Cool, but not a science fair project. And judging by the protest that this kid's mom put up when the kid didn't get his usual "A," it is a safe bet that she put a lot of time in and shared in the disappointment.

More Reports &

2. Our Friend the Sun

Another very large topic, no pun intended. This could be a great topic. Sunlight is fascinating. It can be split, polarized, reflected, refracted, measured, collected, and converted. However, this poor kid simply chose to write about the size of the sun, regurgitating facts about its features, cycles, and other astrofacts while simultaneously offending the American Melanoma Survivors Society. Just kidding about that last part.

3. Smokers' Poll

A lot of folks think that they are headed in the right direction here. Again, it depends on how the kid attacks the idea. Are they going to single out race? Heredity? Shoe size? What exactly are they after here? The young lady who did this report chose to make it more of a psychology-studies effort than a scientific report. She wanted to know family income, if they fought with their parents, how much stress was on the job, and so on. All legitimate concerns, but not placed in the right slot.

4. The Majestic Moose

If you went out and caught the moose, drugged it to see the side effects for disease control, or even mated it with an elk to determine if you could create an animal that would become the spokesanimal for the Alabama Dairy Farmers' Got Melk? promotion, that would be fine. But, another fact-filled report should be filed with the English teacher.

5. How Tadpoles Change into Frogs

Great start, but they forgot to finish the statement. We know how tadpoles change into frogs. What we don't know is how tadpoles change into frogs if they are in an altered environment, if they are hatched out of cycle, if they are stuck under the tire of an off-road vehicle blatantly driving through a protected wetland area. That's what we want to know. How tadpoles change into frogs, if, when, or under what measurable circumstances.

Now that we have beaten the chicken squat out of this introduction, we are going to show you how to pick a topic that can be adapted to become a successful science fair project after one more thought.

One Final Comment

A Gentle Reminder

Quite often, I discuss the scientific method with moms and dads, teachers and kids, and get the impression that, according to their understanding, there is one, and only one, scientific method. This is not necessarily true. There are lots of ways to investigate the world we live in and on.

Paleontologists dig up dead animals and plants but have no way to conduct experiments on them. They're dead. Albert Einstein, the most famous scientist of the last century and probably on everybody's starting five of all time, never did experiments. He was a theoretical physicist, which means that he came up with a hypothesis, skipped over collecting materials for things like black holes and space-time continuums, and didn't experiment on anything or even collect data. He just went straight from hypothesis to conclusion, and he's still considered part of the scientific community. You'll probably follow the six steps, we outline but keep an open mind.

Project Planner

This outline is designed to give you a specific set of timelines to follow as you develop your science fair project. Most teachers will give you 8 to 11 weeks notice for this kind of assignment. We are going to operate from the shorter timeline with our suggested schedule, which means that the first thing you need to do is get a calendar.

A. The suggested time to be devoted to each item is listed in parentheses next to that item. Enter the date of the Science Fair and then, using the calendar, work backward, entering dates.

B. As you complete each item, enter the date that you completed it in the column between the goal (due date) and project item.

Goal   *Completed*   *Project Item*

1. Generate a Hypothesis (2 weeks)

_____   _____   Review Idea Section, pp. 196–197
_____   _____   Try Several Experiments
_____   _____   Hypothesis Generated
_____   _____   Finished Hypothesis Submitted
_____   _____   Hypothesis Approved

2. Gather Background Information (1 week)

_____   _____   Concepts/Discoveries Written Up
_____   _____   Vocabulary/Glossary Completed
_____   _____   Famous Scientists in Field

& Timeline

Goal   *Completed*   *Project Item*

3. Design an Experiment (1 week)

_____	_____	Procedure Written
_____	_____	Lab Safety Review Completed
_____	_____	Procedure Approved
_____	_____	Data Tables Prepared
_____	_____	Materials List Completed
_____	_____	Materials Acquired

4. Perform the Experiment (2 weeks)

_____	_____	Scheduled Lab Time

5. Collect and Record Experimental Data (part of 4)

_____	_____	Data Tables Completed
_____	_____	Graphs Completed
_____	_____	Other Data Collected and Prepared

6. Present Your Findings (2 weeks)

_____	_____	Rough Draft of Paper Completed
_____	_____	Proofreading Completed
_____	_____	Final Report Completed
_____	_____	Display Completed
_____	_____	Oral Report Outlined on Index Cards
_____	_____	Practice Presentation of Oral Report
_____	_____	Oral Report Presentation
_____	_____	Science Fair Setup
_____	_____	Show Time!

Copyright 2003 • B. K. Hixson • Loose in the Lab   193

Scientific Method
• Step 1 •
The Hypothesis

The Hypothesis

A hypothesis is an educated guess. It is a statement of what you think will probably happen. It is also the most important part of your science fair project because it directs the entire process. It determines what you study, the materials you will need, and how the experiment will be designed, carried out, and evaluated. Needless to say, you need to put some thought into this part.

There are four steps to generating a hypothesis:

Step One • Pick a Topic
Preferably something that you are interested in studying. We would like to politely recommend that you take a peek at physical science ideas (physics and chemistry) if you are a rookie and this is one of your first shots at a science fair project. These kinds of lab ideas allow you to repeat experiments quickly. There is a lot of data that can be collected, and there is a huge variety to choose from.

If you are having trouble finding an idea, all you have to do is pick up a compilation of science activities (like this one) and start thumbing through it. Go to the local library or head to a bookstore and you will find a wide and ever-changing selection to choose from. Find a topic that interests you and start reading. At some point, an idea will catch your eye, and you will be off to the races.

Pick a Topic ...

We hope you find an idea you like between the covers of this book. But we also realize that 1) there are more ideas about physical science than we have included in this book, and 2) other kinds of presentations, or methods of writing labs, may be just what you need to trigger a new idea or put a different spin on things. So, without further ado, we introduce you to several additional titles that may be of help to you in developing a science fair project.

1. *Why Toast Lands Jelly-Side Down* Written by Robert Ehrlich. ISBN 0-691-02887-7. Published by Princeton University Press. 196 pages.

This great book brings the basic concepts of physics out of the hypothetical and highly technical, and into the light of everyday life. The author illustrates basic concepts of physics, using inexpensive materials and unique perspectives to show that physics isn't a mythical mathematical mindbender, but a simple fact of life that walks with us everywhere we go.

2. *Physics for Every Kid* Written by Janice VanCleave. ISBN 0-471-52505-7. Published by John Wiley & Sons, Inc. 241 pages.

Janice is at it again, this time with a great book on the introduction to physics. Through 101 inexpensive and safe experiments, you and your child can learn the principles behind why fluorescent light-bulbs glow, and why a curve ball curves. All this from an author who was once a science teacher and presenter at museums and bookstores. You can't go wrong with this great helping of knowledge.

3. *Experiments with Motion* Written by Robert Gardner. ISBN 0-89490-667-4.

Get your dendrites shuffling with this book on motion. As the pages of this book flip by, you'll get tons of examples of physics in everyday life. The book illustrates these simple ideas to you with the use of everyday toys and a little help from good ol' Sir Issac Newton.

Find an Idea You Like

4. *Matter and Energy* Written by Robert Freidhoffer. ISBN 0-531-11051-6. Published by Franklin Watts. 160 pages.

With this book, you'll be the hit of any science show, and you can astound your friends at the same time! It teaches basic scientific laws and principles, cleverly concealed within magic tricks. With this book and a little showmanship, "poof!" ... you'll be the center of attention at any science fair!

5. *Forces, Motion, and Energy* Written by Robert Friedhoffer. ISBN 0-531-11052-4. Published by Franklin Watts. 112 pages.

Get your magic cloak out again, because this is the second book on physics that shows you the basic fundamentals of the world around us through experiments and magic tricks. *Forces, Motion, and Energy* is the perfect follow-up to the first book, *Matter and Energy*, taking you into more principles of how everyday life is filled with magic.

6. *Investigate and Discover Forces and Machines* Written by Robert Gardner. ISBN 0-671-69041-8. Published by Julian Messner. 128 pages.

Ever wondered about why forces are called forces? Curious about why all those little simple machines do what they do? Then this book is for you. You'll get the chance to answer questions on simple machines, forces, and motion, all in these pages. It'll give you crystal-clear instructions on how to perform tests on the world around you and find out why things work the way they do.

7. *The Super Science Book of Forces* Written by Jerry Wellington. ISBN 1-56847-223-4. Published by Thomas Learning. 32 pages.

Time to get tough! This book will show you all the basics you need to know on pushing and pulling, starting and stopping, and slipping and sliding. Jam-packed with facts and examples on the forces in your world. Work hard, and may the force be with you.

Develop an Original Idea

Step Two • Do the Lab

Choose a lab activity that looks interesting and try the experiment. Some kids make the mistake of thinking that all you have to do is find a lab in a book, repeat the lab, and you are on the gravy train with biscuit wheels. Your goal is to ask an ORIGINAL question, not repeat an experiment that has been done a bazillion times before.

As you do the lab, be thinking not only about the data you are collecting, but of ways you could adapt or change the experiment to find out new information. The point of the science fair project is to have you become an actual scientist and contribute a little bit of new knowledge to the world.

You know that they don't pay all of those engineers good money to sit around and repeat other people's lab work. The company wants new ideas, so if you are able to generate and explore new ideas, you become very valuable, not only to that company but to society. It is the question-askers that find cures for diseases, create new materials, figure out ways to make existing machines energy-efficient, and change the way that we live. For the purpose of illustration, we are going to take a lab titled, "Prisms, Water Prisms." from another book, *Photon U*, and run it through the rest of the process. The lab uses a tub of water, an ordinary mirror, and light to create a prism that splits the light into the spectrum of a rainbow. Cool. Easy to do. Not expensive, and open to all kinds of adaptations, including the four that we discuss on the next page.

Step Three • *Bend, Fold, Spindle, & Mutilate Your Lab*

Once you have picked out an experiment, ask if it is possible to do any of the following things to modify it into an original experiment. You want to try to change the experiment to make it more interesting and find out one new, small piece of information.

Heat it	Freeze it	Reverse it	Double it
Bend it	Invert it	Poison it	Dehydrate it
Drown it	Stretch it	Fold it	Ignite it
Split it	Irradiate it	Oxidize it	Reduce it
Chill it	Speed it up	Color it	Grease it
Expand it	Substitute it	Remove it	Slow it down

If you take a look at our examples, that's exactly what we did to the main idea. We took the list of 24 different things that you could do to an experiment—not nearly all of them, by the way—and tried a couple of them out on the prism setup.

Double it: Get a second prism and see if you can continue to separate the colors farther by lining up a second prism in the rainbow of the first.

Reduce it: Figure out a way to gather up the colors that have been produced and mix them back together to produce white light again.

Reverse it: Experiment with moving the flashlight and paper closer to the mirror and farther away. Draw a picture and be able to predict what happens to the size and clarity of the rainbow image.

Substitute it: You can also create a rainbow on a sunny day using a garden hose with a fine-spray nozzle attached. Set the nozzle adjustment so that a fine mist is produced and move the mist around in the sunshine until you see the rainbow. This works better if the sun is lower in the sky; late afternoon is best.

Hypothesis Worksheet

Step Three (Expanded) • *Bend, Fold, Spindle Worksheet*
This worksheet will give you an opportunity to work through the process of creating an original idea.

A. Write down the lab idea that you want to mangle.

_____

_____

_____

_____

B. List the possible variables you could change in the lab.

   i. _____

   ii. _____

   iii. _____

   iv. _____

   v. _____

C. Take one variable listed in section B and apply one of the 24 changes listed below to it. Write that change down and state your new lab idea in the space below. Do that with three more changes.

Heat it	Freeze it	Reverse it	Double it
Bend it	Invert it	Poison it	Dehydrate it
Drown it	Stretch it	Fold it	Ignite it
Split it	Irradiate it	Oxidize it	Reduce it
Chill it	Speed it up	Color it	Grease it
Expand it	Substitute it	Remove it	Slow it down

   i. _____

_____

_____

_____

ii. _____

_____

_____

_____

iii. _____

_____

_____

_____

iv. _____

STRETCHING!

_____

_____

Step Four • Create an Original Idea—Your Hypothesis
Your hypothesis should be stated as an opinion. You've done
the basic experiment, you've made observations, you're not stupid.
Put two and two together and make a PREDICTION. Be sure that you
are experimenting with just a single variable.

A. State your hypothesis in the space below. List the variable.

i. _____

_____

_____

_____

ii. Variable tested: _____

Sample Hypothesis Worksheet

On the previous two pages is a worksheet that will help you develop your thoughts and a hypothesis. Here is a sample of the finished product to help you understand how to use it.

A. Write down the lab idea that you want to mutilate.
A mirror is placed in a tub of water. A beam of light is focused through the water onto the mirror, producing a rainbow on the wall.

B. List the possible variables you could change in the lab.
    i. **Source of light**
    ii. **The liquid in the tub**
    iii. **The distance from flashlight to mirror**

C. Take one variable listed in section B and apply one of the 24 changes to it. Write that change down and state your new lab idea in the space below.

The shape of the beam of light can be controlled by making and placing cardboard filters over the end of the flashlight. Various shapes, such as circles, squares, and slits, will produce different-quality rainbows.

D. State your hypothesis in the space below. List the variable. Be sure that when you write the hypothesis, you are stating an idea and <u>not asking a question.</u>

Hypothesis: The narrower the beam of light, the tighter, brighter, and more focused the reflected rainbow will appear.

Variable Tested: The opening on the filter

Scientific Method
• Step 2 •
Gather Information

Gather Information

Read about your topic and find out what we already know. Check books, videos, the Internet, and movies, talk with experts in the field, and molest an encyclopedia or two. Gather as much information as you can before you begin planning your experiment.

In particular, there are several things that you will want to pay special attention to and that should accompany any good science fair project.

A. Major Scientific Concepts

Be sure that you research and explain the main idea(s) that is / are driving your experiment. It may be a law of physics, a chemical rule, or an explanation of an aspect of plant physiology.

B. Scientific Words

As you use scientific terms in your paper, you should also define them in the margins of the paper or in a glossary at the end of the report. You cannot assume that everyone knows about geothermal energy transmutation in sulfur-loving bacteria. Be prepared to define some new terms for them ... and scrub your hands really well when you are done if that is your project.

C. Historical Perspective

When did we first learn about this idea, and who is responsible for getting us this far? You need to give a historical perspective with names, dates, countries, awards, and other recognition.

Building a Research Foundation

1. This sheet is designed to help you organize your thoughts and give you some ideas on where to look for information on your topic. When you prepare your lab report, you will want to include the background information outlined below.

    A. *Major Scientific Concepts (Two is plenty.)*

        i. _____

_____

_____

_____

        ii. _____

_____

_____

_____

    B. *Scientific Words (No more than 10)*

        i. _____

        ii. _____

        iii. _____

        iv. _____

        v. _____

        vi. _____

        vii. _____

        viii. _____

        ix. _____

        x. _____

    C. *Historical Perspective*

        Add this as you find it.

2. There are several sources of information that are available to help you fill in the details from the previous page.

A. Contemporary Print Resources
   (Magazines, Newspapers, Journals)

   i. _____

   ii. _____

   iii. _____

   iv. _____

   v. _____

   vi. _____

B. Other Print Resources
   (Books, Encyclopedias, Dictionaries, Textbooks)

   i. _____

   ii. _____

   iii. _____

   iv. _____

   v. _____

   vi. _____

C. Celluloid Resources
   (Films, Filmstrips, Videos)

   i. _____

   ii. _____

   iii. _____

   iv. _____

   v. _____

   vi. _____

D. *Electronic Resources*
   (Internet Website Addresses, DVDs, MP3s)

   i. _____

   ii. _____

   iii. _____

   iv. _____

   v. _____

   vi. _____

   vii. _____

   viii. _____

   ix. _____

   x. _____

E. *Human Resources*
   (Scientists, Engineers, Professionals, Professors, Teachers)

   i. _____

   ii. _____

   iii. _____

   iv. _____

   v. _____

   vi. _____

You may want to keep a record of all of your research and add it to the back of the report as an Appendix. Some teachers who are into volume think this is really cool. Others, like myself, find it a pain in the tuchus. No matter what you do, be sure to keep an accurate record of where you find data. If you quote from a report word for word, be sure to give proper credit with either a footnote or parenthetical reference. This is very important for credibility and accuracy. This is will keep you out of trouble with plagiarism (copying without giving credit).

Scientific Method
• Step 3 •
Design Your Experiment

Acquire Your Lab Materials

The purpose of this section is to help you plan your experiment. You'll make a map of where you are going, how you want to get there, and what you will take along.

List the materials you will need to complete your experiment in the table below. Be sure to list multiples if you will need more than one item. Many science materials double as household items in their spare time. Check around the house before you buy anything from a science supply company or hardware store. For your convenience, we have listed some suppliers on page 19 of this book.

Material	Qty.	Source	$
1.			
2.			
3.			
4.			
5.			
6.			
7.			
8.			
9.			
10.			
11.			
12.			

Total $_____

Outline Your Experiment

This sheet is designed to help you outline your experiment. If you need more space, make a copy of this page to finish your outline. When you are done with this sheet, review it with an adult, make any necessary changes, review safety concerns on the next page, prepare your data tables, gather your equipment, and start to experiment.

In the space below, list what you are going to do in the order you are going to do it.

i. _____

_____

_____

_____

ii. _____

_____

_____

_____

iii. _____

_____

_____

_____

iv. _____

_____

_____

_____

v. _____

_____

_____

_____

Evaluate Safety Concerns

We have included an overall safety section in the front of this book on pages 16–18, but there are some very specific questions you need to ask, and prepare for, depending on the needs of your experiment. If you find that you need to prepare for any of these safety concerns, place a check mark next to the letter.

_____ *A. Goggles & Eyewash Station*
If you are mixing chemicals or working with materials that might splinter or produce flying objects, goggles and an eyewash station or sink with running water should be available.

_____ *B. Ventilation*
If you are mixing chemicals that could produce fire, smoke, fumes, or obnoxious odors, you will need to use a vented hood or go outside and perform the experiment in the fresh air.

_____ *C. Fire Blanket or Fire Extinguisher*
If you are working with potentially combustible chemicals or electricity, a fire blanket and extinguisher nearby are a must.

_____ *D. Chemical Disposal*
If your experiment produces a poisonous chemical or there are chemical-filled tissues (as in dissected animals), you may need to make arrangements to dispose of the by-products from your lab.

_____ *E. Electricity*
If you are working with materials and developing an idea that uses electricity, make sure that the wires are in good repair, that the electrical demand does not exceed the capacity of the supply, and that your work area is grounded.

_____ *F. Emergency Phone Numbers*
Look up and record the following phone numbers for the Fire Department: _____ , Poison Control: _____ , and Hospital: _____. Post them in an easy-to-find location.

Prepare Data Tables

Finally, you will want to prepare your data tables and have them ready to go before you start your experiment. Each data table should be easy to understand and easy for you to use.

A good data table has a **title** that describes the information being collected, and it identifies the **variable** and the **unit** being collected on each data line. The variable is *what* you are measuring and the unit is *how* you are measuring it. They are usually written like this:

Variable (unit), or to give you some examples:

Time (seconds)
Distance (meters)
Electricity (volts)

An example of a well-prepared data table looks like the sample below. We've cut the data table into thirds because the book is too small to display the whole line.

Determining the Boiling Point of Compound X_1

Time (min.)	0	1	2	3	4	5	6
Temp. (°C)							

Time (min.)	7	8	9	10	11	12	13
Temp. (°C)							

Time (min.)	14	15	16	17	18	19	20
Temp. (°C)							

Scientific Method
• Step 4 •
Conduct the Experiment

Lab Time

It's time to get going. You've generated a hypothesis, collected the materials, written out the procedure, checked the safety issues, and prepared your data tables. Fire it up. Here's the short list of things to remember as you experiment.

_____ *A. Follow the Procedure and Record Any Changes*
Follow your own directions specifically as you wrote them. If you find the need to change the procedure once you are into the experiment, that's fine; it's part of the process. Make sure to keep detailed records of the changes. When you repeat the experiment a second or third time, follow the new directions exactly.

_____ *B. Observe Safety Rules*
It's easier to complete the lab activity if you are in the lab rather than the emergency room.

_____ *C. Record Data Immediately*
Collect temperatures, distances, voltages, revolutions, and any other variables, and immediately record them into your data table. Do not think you will be able to remember them and fill everything in after the lab is completed.

_____ *D. Repeat the Experiment Several Times*
The more data that you collect, the better. It will give you a larger database, and your averages will be more meaningful. As you do multiple experiments, be sure to identify each data set by date and time so you can separate them out.

_____ *E. Prepare for Extended Experiments*
Some experiments require days or weeks to complete, particularly those with plants and animals or the growing of crystals. Prepare a safe place for your materials so your experiment can continue undisturbed while you collect the data. Be sure you've allowed enough time for your due date.

Scientific Method
• Step 5 •
Collect and Display Data

Types of Graphs

This section will give you some ideas on how you can display the information you are going to collect as graphs. A graph is simply a picture of the data that you gathered, portrayed in a manner that is quick and easy to reference. There are four kinds of graphs described on the next two pages. If you find you need a leg up in the graphing department, we have a book in the series that will guide you through the process.

Line and Bar Graphs
These are the most common kinds of graphs. The most consistent variable is plotted on the "x," or horizontal, axis, and the more temperamental variable is plotted along the "y," or vertical, axis. Each data point on a line graph is recorded as a dot on the graph, and then all of the dots are connected to form a picture of the data. A bar graph starts on the horizontal axis and moves up to the data line.

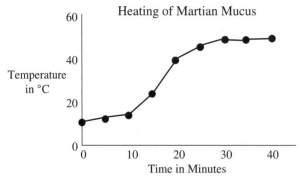

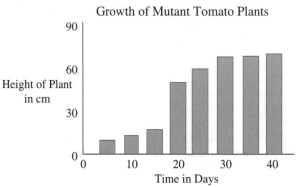

Best Fit Graphs

A best fit graph was created to show averages or trends rather than specific data points. The data that has been collected is plotted on a graph just as on a line graph, but instead of drawing a line from point to point to point, which sometimes is impossible anyway, you just free-hand a line that hits "most of the data."

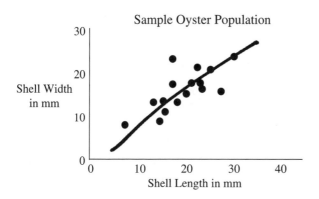

Pie Graphs

Pie graphs are used to show relationships between different groups. All of the data is totaled up, and a percentage is determined for each group. The pie is then divided to show the relationship of one group to another.

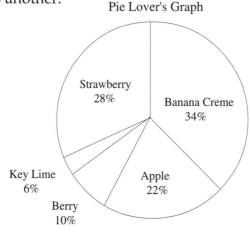

Other Kinds of Data

1. Written Notes & Observations

This is the age-old technique used by all scientists. Record your observations in a lab book. Written notes can be made quickly as the experiment is proceeding, and they can then be expounded upon later. Quite often, notes made in the heat of an experiment are revisited during the evaluation portion of the process, and they can shed valuable light on how or why the experiment went the way it did.

2. Drawings

Quick sketches as well as fully developed drawings can be used as a way to report data for a science experiment. Be sure to title each drawing and, if possible, label what it is that you are looking at. Drawings that are actual size are best.

3. Photographs, Videotapes, and Audiotapes

Usually better than drawings, quicker, and more accurate, but you do have the added expense and time of developing the film. However, they can often capture images and details that are not usually seen by the naked eye.

4. The Experiment Itself

Some of the best data you can collect and present is the actual experiment itself. Nothing will speak more effectively for you than the plants you grew, the specimens you collected, or that big pile of tissue that was an armadillo you peeled from the tread of an 18-wheeler.

Scientific Method
• Step 6 •
Present Your Ideas

Oral Report Checklist

It is entirely possible that you will be asked to make an oral presentation to your classmates. This will give you an opportunity to explain what you did and how you did it. Quite often, this presentation is part of your overall score, so if you do well, it will enhance your chances for one of the bigger awards.

To prepare for your oral report, your science fair presentation should include the following components:

Physical Display
- _____a.   freestanding display board
  - hypothesis
  - data tables, graphs, photos, etc.
  - abstract (short summary)
- _____b.   actual lab setup (equipment)

Oral Report
- _____a.   hypothesis or question
- _____b.   background information
  - concepts
  - word definitions
  - history or scientists
- _____c.   experimental procedure
- _____d.   data collected
  - data tables
  - graphs
  - photos or drawings
- _____e.   conclusions and findings
- _____f.   ask for questions

Set the display board up next to you on the table. Transfer the essential information to index cards. Use the index cards for reference, but do not read from them. Speak in a clear voice, hold your head up, and make eye contact with your peers. Ask if there are any questions before you finish and sit down.

Written Report Checklist

Next up is the written report, also called your lab write-up. After you compile or sort the data you have collected during the experiment and evaluate the results, you will be able to come to a conclusion about your hypothesis. Remember, disproving an idea is as valuable as proving it.

This sheet is designed to help you write up your science fair project and present your data in an organized manner. This is a final checklist for you.

To prepare your write-up, your science fair report should include the following components:

_____ a.   binder
_____ b.   cover page, title, & your name
_____ c.   abstract (one paragraph summary)
_____ d.   table of contents with page numbers
_____ e.   hypothesis or question
_____ f.   background information
               concepts
               word definitions
               history or scientists
_____ g.   list of materials used
_____ h.   experimental procedure
               written description
               photo or drawing of setup
_____ i.   data collected
               data tables
               graphs
               photos or drawings
_____ j.   conclusions and findings
_____ k.   glossary of terms
_____ l.   references

Display Checklist

Prepare your display to accompany the report. A good display should include the following:

Freestanding Display

_____ a.   freestanding cardboard back
_____ b.   title of experiment
_____ c.   your name
_____ d.   hypothesis
_____ e.   findings of the experiment
_____ f.   photo or illustrations of equipment
_____ g.   data tables or graphs

Additional Display Items

_____ h.   a copy of the write-up
_____ i.   actual lab equipment setup

Glossary and Index

Glossary

Air pressure

At sea level, we have approximately 100 miles of air stacked on top of us. This air is pushing down all the time, creating pressure. At sea level, it is about 14.7 pounds per square inch. The higher up you go in elevation, the less air is stacked on top of you, and the less pressure is squishing you.

Archimedes

Greek scientist and mathematician who was fond of taking baths.

Atmosphere

The ocean of air that surrounds the Earth.

Buoyant force

The force exerted upon an object by the molecules in the liquid that is supporting or trying to support the object that is being pulled down by gravity.

Center of gravity

The average mass of an object, predicated on the fact that there is actually a measurement being taken on a planet where there is a gravitational attraction.

Center of mass

Same thing as the center of gravity, only you can find it anywhere in the universe, gravity or not.

Circular motion

An object moving in a repeatable, circular pattern.

Collision

The interaction of two objects heading in pathways that intersect. When the two objects come in contact with each other, a collision is said to have occurred and an exchange of energy usually takes place.

Conservation of momentum
A principle of physics where all of the energy in a system or interaction is accounted for. In the case of dropping two balls on the floor, with one ball on top of the other, the energy that is transferred from the lower ball to the upper ball occurs because there is a conservation of momentum.

Density
The relative measure of how compact the atoms in a material appear to be, relative to the surrounding environment. Density is measured in terms of weight per volume, i.e. grams per liter, pounds per square inch, or metric tons per nano-ounce (for black holes only).

Distance
A linear measurement from one place to another. Can be taken in either Old English (inches, feet, miles) or metric measurements (meters, centimeters, or kilometers).

Drag
A form of dress preferred at certain entertainment establishments. Also a term used to describe how much friction is pushing against an object and preventing it from moving freely.

Effort arm
The side of the lever where you add the weight to push the lever downward.

Effort force
The weight that you add to the effort arm in order to try to get it to move downward.

Glossary

Friction

The amount force resisting the movement of a solid, liquid, or gas. The friction is a force that is caused when two or more objects collide with each other reducing the speed of the object and potentially converting some of the energy to light or heat.

Fulcrum

The pivot point of a lever—typically the pencil under the ruler in simple levers. Also, the center point in a teeter-totter.

Gravity

A downward force that is created by an extremely large mass, such a planet or star. The mass of the object creates the downward force that affects all objects that have mass, pulling them toward the center of the object.

Ideal Mechanical Advantage

The mathematical term used to describe how effective a simple machine is at helping a person do work. The larger the number, the more efficient the machine is at helping to do the job.

Inclined plane

A ramp or any other simple machine that makes it easier to move from one level to another.

Inertia

The tendency for an object to resist movement. The foundation of Newton's First Law. The more mass an object has and the greater the friction is, the more inertia the object is said to possess. For example, a large, flat stone has a lot of inertia. A large, round steel ball of the exact same mass has less inertia because there is very little friction between the ball and the surface that it is resting on.

Kinetic energy

This is the energy that is used by an object that is moving. Hold a ball in your hand, and it has lots of potential energy. Drop the ball, and it has kinetic energy as it falls toward the ground.

Lever, first-, second-, and third-class

A lever is a simple machine that is defined as having a fulcrum, load, and effort. Depending on the arrangement and position of these three things, the lever is defined as first-, second-, or third-class.

Mass

The amount of stuff that an object possesses. It remains the same, regardless of the circumstances. For example, when you are on Earth, your mass and your weight are the same thing. However, when you are in space, there is no gravitational attraction, so you do not have any weight. You are weightless, but you still have mass.

Momentum

The amount of energy that you have generated to get you moving in a certain direction. The more momentum you have, the harder it is to stop or change direction.

Newton's Laws

There are three of them, to be exact. The First Law says that an object at rest tends to stay at rest, unless a force acts upon it. (Inertia for the kid starting out.) The Second Law states that for every action, there is an equal and opposite reaction, also known as the "Schoolyard, playground rule." And finally, force equals mass times acceleration.

Potential energy

This is the term that is used to describe the energy that is stored in an object. It can be a ball held above the ground, the chemical or electrical energy stored in a cell, or anything else that holds energy in reserve until it is needed.

Glossary

Precession
This is a term that describes the back-and-forth wobbling of planets. This back-and-forth wobbling is responsible for creating the seasons we experience.

Pulley
This is a simple machine that is an adaptation of the wheel. The pulley is a grooved wheel that allows you to lift and move heavy objects. The more pulleys that you have in sequence, the easier it is to move the object.

Resistance
A term that is used to describe the reluctance of an object to move due to another force pushing on that object. When you drive a car down the road, the air pushes against the car, causing wind or air resistance. Water can also do the same thing. Just try running across a swimming pool if you don't believe us.

Resonance
The ability of a material to mimic or match the frequency of an object. When the two objects match, they are said to have resonance and will begin vibrating at the same rate and producing the same frequency.

Screw
This is an inclined plane, wrapped around a pole.

Speed
How fast an object travels from one spot to another, based on the equation: s *(speed)* $= d$ *(distance)*$/t$ *(time)*. A typical unit for speed would be given in miles per hour.

Spring balance

This is a spring inside a plastic tube that measures both the downward force of an object in *Newtons* and the mass of the object in *grams*. Kind of a one-way balance or scale.

Stored energy

Also known as potential energy. This is energy that is being saved until it is needed to move an object, cause a force to occur, or otherwise change the local environment.

Vibration

A measure of how fast an object is moving back and forth over a given distance. When you strike a piano key, the string begins to vibrate back and forth. The period of the vibration and the pitch of the string are dictated by the length and width of the string.

Vortex

Washington, D.C. Just kidding. The vortex is the center of a spinning fluid, either liquid or gas. The eye of a hurricane is a vortex, the center of a tornado is a vortex, and the swirling water descending down into the bottom of your toilet is also a vortex. The objects surrounding the vortex are drawn into it because of the angular momentum of the fluid as a whole. That ought to make it clear as mud.

Wedge

Two inclined planes, slapped side-by-side. Also known as a knife.

Index

Index

Notes

Notes

Notes

Notes

Notes

Newton Take 3 • B. K. Hixson

Notes

More Science Books

Catch a Wave
50 hands-on lab activities that sound off on the topic of noise, vibration, waves, the Doppler Effect, and associated ideas.

Jr. Chemhead
50 hands-on lab activities that delve into the world of chemistry and the characteristics of atoms, molecules, and other basic chemistry ideas.

Newton Take 3
50 hands-on lab activities that explore the world of mechanics, forces, gravity, and Newton's three laws of motion.

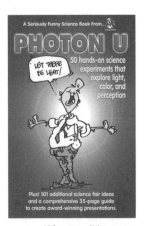

Photon U
50 hands-on lab activities from the world of light. Starts with the basic colors of the rainbow and works you way up to polarizing filters and UV light.

Electron Herding 101
50 hands-on lab activities that introduce static electricity, circuit electricity, and include a number of fun and very easy-to-build projects.

Opposites Attract
50 hands-on lab activities that delve into the world of natural and man-made magnets as well as the characteristics of magnetic attraction.

Rockin' My Life Away
Listening to Jerry Lee Lewis

Rockin' My Life Away

Listening to Jerry Lee Lewis

Jimmy Guterman

RUTLEDGE HILL PRESS
Nashville, Tennessee

Published in Nashville, Tennessee, by Rutledge Hill Press, 513 Third Avenue South, Nashville, Tennessee 37210

Typography by Bailey Typography

Photographs on pages 10, 46 (London Express), 52, 91, 102, 105, 108, 120 (London Express), 145, 159, 176 (© Graham Barker), 182 (Philip Parr), 189, and 196 courtesy of Murray Silver.

Photographs on pages 57, 61, 65, 68, 73, 141, 151, 169, 172, 186, and 205 courtesy of the Country Music Foundation.

Photographs on pages 79, 82, 96, 101, 111, 114, 117, 125, 163, and 190 courtesy of Showtime Archives (Toronto).

Photograph on page 193 © 1984 by Louis Cahill and used by permission.

Library of Congress Cataloging-in-Publication Data

Guterman, Jimmy.
   Rockin' my life away : listening to Jerry Lee Lewis / Jimmy Guterman.
     p. cm.
   Includes index.
   ISBN 1-55853-081-9
   1. Lewis, Jerry Lee. 2. Rock musicians—United States—Biography.
I. Title. II. Title: Rocking my life away.
  ML420.L534G9 1991
782.42166'092—dc20
[B]   91-29525
                                              CIP MN

Printed in the United States of America
1 2 3 4 5 6 7 8—97 96 95 94 93 92 91

Contents

For Jane Kokernak

Acknowledgments

Rockin' *My Life Away* is the story of Jerry Lee Lewis through his music, so the prime source material for this book is on record, tape, or compact disc. Nonetheless, many people were generous enough to help expand my knowledge of that music, either by supplying me with tracks I had not heard before or by helping me hear familiar cuts in new ways. Upon completing this book, I remained humbled by Jerry Lee's work. I know that no book, certainly not this one, can solve all the mysteries suggested by such an all-encompassing artist. All I can hope for is that this modest examination is worthy of its unmatchable subject.

This project is about trusting art, not artists, but many performers and producers took the time to set me straight on a variety of issues. Thanks in this area go to many, among them Jack Clement, Roy Dea, Jim Dickinson, Linda Gail Lewis, Charlie Louvin, Bob L. Moore, Andy Paley, Shelby Singleton, and especially Mack Vickery.

For puzzle pieces and general support, I thank James Austin, Ari Bass, Anatole Broyard, Mark Caro, Gail Clark, Charlie Conrad, Al Cooley, Charles Cross, Colin Escott, Gary Hardy, Richard Helm, Pete Howard, Nick Hunter, Maria Jimenez, Brian Johnson, Paul Kingsbury, Phoebe Lewis, Dennis MacDonald, Noel and Janice Monk, Cal Morgan, Owen O'Donnell, Oedipus, Herb O'Mell, Maury

O'Rourk, Mark Pucci, Tim Riley, Jason Ringenberg, Don Rose, Mason Ruffner, Lydia Sherwood, Murray Silver, Sidney Singleton, Brent E. Sparks, Donald W. Spicer, Charlie Springer, Howard Thompson, Richard Weize, and Dave Yeskel. Thanks also to the too-many-to-list fans and professionals who supplied me with rare and unreleased recordings and sessions. Special thanks go to Kay Clary, Jack Emerson, and Andrew McLenon.

Three significant books about Jerry Lee Lewis preceded this one, and each tells part of the story. Robert Palmer's *Jerry Lee Lewis Rocks!* is a personal essay; Murray Silver's *Great Balls of Fire* is the adventure as Myra saw it; and Nick Tosches's *Hellfire* is a celebration of the Killer myth.

Milo Miles was my editor at the *Boston Phoenix* back when that newspaper published pop music criticism, and I'd like to belatedly thank him for being a forceful advocate who taught me a great deal about craft and detail. I'd also like to acknowledge the work of Peter Guralnick, Greil Marcus, and Dave Marsh, all of which inspired my choice of occupation and subject.

Any investigation of Jerry Lee Lewis's music would be impossible without the pioneering reissue work of Hank Davis, Colin Escott, Martin Hawkins, and, most of all, Richard Weize. Colin and Martin's Sun Records discographies, liner notes, and histories were essential reference works.

At Rutledge Hill Press, I am grateful to Larry Stone for his enthusiasm, his guidance, and his patience, and to Kath Hansen for getting the ball rolling.

Personal thanks go to Deanna and Edward Schey, the Kokernaks, and John Guterman.

Rockin' My Life Away
Listening to Jerry Lee Lewis

CHAPTER 1

A Jerry Lee Lewis Solo

"Some people call me an idiot, but I know who I am. I am The Killer.*"*
—*Jerry Lee Lewis*

A third of a century later, he is back where he started, and he is holding court.

It is the first night of February 1990, and Jerry Lee Lewis is once again singing and shouting in the eighteen-by-thirty-foot studio at the Memphis Recording Service, 706 Union Avenue, Memphis, Tennessee, a room that once functioned as his spiritual home. Fifty-four years old, Jerry Lee doesn't feel much like the kid from Ferriday, Louisiana, who barged into that building in September 1956, demanding that Sun Records label head Sam Phillips hear at that moment how great he was. It is not that he looks bad. He hasn't been renovated as undoubtedly as the studio, but he is as presentable as he has ever been. Jerry Lee's wavy blond hair, newly cut, is packed tightly and neatly. It is nothing like the wild mop it was three decades ago, all flying curls and dangling strands. His defiant sneer has vanished. He has put on some weight, though certainly not the thirty-three years' worth of girth one might expect of an entertainer in the late autumn of his career. Jerry Lee has looked far worse, as many friends, family, fans, and health-service professionals can vouch. Compared to what happened to some of his contemporaries, people like Elvis Presley—a man rarely far from Jerry Lee's thoughts—he is in good shape.

The most pronounced difference is in his eyes. Once they were as ferocious as a pair of fireballs. That was one of the nicknames he encouraged: the Ferriday Fireball. When Jerry Lee first looked for a place in Sam Phillips's dream, he was as singleminded as a kid who knew he was talented could be. He stared straight at the person he was addressing, certain that his God-given prowess could sway anyone. Indomitable, Jerry Lee employed false modesty if he thought it would help him, so the directness in his eyes could be misread as earnestness. He was powerful, he knew he was powerful, and his eyes were among the first weapons he employed. Now his gaze wavers, and not merely because he needs reading glasses. He looks down or looks away almost as frequently as he locks in with another's eyes. Jerry Lee can still size up or dress down someone if he so deigns. When he bothers to use them, his eyes are as unrelenting as they have ever been. Yet the decades have made them something they never were in his salad days: now they are unpitying. If Jerry Lee bothers to notice someone new crossing his path in a studio or a backstage somewhere, it usually is not to beget a friendship.

Friendly or not, Jerry Lee is intent on being a professional tonight, and that means appearing to be committed to his work and not in the condition that his legend often necessitates. But from the moment Jerry Lee first arrived in Memphis thirty-three autumns back, "good shape" for the Ferriday boy was always a relative term. How could a twenty-year-old kid about to careen into his third marriage of dubious legality be in good shape? How could a religious young man tortured by the suspicion that he was playing evil music and committing loathsome acts be in good shape? Jerry Lee's subsequent behavior, by turn destructive and self-destructive, was well-documented as it happened; many of his legions were sure that it was his honesty that brought him down so many times. His self-inflicted punishments went far beyond what any fair court or deity would mandate. (There could be no jury of his peers, of course, because he knew he had no equals.) Jerry Lee's death was reported once and expected several times more, but he laughed at how the public view of his life had led to such expectations. He was The Killer, he would tell anyone who came within earshot, and he would last as long as he damn well wanted. He was in charge.

But he is not a kid anymore. His most purposeful performances of the past decade and a half—songs like "Middle Age Crazy," "I Wish I Was Eighteen Again," "Thirty-nine and Holding," and "Rockin' My Life Away"—derive much of their considerable staying power from Jerry Lee's knowledge that his glory days, at least in terms of _Billboard_ chart standings, are now mostly the stuff of myth and memory, and from his fear that his time as a top-rank performer has passed. Jerry Lee Lewis is not content to be a good singer and pianist who was once one of the greats. He wants only to be the best at this instant, and his terror is that of the aging competent who remembers.

Kids don't smoke custom pipes. Jerry Lee may have driven to the studio from his ranch in northern Mississippi in a flashy powder-blue-topped Jaguar that screams his idea of rock-star attitude, yet he reads the words to the tune he chooses to sing tonight, "It Was the Whiskey Talkin' (Not Me)," through the half-height reading glasses that edge down to the tip of his nose. He concentrates, tests phrasings, listens, lets his gaze glide up and down the room's eleven-foot-high walls, concentrates, swigs some of the song's namesake, and asserts himself at irregular intervals.

Although "It Was the Whiskey Talkin' (Not Me)" is as strong a new tune as any he has recorded in the past four years (skeptics may consider this faint praise), Jerry Lee's recording of the number is essentially a contrived event. Quite simply, he lucked into the gig. The producer, Andy Paley, wrote the song with Jerry Lee in mind more than a decade ago when he was a staff writer for Warner Publishing and Jerry Lee was one of the rulers of country radio. For reasons too obscure and random to recount, the song was not then presented to the Killer. Now Paley is supervising one element of the soundtrack for a film version of the *Dick Tracy* comic strip, following director and star Warren Beatty's directive that the movie's music should reflect his version of what Chicago radio might have sounded like in the 1930s. "It Was the Whiskey Talkin' (Not Me)" fits into that niche; it's a pleasant, if not spectacular, trot along the pop side of Bob Wills-style western swing. The blame-the-booze-not-the-boozer lyrics of the song are not particularly convincing, but they do appear custom-made for Jerry Lee's latter-day recording persona. "Think about it," he often says between takes, more as an ominous general warning than as a reference to anything specific.

Now in the fourth decade of his professional recording career, Jerry Lee is used to putting across songs custom-written for him. He is a stylist, he likes to say, not a writer. His own rare compositions tend to be slight and formulaic. One of his greatest gifts is to take a composition, even one associated with another performer, and redefine it in such a way that others' versions of the song no longer matter. Custom-written numbers don't show up in his mailbox as frequently as they did back when Paley wrote "It Was the Whiskey Talkin' (Not Me)," so Jerry Lee is luxuriating in the tune. He is also savoring the knowledge that this tune will appear in what will likely be a hit film. He has suffered bad luck with films lately: his contribution to the film *K-9 Cop* was a dog, and his own biopic, *Great Balls of Fire*, portrayed him as a grotesque somewhere between Gomer Pyle and the Disney dog Goofy. So he is working, extra hard, on "It Was the Whiskey Talkin' (Not Me)." He needs a hit. He wants a recording deal again.

A playback of the tune fills the studio, Jerry Lee's voice darting between horn blasts. The mood in the room is buoyant but professional. "I can't figure it out, but it sounds great," Jerry Lee hears someone, he's not sure who, tell him. "All of it sounds great. Awesome."

Jerry Lee pushes his glasses up his nose, grins, and points at the ingratiating speaker. "He knows somethin', but he ain't sayin' nothin." Jerry Lee laughs and prepares to take control of the situation. It is the sort of thing he likes to say he can do in his sleep.

"I'm being serious," he hears.

"Well, I appreciate that."

"I _am_ being honest," he hears.

"I appreciate you for saying that, young man," Jerry Lee says, in one of the trademark expressions of feigned deference that still charms fans and seduces producers and executives. Others think they are in charge, but Jerry Lee knows better. "I just want to know. I'm watching people in the room and I get real sensitive. I watch people's eyes. Now who is this guy here? Hey, who are you?"

"That's James," producer Andy Paley pipes in.

"Come here, boy," Jerry Lee instructs and the young man walks toward him. "Who are you?"

"I'm James. I'm the studio manager."

"OK, James. What do you think?" Jerry Lee is insecure. His last single that crossed over from _Billboard_'s country charts into its more lucrative pop list slipped off more than sixteen years ago. He needs a hit, but he also needs to play, and he appears more alert for this face-off than he was for some of the vocal overdubs he committed to tape earlier this evening and the night before.

James is nervous and, like many young men, southern U.S.A. and elsewhere, his discomfort summons up his manners. "I think it sounds real good," he says. "We got a lot of good vocals on there. Last night I liked everything that was on there. Tonight I love everything. And if Andy says he likes it—"

Jerry Lee interrupts James and points at him. "Do you love God?" he demands. Those looking carefully can discern a hint of the old spark behind his reading lenses.

James keeps talking, hoping that he can return Jerry Lee's attention to the tune. ". . . it's gotta be good. He can't lie—"

"Do you love God?" Jerry Lee drawls again.

As he looks around, Jerry Lee takes in the large photographs on the wall, all taken during Sun's fifties heyday, a time label head Sam Phillips had moved on from his seminal blues productions—he was the first to record Chester Burnett (aka Howlin' Wolf), among many other top-rank bluesmen—to a blues-drenched form of country-and-western that, after some woodshedding, exploded into rock and roll. Phillips's grinning image is on the wall. Jerry Lee is there as well, along with Elvis Presley, Carl Perkins, Johnny Cash, and several other white performers who helped make the Memphis Recording Service the center of the pop-music universe.

Once upon a time, Jerry Lee was the reddest, hottest core of that center, and he stretched it when he could. In October 1957, anxious to deliver a worthy follow-up to his million-selling Sun smash "Whole Lotta Shakin' Going On," Lewis settled into the studio one evening to take a pass at "Great Balls of Fire," a submission from ace New York songwriter Otis Blackwell. Lewis was accompanied by guitarist Roland Janes and drummer J.M. Van Eaton, the core of his band, although Janes did not play on the released version. Missing was the fourth member of his stage quartet, Jerry Lee's cousin and future father-in-law, J. W. Brown. Another Sun regular, perhaps Billy Lee Riley, a star in his own right, toyed with an upright bass but went mostly unheard.

Jerry Lee, the only great rock and roller who also had been expelled from the Southwestern Bible Institute of Waxahachie, Texas, was exploring "Great Balls of Fire" before attempting to record it for a single when he noticed the frankly Pentecostal imagery of the song's title and he flipped out. Shouting "H-e-l-l!" he launched into a protracted argument with producer Phillips that was as brazen and enthusiastic as the song in question. The altercation exemplifies two of the great Jerry Lee Lewis dilemmas: his desire to be both the most profane pop performer and the purest purveyor of sacred music, and his demand for permission to hop from one to the other at whim. Never in the argument did he suggest that he wouldn't record "Great Balls of Fire." The dispute took in all sorts of Biblical quotations, some of which Jerry Lee made up, and its intensity was in no way compromised by the inebriation of the debaters. Jerry Lee demanded that Phillips accept Jesus Christ as his Savior; Phillips demanded that Jerry Lee interpret the Bible in a new way; the underpaid sidemen tapped their instruments and mumbled that they wanted to cut the song already and go home.

Jerry Lee and Phillips loved this kind of brawl, but this quarrel was not only amusement, even if they both were entertained by it. Jerry Lee had recorded a version of the song a few weeks earlier for the soundtrack of the film *Jamboree*, so undoubtedly he knew all the words before that evening. His testiness was replaced a few minutes later by expressions of desire that were far more worldly. They loved to face off, show off, and (although each was too proud to admit it) learn from the other.

Tonight at 706 Union there is no one with the authority to counter Jerry Lee, no one who can stand with him among the giants pictured on the walls. So tonight he will solo and see whom he can draw into his wake. Jerry Lee is playing a game.

His question to James, "Do you love God?", hangs in the air. This time James knows he cannot run away. "Yes sir, I sure do," he says.

"Are you a Baptist?" Jerry Lee inquires. As with most

of his recent solos, he has waited a moment before picking up steam.

"A Baptist Christian," James responds, stating his affiliation precisely in an attempt to ward off future questions. He is not smiling.

Jerry Lee smiles as he leans toward his punch line. "I knew you were fucked up."

"Uh oh," James says.

"You know the only thing wrong with Baptist folk?" Jerry Lee asks.

"What is it?" James plays along.

"They just need to get saved," Jerry Lee says. Sacred issues are as omnipresent in his mind as memories of Elvis, but that does not mean that he will address them in a sacred fashion. The half-dozen folks in the studio absorb the outburst and act as appalled as their jaded selves can be.

Alas, James makes the mistake of taking Jerry Lee seriously. "Oh! My grandfather was a preacher. I'm not gonna tell him—"

"Young man," Jerry Lee says, "I'm just putting you on."

"I know it." James swallows.

"Baptist folks are good," Jerry Lee continues. "They just don't preach the full gospel."

"I'm not as good a preacher as I ought to be," James admits.

Jerry Lee has his invitation. "Well, let me go back to where we started: the Book of Acts, second chapter. Read it. Pentecostal. You are what you are. You're realistic and you're real—or you're not." He looks toward the control room. "Now I'm watching you people in there and I know what you're thinking. I know what you're thinking, I know what you're looking at. You ain't fooling Jerry Lee Lewis for a minute."

"I'd never try to," James says, once again on the defensive. "You've been around long enough to read me the Book."

Jerry Lee chuckles. "Now that boy's got a little more sense than I thought he had. That's good."

James goes on, too nervous to stop now. "He's got us jumping in there so fast we ain't got time to think."

Distracted, Jerry Lee turns away from James for a moment and studies the oversize photograph of Elvis on the wall. "Now if I could just recall this dude back here for about fifteen minutes," he says, gesturing toward the larger-than-life king of rock and roll, "we could show you a trick." He nods, swigs, and continues. "Never be another Elvis Presley. He had that something. Dynamic, you know, something that would make you want to drive ten thousand miles to see him if you only had fifteen cents in your pocket. You'd get the money somewhere to go. Ain't nobody could outdraw Elvis Presley."

"I never had the honor of meeting him," Paley says.

"Really?" Jerry Lee fakes incredulity. "Well, we had some good times right here in this old studio out here. He told me, he said, 'Wh-what's goin' on?'" Jerry Lee stops for a moment, delighted that his Elvis imitation catches some of his dead peer's self-mocking mannerisms. "He said, 'Wh-why did you, you didn't have to go into the Army?' I said to him, 'Shit, I never was that crazy.'"

"He got a little upset about that," Jerry Lee says after he stops laughing. "But he was some man. He served his time, he done it. He was so far ahead of his time." He lowers his voice. "He was so great." He begins to sing a line from a tune associated with Presley—"Landlord ringing on the front door bell"—and then imitates Presley's Sun-period vocal stutter: "B-b-b-baby, baby, b-b-baby."

Again, he laughs. "Well, he had something different, didn't he? He was a real gentleman, son. I'll never forget— I know people don't want to hear this bullshit I'm talking about—he pulled out right here and parked, he had that 1956 Lincoln Mark I, I believe it was, I think it was. White one. When he got out of the damned car, I wanted to see what he looked like. He rolled out of that car and he walked in and he looked just exactly like he looked—*dangerous*. We had some times. But those days are gone, aren't they?"

"Not completely," someone pipes up. "We got Jerry Lee."

"Well, ole Jerry Lee is really trying to get it together," he continues. "I know I haven't quite gotten there yet, like I really need to get it there, but I am really working on it with everything I've got to get it there. I've had a rough struggle. I got strung out for a couple of years on all kinds of drugs, junk, whiskey, and everything else. And you just got to back off, man, or you're not gonna make it. Record companies are not gonna buy you, they're not gonna produce you, they're not gonna release a record on you, they're not gonna back you up, if you don't back yourself up."

Caught up in his own preaching, his voice rises: "And they can spot you a mile off if you've got a shot of Demerol or something. They can detect it just like that." He snaps his fingers. "Whiskey's bad enough, but that other kind of stuff . . . man. Brother, I don't mean to be getting into that, it's just a pleasure talking to somebody. You're one of the sharpest people I've talked to."

"Well, that's a huge compliment coming from you."

By now, few in the room remember that they are here to help Jerry Lee finish the vocals to "It Was the Whiskey Talkin' (Not Me)." They are witnessing a performance. Jerry Lee loves it. Except for the informality, for him there is no difference between playing a sold-out thousand-seat hall or a studio with half a dozen professionals and hangers-on. He is still performing. "People talk to you somehow, they talk to me, they get so, I don't know, they just talk in circles. They think they're fooling me, they're trying to put something over on me and I can't hear a prayer."

Suddenly, he remembers what is really on his mind: "Weeds die and roses bloom, but I can't figure out what to do with that fucking wife."

Jerry Lee's laughter has become more hoarse as his mind wanders outside the studio to ponder his latest public argument with his wife, Kerrie, and her father, Jerry Lee's on-again/off-again manager. "She really made me mad this trip," he says. His phrasing owes much to his whiskey. "I told her she ought to go back to her daddy, her manager, Bob McCarver." He laughs loudly. "Well, I'm hotter than fresh-fucked sheep!" He laughs again. "Woo! That broke me out in a sweat. Lord, you're gonna pay for what you did wrong, you know that."

"It'll come back to you," Paley says.

"Don't it?" Jerry Lee continues. "What goes around comes around, what comes around goes around. Well, I'll tell you one thing, I'll never get married again if I live to be three thousand years old!" His voice rises the eleven feet to the ceiling. "I'll swear to God that's the truth! Mark my word on that! Jerry Lee's had his share of women, but they always seem to leave. Thank God for some favors." He chuckles. "Well, my life would make a damn good country song, son. I've been there. And I'm still a living, a living motherhumper."

He fingers the keys of his piano and keeps talking. "I _know_ some things. I've _learned_ some things. I've got to get with it." He talk-sings the first lines from his 1975 hit, "A Damn Good Country Song": "I took enough pills for the whole damn town/Jerry Lee Lewis, he done drunk enough whiskey to lift any ship off the ground." He chuckles, and pays more attention to his singing. "God knows, I've earned my reputation/But they'll never let me get my salvation/My God, Jerry Lee would make a damn good rock-and-roll song/I've had my share of women, son/But they always seem to leave."

Now he's singing full power. "I'll put me another

quarter in that pinball machine/Yes, Jerry Lee's been wrong/Looks like the change that came over me took a little too long/My life would make a damn good country song/Jerry Lee Lewis's life, son/Would make a damn good country song." He ends with a flourish.

"There you go," he says as applause fills the room.

Having warmed up, Jerry Lee believes he is now prepared to cut the number he's there for; his announcement, "Let's cut it," throws the assembled off-guard. "Well, now that I've psychoanalyzed everybody and proved myself wrong again, I . . . thank you for talking with me, Killer." *Call someone else by my most persistent nickname*, he thinks, *and he'll be loyal to me for life.* "I . . . I need talk sometimes, I need help sometimes. Nobody wants to talk to me. They just look at me like I'm crazy or something. You're a good man. I'll tell you what, I think I might just start recording here."

Applause.

Jerry Lee testifies to himself (so much for "Let's cut it"). "As a matter of fact, I swear to God, last night I . . . I, I laid in my bed this morning, about four-thirty, I said, 'That's where I'm gonna start doin' my records.' And nobody could tell me, but this is something I had to make up my mind to do. I don't know, I just made it up when I came in last night, I got to thinking about it. This is home!" Others in the room murmur their assent. "You gotta go back home, man, the prodigal son, man, you know. Hell, I done blowed and strowed and it's time to get back in the saddle. Open me with welcome arms, daddy."

Jerry Lee mumbles, pauses, and adds, "Well, now that I have disbursed all the ignorance of my great thoughts and thinking of my casual-type, nimble brain, let's record." After a verse and chorus from Ray Price's "For the Good Times," a longtime standard in Jerry Lee's stage show, he is indeed ready. "Hey man, this damn song could be the biggest thing. God, I wish I'd've gotten a hold of this thing with a band." Quickly, Jerry Lee remembers that he is at the Memphis Recording Service tonight to make Paley happy, so he changes his tune. "But then again, you're not going to beat the band you've got on there. But you see, Andy, I've got a bad hangup, a bad problem with overdubbing. I never thought I could overdub."

Paley encourages. "But somehow you could."

"Well, I did," Jerry Lee answers, his ego rising. "I went in and did the vocal on 'Middle Age Crazy' a month after I put the track down. I hadn't done it before."

"You'd never know," Paley says.

"No, and it was a big record," Jerry Lee reminds himself.

"Let's try it," Paley says. "You're overdubbing good."

"This is a hit," Jerry Lee says. "Now I think I can cut a hit on this song. Let's get with it."

The next take is a strong one, Jerry Lee somehow finding new nuances in a number that he has by now sung dozens of times. "Boy, that song's something else," Jerry Lee says after he finishes. "Damn, that song excited me. Ain't nothin', son, got me out of bed, son, in the last ten years."

"I'm proud of that," Paley says. He has waited ten years for Jerry Lee to cut the track; he is not kidding. "Glad to be of service."

"Glad to be a servant," Jerry Lee mimics.

A few more passes at "It Was the Whiskey Talkin' (Not Me)" yield nothing special. By the third effort Jerry Lee is playing around, showing off, leading into sloppy solos with improvised couplets like "If you can find a stool high enough/You can kiss ole' Jerry's ass." He apologizes.

"It's all right with me," Paley says.

"No, I just want to get my voice opened up, Killer. It's taking me a little while. When my wife comes back, it'll close up again."

The next take deteriorates into more improvised couplets: "I guarantee you this/It was the whiskey that made me want to piss/It was the whiskey doing things like this."

"Sorry, Andy," Jerry Lee says. "Fuck, I ain't sorry. John Wayne said, 'Never apologize. It shows a sign of weakness.' I ain't apologizing; I'm just saying I was wrong."

By now, Paley is satisfied enough with the various takes to know that he can piece together a full performance from the many takes. He is almost home. He says, "This is the only line we need right here: 'Just lettin' off a little steam.'"

"Whoever wrote that is baaad," Jerry Lee says.

Andy repeats: "Just lettin' off a little steam."

"I'm just playin' with you, son," Jerry Lee says and belches as Paley repeats, "Just lettin' off a little steam."

Jerry Lee decides to comment on his expulsion. "Now that was the most ill-mannered, ridiculous, uncouth thing that I've ever done in my fucking life." He gestures toward the lyric sheet that has fallen to the floor. "Now hold that damn piece of paper up where I can see it and let's get to letting off some steam."

He sings the line and then decides it's not true. "Just lettin' off some steam? Well, that's a bunch of shit. I'm the meanest motherfucker that ever shit through a meat ass." Paley laughs, Jerry Lee and Paley duet the verse in question, and Jerry Lee quickly loses interest.

"I'm sounding worse all the time," Jerry Lee says after another aborted take. Now he yells. "I'll drink this whole fucking fifth if I don't get mad in a minute and kill! I'm really getting upset. Call Sam." Then quieter, "Please don't do that."

Paley feels the session getting away from him. "Please don't get upset," he implores.

"I'm as nervous as a queer at a weenie roast," Jerry Lee says. "I oughta married one o' them Rock Hudsons or somebody, I would've been better off."

Another overdub attempt is closer to what Paley wants,

but Jerry Lee wants more. "Why don't we do the whole song?"

An alarmed Paley says, "Wh–wh . . . that was good, though. Let's just get the ending. Let's get the ending."

"Yassuh," Jerry Lee says. "Yassuh boss."

More overdubs follow, and eventually Paley gets what he wants. Yet completing the song is anticlimactic. The show Jerry Lee is putting on tonight is greater than any movie-soundtrack tune. "Are we outta here?" Paley asks.

Jerry Lee sings and plays his response, improvising half-remembered words to a half-remembered melody:

"Are we outta here/I think we were before I came/I think I was in vain/A motherhumpin' man I used to be/I got news in 1990/Son, they're gonna see/A different motherhumper by the name of Jerry Lee/'Cos I just am what I am and I just really don't give a damn."

By now Paley has joined in on drums and Jerry Lee is cruising, playing far harder than he was for take after take of "It Was the Whiskey Talkin' (Not Me)." He sings: "'Cos people ain't gonna tell me what I can do/Doctor, lawyer, bum at a bar, a rockin' motherhumper or a movie star/ There's a rockin' rollin' Jerry Lee Lewis from Tennessee/ Memphis, Tennessee, is rock and roll, son/Nashville, Tennessee, is hillbilly heaven/I ain't got nothin' against ole' hillbilly heaven/My voice is leavin', that must mean I must have some of the devil/You demon-possessed mother, play your drums for Jerry Lee/Go back to your little girl in L.A. and tell her how true you've been/You'd screw up a two-car funeral with Sam Phillips in the lead/Ha ha/Thank God I'm perfect/Shine on, shine on, shine on, harvest moon up in the sky/Jerry Lee Lewis ain't had no lovin' since January, February, June, and July/There's no time, baby, ain't no time for stayin' out late to spoon/You oughta get down on your knees for me and shine on harvest moon."

Jerry Lee indulges himself in a brief upper-key solo

and returns to his tale. "Well, Jerry Lee, he's been waiting for a wedding in June/Honey, I might be a little hoarse but pretty soon I'll come through/They're gonna put a coon on the moon in June or the jig is up they say/Probably be old Charley Pride I pray, pray, pray, and pray." He solos through the nervous laughter, plays another chorus, and resolves into a standard: "Mona Lisa, Mona Lisa, men have named you." Paley's drums nearly swing and Jerry Lee's piano certainly does, until the Killer loses interest and complains, "Pick it up son, you're draggin' on Jerry Lee. You screwed me up."

"No I didn't," Paley protests as he drops his sticks.

"Jealousy. I have that problem everywhere I go." Jerry Lee chuckles. "You're draggin' ass on me, too."

"I'm sorry, Jerry." Unlike James, Paley won't be drawn out.

Jerry Lee nods an acceptance to Paley's apology. He looks at the picture of himself and his fellow Sun artists on the wall, and he remembers once more. He looks around, taps the top of the piano, and he recalls the simple joys of discovering music in this room. That's what he does best and the vast majority of people who have heard his name don't know it. They know the dirt; they know defrocked televangelist Jimmy Lee Swaggart is his cousin; they know Jerry Lee is rumored to have murdered one of his half-dozen wives; blah blah blah. Jerry Lee knows he should be famous for only one thing: his more than thirty years of music. Instead he is famous to most because he enjoyed two early rock-and-roll hits with suggestive titles, because he ruined his career by marrying his thirteen-year-old cousin, and because he is one of the few early rock-and-roll titans who isn't dead.

He has suffered through years of indifference from a modern pop-music industry he helped build. He has endured books about him full of transparently made-up quotations. He has suffered through a flop film based on his life that treated him and the culture that formed him as a joke. He appears in the tabloids not for his records, but for business judgments so wrongheaded that they are matched only by his romantic miscalculations. People get so high on the myth of Jerry Lee that often many forget that the guy sings and plays piano.

Jerry Lee's true story is in his bold, unquenched music far more than in his ultimately common deeds. It is his music that speaks loudest; it is his music that tells the greatest truths. When you're listening to Jerry Lee Lewis, you're listening to him rocking his life away, listening to his music. Long after he passes on and the tabloids pick at his bones ("Killer's Ghost Disrupts Graceland Tour," the headlines will read), his music will remain. Long after his life story is supplanted in most people's minds by Dennis Quaid's incompetent impersonation of him in _Great Balls of Fire_, his greatest records will still reveal mystery after mystery. The records will tell a story that will sway even the most fervent critic of the man. Jerry Lee Lewis lived his life through his music; we can understand his life only through his music.

CHAPTER 2

Ferriday

"We were just farmers."
—Jerry Lee Lewis

Before we can hear the music, we need to know what led to it. "There's only been four of us," many have reported Jerry Lee boasting. "Al Jolson, Jimmie Rodgers, Hank Williams, and Jerry Lee Lewis. That's your only four fuckin' stylists that ever lived."

The youngest of that elite group of American music originals was born poor on Sunday, September 29, 1935, in Ferriday, Louisiana, a medium-size city in the east center of the state, near the Mississippi border. The larger Louisiana city Alexandria was more than an hour's drive away; the nearest community of any size was Natchez, just across the great Mississippi River. United with Mississippi by its dependence on the river, Ferriday had more in common with Mississippi boroughs than Louisiana ones, both musically and economically. It is no accident that Jerry Lee always considered Mississippi, which is all that separates Ferriday from Memphis, as much his home state as Louisiana.

Jerry Lee was the second son born into the stormy marriage of Elmo and Mary Ethel ("Mamie") Lewis. Elmo, Jr., was closing in on his sixth birthday when his little brother showed up a bit prematurely. Those with a pen-

chant for the romantic are welcome to suggest that Jerry
Lee, born feet first, just could not wait to get into this world
and start rocking. Throughout his personal and professional life, he always worked on his own schedule.

Elmo, Sr., was already rocking. A cotton farmer, he
had been the victim of two horrible punches, knocked to
his knees by poor harvests and then to the dry ground by
the Great Depression. One of his few means of escape was
his collection of Jimmie Rodgers 78-r.p.m. records; through
his father Jerry Lee became a dedicated fan of the Singing
Brakeman. Another one of the former bootlegger's diver-
sions was selling homemade whiskey without giving the
government its share of his proceeds. This had already
landed him in prison at least once before Jerry Lee was
born.

Music and booze were no more than temporary diver-
sions. The Lewises were poor, saved from outright home-
lessness only by the shotgun home lent to them by one of
Elmo's relations. They lived without indoor plumbing or
electricity—the record player was a windup model. Elmo
and Mamie endured frequent rows. Mamie's anger at their
economic predicament and her husband's inability to rescue
them from their insolvency vented itself frequently and
Elmo would usually either back off or take off. Those looking for the origin of the many battles Elmo and Mamie
fought over Jerry Lee's destiny have only to consider their
son's name. Elmo insisted that he had named the child after
two relatives while Mamie stressed that she had named him
either after *different* relatives or after one of her favorite
silent-movie stars. In these ways—dire economic circumstances and a passive husband stumbling along the margins
of the law—the circumstances of Jerry Lee's first few years
were similar to those of another kid, eight months his senior, who was growing up in northern Mississippi: Elvis
Presley. Grafted onto this situation was something Elmo
and Mamie whispered about, something called "It," that
had infected members of Elmo's family.

Some photographs of Jerry Lee from this period have survived, and they all reveal an aspect of the Killer's look that has also lasted, his sneer. Much has been written about the lecherousness of Jerry Lee's smirks, but such provocativeness on his part definitely began in a presexual period. In his early years of hardship, long before he had a hint of what he was going to do with his life, Jerry Lee sported a natural sneer, one far more friendly than the one many have subsequently divined.

They did have music, and Mamie loved to hear her two Elmos sing tunes by their favorite Mississippian, Jimmie Rodgers. Rodgers's career was brief: he recorded professionally for the first time in 1927 and was dead of tuberculosis within six years. However, what his first producer called a mix of "nigger blues and old-time fiddle music," coupled with the expressive, malleable yodeling that was his trademark, made the former railroad man an instant star.

Rodgers's influence was diverse, immediate, and profound on the second generation of country-and-western stars. Bob Wills expanded upon his ideas about merging white rural music with New Orleans-style jazz. Tex Ritter and Gene Autry transformed his wild, romanticized tales of a brakeman's life (with titles like "Train Whistle Blues," "In the Jailhouse Now," and "My Rough and Rowdy Ways") into less adventurous, more romanticized tales of a cowboy's life. Woody Guthrie took up his mantle as a plainspoken rambler.

Rodgers is often designated the Father of Country Music, although the elements of his style that have frequently been dismissed, such as his nasal voice and his idiosyncratic timing, are the ingredients that earned him his title. His commercial ascendancy and the success of his contemporaries, such as the Carter Family and dozens of front-porch string bands, showed that this new form of music he was inventing would have much more to do with direct, unencumbered expression than it would with the tightly arranged big bands then at the height of their popularity.

Also, one did not need thirty instruments to replicate this music, and the Elmos were content to sit on the floor and harmonize with Rodgers and his primitive guitar accompaniment.

The Lewises also had church. For whites in the mostly rural South, informal evangelical sects were the rule, the rock that united families and communities. Religion, especially the more visceral variety, is frequently a refuge for those who have been mistreated in this life. Flannery O'Connor, a southern Catholic with a keen eye for the nuances of her Protestant neighbors, once said in a lecture, "While the South is hardly Christ-centered, it is most certainly Christ-haunted." This observation, albeit somewhat flippant, alertly describes the predicament of families like the Lewises. Their everyday problems were too pressing and unavoidable for them to devote their time to much other than survival, but it was belief in something beyond this world that made it possible for them to get through day after day of drudgery and fear. At Mamie's command, the Lewises were churchgoers, first to the local Baptist church and later to the Assemblies of God hall. What little leisure time she enjoyed went in that direction.

In his youngest years Jerry Lee was brought to a makeshift church, more a tent than a solid building, that had been founded by traveling preachers representing the Assemblies of God, one of the more popular Pentecostal sects. Pentecostalism was a culture based on separation from worldliness, and the Assemblies of God was more activist in its methods of disassociation than most. Not only did the Assemblies of God believe in the standard Pentecostal movement's emphasis on ecstasy through glossolalia (speaking in tongues) and the purity of women through enforced plainness and rigid social morés, but it also insisted that even believers had to be repeatedly prodded along the road to salvation. It was a sect for people who wanted to be saved every day.

The uninhibited Assemblies of God services were more than a little scary to the young Jerry Lee. People danced excitedly, in ways he had never seen his parents respond to his father's Jimmie Rodgers records, and people spoke in words and ways he could not comprehend. But Jerry Lee enjoyed the Assemblies of God rituals for another reason: there was music. His uncle Willie Leon Swaggart and his aunt Minnie Bell Swaggart, who had inducted the Lewises into the Assemblies of God, brought their fiddle and guitar to the proceedings and by all accounts kicked up as much dirt with their accompaniment as did the dancers and glossolaliacs. Jerry Lee and his cousin Jimmy Lee Swaggart listened to Jimmy Lee's parents play, and they were both moved by what they heard and saw. They got to sing along. They were poor but they felt like part of a community, part of a big family.

One member of the Lewis family who did not attend many of these services was Elmo, Sr., who had been arrested once again for liquor-law violations and was residing in a New Orleans federal prison. While her husband was away, Mamie held sway over Jerry Lee and impressed upon her son that his father was not worth his time. (The Elvis parallel is clear.) Jerry Lee saw his father only once during Elmo's nearly year-long incarceration, and those circumstances were tragic. On a Saturday afternoon in early August 1938, Elmo, Jr., eight years old, was killed by a drunk driver. His father was allowed to attend the funeral, which took place on land owned by a relative, in handcuffs. The inscription on his dead son's stone read: Budded on Earth to Bloom in Heaven.

Elmo returned from prison a few months later to learn that he might as well have stayed in New Orleans. His family, particularly the Calhouns and the Swaggarts, had supported Mamie and Jerry Lee adequately while he was away, and absence had not made Mamie's heart grow fonder. Elmo did what his wife told him to do and complained about it elsewhere. Jerry Lee envied his father's rough and rowdy affairs from afar, but he was and would remain his mother's son. Jerry Lee was now singing along with Elmo's Jimmie Rodgers records, not singing along with Elmo.

Jerry Lee grew up during World War II in several homes, including his own and the somewhat more spacious one of his uncle Lee and aunt Stella Calhoun while Elmo and Mamie hit the road briefly in 1942, chasing weapons-manufacturing work. The Swaggarts also sought such jobs. By then the Assemblies of God tent had become a genuine wood building in which Jerry Lee and his favorite cousins, Jimmy Lee Swaggart and Mickey Gilley, beheld services that were made more spectacular by an assembly line of fire-breathing preachers.

Also by then Jerry Lee had noticed the Calhouns' spinet piano. There was an upright in the church that Jerry Lee, Jimmy Lee, and Mickey were all encouraged to explore, but it was the Calhouns' that Jerry Lee favored. His school work was consistently poor enough that Elmo felt the need to spank him over it; the Calhouns' piano was for Jerry Lee both an escape from these everyday traumas (it did for the eight-year-old what the Assemblies of God did for Mamie) and an alternate means of satisfying his parents.

Elmo and Mamie gave Jerry Lee a sister, Frankie Jean, shortly after his ninth birthday. Around the same time, Jerry Lee gave Elmo and Mamie a present of his own.

He had been battling the Calhouns' spinet for months, and by Christmas 1944 he had beaten his first recognizable song out of it, the nineteenth-century carol "Silent Night." For an untutored nine-year-old with minimal interest in schooling and nothing approaching leadership from his father, Jerry Lee's serendipitous discovery that he could listen to a song, reproduce it, and get the immediate approval of his entire family was revelatory. Mamie pronounced him a budding genius on the spot, and she instructed Elmo to use what little they had as collateral to get the child a piano.

Elmo soon dragged a used Starck upright into their home.

The war ended, the flooding of the Mississippi River had a deleterious effect on the family harvest, and his grades fell to nearly straight F's, but Jerry Lee did not care because he had a piano. At first he played variations of "Silent Night" that became more raucous with each iteration. The Calhouns' house had a radio, so in addition to the Jimmie Rodgers tunes that were the staple at home, Jerry Lee's ears were opened to a broader array of sounds. Most important was a song called "Boogie Woogie," which he had heard in two versions, that of the Tommy Dorsey Orchestra, and the original version by Clarence ("Pinetop") Smith, who identified it as "Pinetop's Boogie Woogie." A delightful instrumental journey, "Boogie Woogie" was the first major hit record to feature the striking new piano style that gave the song its name. By the time Jerry Lee was ready to hear "Boogie Woogie," the form had apparently peaked. John Hammond's 1938 breakthrough concert at Carnegie Hall in New York City, "From Spirituals to Swing," had featured three boogie woogie pianists: Albert Ammons, Pete Johnson, and Meade Lux Lewis. By the mid-forties, most boogie-woogie piano players in large bands were often too overwhelmed by loud horn sections to make themselves felt.

Boogie-woogie sounded like noise to many of the jazz fans who first heard it, but more discerning listeners, among them the amazed young Jerry Lee, could tell that it was the most unruly, most inviting piano style they had ever heard. Boogie-woogie was propelled by eight-to-the-bar rhythms that could turn the pianist's right hand into an instant jukebox. Play the boogie-woogie, and people would move. Even if a pianist's right hand—the melody hand—was not particularly adept, the boogie-woogie beat would stomp out all objections. Jerry Lee played "Silent Night" boogie-woogie.

Jerry Lee's vacillation between the sacred and the profane has been an enduring part of his myth, but the fact remains that his early boogie-woogie workouts, an obvious affront to church piano patterns, met no objection from his God-fearing mother or, apparently, anyone else. Mamie encouraged his explorations. One preacher, a Brother Janeway, who passed through Ferriday's Assemblies of God church, was noted for a staccato piano style, sparked by a wandering left hand that many listeners felt could boogie them toward the Promised Land. Mamie never hid her desire that Jerry Lee's burgeoning talents be put in the service of Jesus, but at least in his first few years of piano playing, perhaps until as late as 1950, there is no evidence of her forcing Jerry Lee down one musical path or another. Perhaps she was simply grateful for evidence that her remaining son might develop into something more than his father.

Music was everywhere for Jerry Lee: in church, on the Calhouns' radio, and on the new records Elmo bought to augment his Jimmie Rodgers 78s. The pumping rhythms of Freddie Slack's "The House of Blue Lights" made it a favorite (young Jerry Lee was allowed to listen to a song with a title that hinted at a house of ill repute), as was a hammering version of the Cajun standard "Jolé Blon" by Aubrey "Moon" Mullican. (Moon's follow-up was called "Jolé Blon's Sister.") Mullican was using his piano to pull off some of the same fusions that Jimmie Rodgers had achieved on his guitar; but, although Rodgers was the greater artist, the younger Mullican was able to incorporate Rodgers's achievements into his mix.

Mullican was a country singer in the Texas style, which meant he raided jazz for rhythms to complement his country cadences. He was country and western with an emphasis on western. Mullican's attitude also made an impact on his young fan. He shouted his words and was far more interested in being heard than in being precise. Mullican once said, "You got to make those bottles bounce on the table," a notion Jerry Lee would remember when he entered the honky tonks of Natchez. Esteemed as a singer and pianist, Mullican was nonetheless best known in Louisiana as the leader of the band that accompanied Jimmie Davis, the future governor and author of "You Are My Sunshine," during his first campaign.

Jerry Lee tried to learn everything as quickly as possible. He heard blues records on a Natchez radio station after his home finally had electricity. But at that time the black music of the Delta was too foreign for him to assimilate, even if the country blues of Charley Patton and Robert Johnson had now been electrified and ostensibly made more accessible by several Memphis-based performers. He made tentative attempts at translating Jimmie Rodgers's guitar ideas onto piano chords, and he learned to yodel in Rodgers's blues-derived manner. He committed himself to drills of Al Jolson tunes, whose films he devoured, so he could better project his voice. Most important, he latched onto Gene Autry's "You're the Only Star (In My Blue Heaven)" as a means by which he could make country music swing in a new way. From the start he was looking to be a unique stylist. Eventually he was willing to play outside the house in front of people other than his family, and his performances of sacred songs were loose enough to be appreciated and close enough to the original to be permitted. In the summer of 1947, Mamie gave birth to Jerry Lee's second sister, Linda Gail.

Since school was no longer a priority for Jerry Lee, in his parents' minds as well as his own, his hours not practicing or praying were devoted to carousing with his cousins Jimmy Lee and Mickey. Jimmy Lee, still a teenager, had already pledged his life to the Lord, but he was nonetheless encouraged by Jerry Lee and Mickey to accompany them on their jaunts both in Ferriday and across the river. They sneaked into blues bars and heard venerated piano players like Sunnyland Slim and Memphis Slim; they also indulged in some petty theft. Not yet fourteen, Jerry Lee was already

having it both ways: his mother delighted at his development as a church pianist and his cousins were thrilled to be
hearing some juke blues, overturning garbage cans, and
raising a bit of hell. Around this time, Jerry Lee's wild behavior, among other things, earned him the nickname
"Killer."

The final element of Jerry Lee's musical education ar-
rived one Saturday night, when he tuned to the syndicated
"Louisiana Hayride" radio show and first heard Hank
Williams. Williams was as much a trailblazer as Jimmie
Rodgers, but he was an even greater writer and performer.
The characters in his songs wavered incessantly, but his
portrayals of them never did. Jerry Lee heard Williams put
across songs like "I Saw the Light," an astonishing prodigal
son parable; "Honky Tonkin'," a paean to hard living; and
"Move It On Over," a hilarious tale of a honky-tonkin' husband who is literally in the doghouse. The breadth of these
recordings was stunning to Jerry Lee. Here was someone
who could sing about both sides of the line, sin and salvation, and make them sound like the same, real life. Jerry
Lee has said that his favorite of the early Williams tunes he
heard was "Lovesick Blues," which was not, tellingly, a
Williams original; it originated in Tin Pan Alley. For Jerry
Lee, it had everything: a steady beat that never got in the
way of the singer, a resigned tale of fractured love that
somehow worked with its spirited delivery, and a yodel
more lonesome and blue than anything Jimmie Rodgers
ever concocted. When Jerry Lee connected immediately to
Williams's music, it was not only because he heard someone
he liked, it was also because he heard someone he wanted to
be.

With Williams's songs ringing in his ears even when he
was not listening to them or replicating them on his Starck,
Jerry Lee decided he was a songwriter, too. He never recorded the first song he wrote, a ragtime-style ditty he often
sang with his cousin Mickey, called "Yo Yo":

Yo yo, I know
You're my little pet.
You must've come from heaven
'Cause you ain't stepped out yet.

With a string around my finger
I'm happy as can be
'Cause every time I throw you down
You come right back to me.

★　　★　　★

Elmo got a job working construction at the Angola
Penitentiary, the same place he had served time a few years
previously, and a reformatory known in town for the musical prowess of its mostly African–American residents. Jerry
Lee spent much time shuttling between the family's new
home closer to the prison and his beloved Ferriday. His relationships with his sisters took their cue from the way he saw
Elmo and Mamie interact: he would bully Frankie Jean,
and she would find out what mattered to him and damage
it. The job in Angola did not last long, and the family
moved back to Ferriday, this time to a house with electricity
and indoor plumbing. Aside from a high-school football injury and his first attempts at romance, nothing happened to
Jerry Lee in Angola.

In 1949 Ferriday got a Ford dealership, Babin–Paul
Motors, and a hillbilly band performed at a November
party hyping the new cars. In one of his few enterprising
moments that did not involve moonshine, Elmo talked one
of the proprietors into letting Jerry Lee take over the
eighty-eights. Those at the event differ on what Jerry Lee
played and sang. Some report it was the Bill Nettles's hit,
"Hadacol Boogie," others insist it was Granville ("Stick")
McGee's proto-R&B "Drinkin' Wine Spo-Dee-o-Dee"; but
everyone agrees that after a few seconds of indecisiveness,
Jerry Lee was tremendous, as evidenced by the nearly thirteen dollars he earned when a hat was passed. For the

Lewises, that was big money. Jerry Lee knew what he was going to do with his life. Within a month, he dropped out of high school. No one argued.

Jerry Lee wanted to play clubs, and he was competent to do so, but the local authorities did not look kindly upon underage piano players in juke joints. Jerry Lee tried to find work elsewhere, traveling as far as New Orleans; but, as Elmo put it, his son didn't look any older in New Orleans than he did in Ferriday. He contented himself with flat-bed shows and talent contests, usually taking in ten dollars or so.

Mamie was pleased that her son was making something of a living as a musician, but she was still committed to the idea that his talents be used for their church. She was unable to fathom a way in which Jerry Lee could do both. Since she could not resolve the dilemma, she decided it was all Jerry Lee's fault. Mamie was proud that her son was talented, but the real reason she encouraged Jerry Lee's predilection for music was simple economics. Even with Elmo's somewhat better standing in the community, even with the help they still received from their families, they were far from safe or comfortable. They needed the money, even if Mamie feared that Jerry Lee's occupation would make his entrance into heaven questionable. When Jerry Lee came home from a gig, he knew what the pattern would be. Mamie would rail at him about how he was doing the devil's work by playing that boogie-woogie music. Then she would demand the money.

As the months passed, Jerry Lee returned home with more money in his pockets. Fifteen years old, he was finally allowed to work in a Natchez nightclub and he earned himself a twenty-minute Saturday-night slot on Natchez's WNAT, where he played Jimmie Rodgers songs, other countrified blues, and a smattering of gospel. His extracurricular adventures accelerated since he could drive, and Elmo made some noise himself by being accused of trying to kill his brother-in-law Lee Calhoun over a piece of land. These events, coupled with his fear that Mamie and Jimmy Lee might be right about whom he was serving during his evening adventures, led Jerry Lee to enroll in the Southwestern Bible Institute in Waxahachie, Texas.

He did not last long. His attention span snapped quickly, and the institute's faculty did not take well to his sneaking out to bars or inserting boogie-woogie riffs into songs like "My God Is Real" during services. After three months, he was expelled and returned to Ferriday.

At the time, Jerry Lee was nonchalant about being booted from the institute, but being expelled from such a school must have touched him deeply. Mamie's screams that he was doing evil by playing secular music rattled in his brain, and he knew that his inability to satisfy his teachers in Waxahachie indicated that he was cut from a different cloth. Jerry Lee has bounced back and forth between hard-edged rock and roll and polite spirituals more times than Little Richard and Prince combined. Mamie never resolved the paradox, and she never gave her son the tools to do so. Waxahachie came and went quickly for Jerry Lee, but it stayed with him.

By this time, Jerry Lee was a married man, at least on paper. Sixteen years old, he had married a preacher's daughter one year his senior named Dorothy Barton. On his February 1952 marriage license, he listed his occupation as farmer. Barton's romance with Jerry Lee had proceeded despite her parents' protest. They detested Jerry Lee, which was reason enough for them to try to break it off, but a more sensible reason for separating Jerry Lee and Dorothy was that they were both innocent kids who had no clue what marriage was about. Neither knew how to make a living, and they were also extremely ignorant sexually.

As Jerry Lee remembered more than three decades later, "On my wedding night with Dorothy, we just sat up for hours, didn't want to shut the lights and go to bed. I said, 'Do you wanna?' and she said, 'I don't know, do you?' So I said, 'Well, this is what we got married for, ain't it?' Boy, afterwards, I didn't know where the blood was comin' from, you know, if it was from her or me. I wiped myself off and saw it wasn't me and called old man Calhoun and said, 'Somethin's wrong with Dorothy, she's bleedin' to death.' Man, they didn't teach us nothin'."

To please Mamie and Dorothy's father, Jerry Lee preached for a time, but that did not take any better than the marriage. Those present swear that his sermons were as vivid and intense as the piano solos he played when he slipped into Ferriday and Natchez clubs late at night, but it was the excitement of the jukes and the relative ease with which he could make a living there that settled the question. He had also picked up some work as a drummer in Paul Whitehead's band at the Wagon Wheel in Natchez, which catered to both country and blues crowds. He was able to play piano when Whitehead moved to accordion or trumpet. Thirty-seven years later, Jerry Lee's onstage repertoire was cluttered with many of the same songs he played with the Whitehead group: "Drinkin' Wine Spo-Dee-o-Dee" (a cleaned-up version of "Drinkin' Wine Mother-fucker"), Hank Thompson's "The Wild Side of Life," Ernest Tubb's "Slippin' Around," and Johnny Temple's "Big Legged Woman." It was with Whitehead's band that Jerry Lee learned the worth of, and excitement that could be generated by, the hardest-edged, bluesiest of country sounds. Around the same time he heard a local bluesman named John Littlejohn play a song that sounded interesting, called "Whole Lotta Shakin' Going On."

• • •

By the end of 1954, Jerry Lee's second marriage was in trouble. He had ended his first marriage unilaterally, without bothering to get any approval from the state of Louisiana, or from Dorothy, an oversight that would one day cause him much grief. Jane Mitcham, wife number two,

met Jerry Lee at church, made a living selling sewing machines, and gave birth to Jerry Lee Lewis, Jr., in
November. Jerry Lee did not spend much time with Jane or
his son; he was either out playing or in listening to the radio. Church was no longer part of his weekly routine.

The music he heard on the country stations was per-
ceptibly more uptempo than it had been six years earlier,
when he started listening seriously. A boogie-woogie pianist
named Merrill Moore was playing hard, fast versions of
Freddie Slack tunes, and a journeyman country singer
named Bill Haley was softening Joe Turner's "Shake, Rattle, and Roll" into something that seemed different. Haley's
"Shake, Rattle, and Roll" wasn't country. It certainly
wasn't blues, and it wasn't slick enough to be pop. Jerry
Lee filed the genre-busting idea.

He promptly forgot it when he got another one, a better one. Some little label had a new singer who didn't just
sound different; he sounded outright weird. Oddballs,
singers like Howlin' Wolf and B. B. King, only got onto the
blues stations, not the country or pop channels where quiet
conformity ruled. "Da da-da dee dee-dee dee, Dee-dee dee-
dee dee," Jerry Lee heard Elvis sing. There was hardly anything other than Elvis's voice on "That's All Right," just a
couple of guitars. Even more than the Bill Haley performance, which was much lighter, "That's All Right" did not
sound like it belonged anywhere. It moved, though, and
Jerry Lee learned that the company in Memphis that put it
out was called Sun.

The confidence Jerry Lee gained from performing in
Ferriday and Natchez clubs, combined with his hope that
the introduction of these strange sounds to the radio might
mean there was room for someone like him, led him to
Shreveport on a trip funded by his aunt Stella Calhoun. He
auditioned for the "Louisiana Hayride" package tour, the
program through which he had first heard his idol, Hank
Williams. Jerry Lee auditioned for Slim Whitman, a coun-

try star with severe pop leanings. Whitman brought Jerry Lee to the KWKH studios, where the nervous kid recorded two songs directly to acetate. It was only the second time Jerry Lee had been recorded. In the summer of 1951, he had shown up at a make-your-own-record booth in New Orleans and cut a pair of tunes, Lefty Frizzell's "Don't Stay Away ('Til Love Grows Cold)" and an original instrumental that never earned a name. That time the only audience was Jerry Lee and his buddy Cecil Harrison. At KWKH far more was at stake.

For the first number, Jerry Lee chose "I Need You Now," then a chart-topping pop hit for Eddie Fisher. The song was nothing special, just a come-back-to-me lyric pasted on standard chord changes, but Jerry Lee's solo performance, kicked off by a boogie-woogie figure he swiped from a Moon Mullican single, strips the song to its barest essentials and makes it real. His voice is higher than his first officially released performance two years later, but what is most remarkable about the track is that he is already "the Killer" in style and demeanor. One myth about Jerry Lee (a similar one exists for Elvis) is that he entered the Sun Recording Service as a *tabula rasa* for Sam Phillips and Jack Clement to shape, but even a cursory listen to "I Need You Now" indicates that Jerry Lee arrived at 706 Union Avenue close to being fully formed musically.

The second tune, Hank Snow's "I Don't Hurt Anymore," was even sturdier. Everything about the performance was more thought out, probably because the Snow tune had been out four months longer than "I Need You Now" and Jerry Lee had had more time to assimilate its nuances. The singing was more assured; he played with the phrasing and bent the melody to his wishes. He stomped into the solo, which set the pattern for a lifetime of piano breaks. There was nothing economical about the solo. Jerry Lee tried to cram in as much as the song would stand. He climaxed "I Don't Hurt Anymore" the same way he capped

"I Need You Now," in a persuasive upper-register cry. Although they were never released, these performances meant a great deal to Jerry Lee for a long time. As recently as the mid-seventies, he played the acetates for virtually anyone who visited him. However, they did not mean anything to Slim Whitman, who is reported to have said, "Don't call me, I'll call you."

Far from discouraged, for he knew he was great, Jerry Lee next assaulted the capital of country music, Nashville, a town he later memorialized as "hillbilly heaven." He found some work there but soon returned to Ferriday because he was broke. Legend states that conservative C&W icon Chet Atkins himself dismissed Jerry Lee and told him to learn how to play the guitar. Atkins says he does not remember such a suggestion, although Jerry Lee did subsequently study the six-string. Whoever turned him down and for whatever reason, Jerry Lee landed back at the Wagon Wheel.

He tired of Natchez clubs quickly and hammered out a tentative reconciliation with Jane. Through 1955, Jerry Lee heard more and more Elvis Presley records on the radio and decided that Elvis's record company, Sun, might be more open to a wild child like him than the buttoned-up Nashville major labels. Through the fall, Jerry Lee and Elmo worked Elmo's hens hard, pulled a record number of eggs out of them, and used the money they made from selling more than thirty dozen to finance a trip to Memphis to show this Sam Phillips how great Jerry Lee was.

CHAPTER 3

Sun Rising

You went to Memphis to find yourself
Read every Elvis book on the shelf
Even popped a pill or two
*   to feel like a honky-tonk star.*
*   —Jason Ringenberg, "Broken Whiskey Glass"*

For fans whose primary connection to country music was through their radios, 1956 was a great year. Aside from Elvis, folks could hear genre-shattering new songs like "Why Baby Why" by Red Sovine and Webb Pierce and assertive returns to the hard country of two decades earlier like "Cash on the Barrelhead" and "I Don't Believe You've Met My Baby" by the Louvin Brothers. The year's biggest country hit was Ray Price's "Crazy Arms," a tremendous heartbreak ballad written and, to a lesser degree, performed in the mold of the late Hank Williams. The song had been written by Price's guitar player while he was drunk, after his wife left him. This was a year in which the record companies allowed the country audience to respond to the unadorned stuff, a situation that gave Sun Records a shot. (One could argue that without Sun, the major labels in Nashville never would have loosened up enough to release such songs and promote them as hits.)

47

At his peak, at ease, London, 1958

Broke and half-crazy after the long car ride from Ferriday, Jerry Lee and Elmo arrived at the Sun Recording Service one afternoon in September 1956 and learned that Sam Phillips was not around and was not expected for several days. Jack Clement, a former dance instructor and Sam's staff engineer/creative consultant/court jester, was there; but he was dubious about listening to unwashed talent that walked in off the street and tracked up the floors. As a result of Sun's recent success—since Elvis, Sun had recorded Johnny Cash, Carl Perkins, and many other new stars—Clement had to sift through a considerable amount of garbage when it was his turn to mind the store. After Phillips had to sell Elvis Presley's recording contract to RCA in 1955 and Sun became famous as Presley's original label, the number of Elvis wanna-be's who showed up demanding that they were every bit as noteworthy as the Hillbilly Cat increased exponentially. Unfortunately all that many of them had in common with Elvis was their truck-driver sideburns.

However, Sun would not exist were it not for such unannounced hungry kids. The label had scored its first two non-Elvis Number One country hits that year, Cash's "I Walk the Line" and Perkins's "Blue Suede Shoes," thanks to music that came to it. Phillips may have been a genius in directing talent, but it was always talent that found him. He could work up a hit, but he was no talent scout in the traditional sense, like a Ralph Peer or a Don Law. Everything about the place was casual. When Roy Orbison sold his song "Claudette" to the Everly Brothers, who scored a major hit with it, he did so by simply singing it for them and writing its words on the top of a cardboard box.

First Elmo promoted Jerry Lee, and then his son stepped forward to announce that he could play piano like Chet Atkins played guitar. This sounded bizarre to Clement, but Jerry Lee knew what he was talking about. None of his heroes, the three "fuckin' stylists" who had preceded him, were piano players: Al Jolson was a singer; Jimmie Rodgers and Hank Williams were singers and guitarists. Jerry Lee wanted to sound like a guitar player on his piano; he wanted his piano to talk in a different language, the tongue Rodgers and Williams so effortlessly spoke.

Intrigued by Jerry Lee's strange boast and his taunting goatee, a recent addition that would soon vanish, Clement pointed the wavy-haired kid toward the studio spinet. The Killer banged out spirited versions of the George Jones number "Seasons of My Heart," Hank Thompson's "Wildwood Flower," and a few other of the year's country hits. Clement was impressed, but he also impressed on Jerry Lee his belief that the country market was shrinking, thanks to Elvis, and that if he wanted to record at Sun he would have to come up with some rock-and-roll songs. This made no sense to Jerry Lee, who did not separate blues, country, rock and roll, or gospel any more than he differentiated between his behavior in church and in the back seat. For him, it was all part of the same thing. Clement encouraged Jerry Lee to write a rock-and-roll song and return soon, but Elmo's son left Sun disappointed and confused. Before they embarked on the long drive back to Ferriday, Elmo and Jerry Lee tried out some other Memphis companies, most notably the crumbling Meteor label, but could not find a snug fit anywhere.

Within days of reasserting himself in Ferriday, Jerry Lee rummaged through his memory and devised his rock-and-roll tune. He was again living with his parents and sisters, separated for at least the second time from Jane. Her sister Jewell was raising Jane and Jerry Lee's second son, Ronnie Guy, because the infant looked so unlike Jerry Lee, Jr., or Sr., that the Killer insisted that he was not the father.

The song was "End of the Road." It was dark like a blues song, rocking like a boogie-woogie; it had everything. For some uncharacteristic reason, Jerry Lee planned to relax in Ferriday for a few months and then return to

Memphis, but this plan changed when his cousin on Elmo's side, J. W. Brown, whom Jerry Lee had never met, passed through town on his way home *to* Memphis. Brown, ten years older than his cousin, wanted to start a band and he had heard that Jerry Lee could play piano. Was he interested? Jerry Lee rode back to Memphis with J. W. and was welcomed to his cousin's home by J. W.'s wife, Lois, and their twelve-year-old daughter, Myra Gale.

Jerry Lee and J. W. met with Phillips, everybody sized up everybody else, and on November 14, 1956, Clement supervised Jerry Lee's first Sun session. J. W. was a bystander that night, being too new to the bass to be of much use yet. Aside from Jerry Lee, the only other musicians at the session were Clement's studio stalwarts: guitarists Roland Janes and Billy Lee Riley, and drummer Jimmy Van Eaton. Riley played only one note at the end of one song, so the session was essentially a three-piece date. Although this was the first time Jerry Lee had recorded with accompaniment other than himself, the session sounds like a complete band with no holes, no tentativeness. Two hundred miles east in Nashville, producers like Owen Bradley and Billy Sherrill were discovering how many strings and horns and background vocals they could drop on a song and still have something under it that was recognizable as country music; at Sun the method was to discover how little one needed to put across a song. Direct expression was what mattered most.

Jerry Lee was anxious to record the song he had written at Clement's direction, "End of the Road," and that is where the band started. The opening piano figure was honky-tonk à la Moon Mullican, and there was a palpable amount of echo glued on his voice as he sang, "The way is dark/Night is long/I don't care if I ever get home/I'm waiting/At the end of the road." The echo on his vocal as well as its natural deepening gave it more presence than it had exuded on the KWKH demonstration acetate two years earlier.

Slapback echo was an integral part of the Sun recording formula, from bluesmen like Little Junior's Blue Flames through Elvis's angular sides to the more recent rock and rollers like Roy Orbison, and it suited Jerry Lee better than most. But, as with the KWKH cuts, "End of the Road" indicates that Jerry Lee arrived at Sun with his method and his repertoire already set. (Recent research by Colin Escott suggests that the released version of "End of the Road" may in fact have been recorded at a later session, but there is strong evidence that some version of the tune was recorded that night.)

Next up was "Crazy Arms," the Ray Price smash of a few months previous, and it was essentially a duet between Jerry Lee and Van Eaton. Roland Janes's acoustic bass was so far off-mike it was barely audible, and Billy Lee Riley played only one guitar note at the very end of the song. He was in the bathroom for most of the performance and returned to twang once, unaware that Clement was recording the take. "Crazy Arms" was traditional country, and Van Eaton did not exactly swing. However, even the laziest disk jockey who heard it, mostly because it was already a notable number and therefore was the song from the session picked to be a single, could tell that this was something new. It was as delightful and inexplicable a mixture of American musical forms as the one that Elvis had worked up with Scotty Moore and Bill Black in the same studio two years earlier.

Clement was pleased with "End of the Road" and "Crazy Arms," but he had time to kill and wanted to hear how broad Jerry Lee could go. The Ferriday fireball responded with "You're the Only Star (in My Blue Heaven)," his favorite sentimental-yet-effective Gene Autry ballad. Jerry Lee's version was less sentimental and more effective. He held his vocal notes for a longer time than necessary; that, along with a dash of falsetto that he sprinkled into the mix, lent the slightest air of camp to his performance. In his first night as a professional recording artist, Jerry Lee was already making fun of himself, laughing at himself. The

performance was less than masterful, but no one can listen to it and argue that Jerry Lee was not enjoying himself. His brief solo danced up and down, and Janes's improvised solo showed him going for something different from a Sun guitarist's Scotty Moore-derived norm. These three players—Lewis, Janes, and Van Eaton—were beginning to find common ground, beginning to develop into a real band.

The last song they attacked that night, Ted Daffan's World War II hit "Born to Lose," was a midtempo ballad of regret that provided Jerry Lee with a vehicle for some profound singing that transcended the tale of self-pity and compensated for when he forgot the words. Janes's wobbly background guitar and brief solo had a touch of Les Paul, and Jerry Lee's boogie-woogie piano solo emphasized his left-hand rhythm dexterity.

Although Phillips deemed only two songs from this session worthy of release ("End of the Road" was the flip side of the "Crazy Arms" single; neither side charted), these four cuts persuasively outlined Jerry Lee's concerns as a musician. Even the ballads rocked along steadily, he straddled multiple styles and showed no interest in conforming to morés, and he played each song in full. There were no fadeouts. The songs ended exactly as they would in front of an audience.

Jerry Lee left that evening convinced he was going to be a big star. He telephoned Ferriday and talked Jane into moving in with him at J. W. and Lois's home. Cousin Myra volunteered to babysit for Junior.

Jack Clement left that night sure that he had found Sun a new session piano player. Phillips agreed. "I can sell that," he said when Clement played him a tape of "Crazy Arms," even before Jerry Lee started singing. "Why'd you let the guy get outta here that other time?" They decided to credit him on the record as Jerry Lee Lewis and His Pumping Piano.

Imminent stardom notwithstanding, Jerry Lee needed to make a living. The Browns' attempts to secure him day jobs were fruitless, so he checked his rapidly expanding ego and allowed himself to be used as a session man for Sun. He got a call the morning of December 4, 1956, from Jack Clement. If he played on a Carl Perkins session that day, Phillips would pay him fifteen dollars. Jerry Lee was there.

Perkins, a native of Jackson, Tennessee, an hour and change east of Memphis, was the greatest of the Elvis wanna-be's who were drawn to Sun, and he was one of the few rockabilly singer/guitarists who developed a lanky style that was not a regurgitation of Presley's salad recordings. Even more than Presley's, Perkins's Sun recordings defined rockabilly. "They took a light from the honky-tonk/Put the gleam in your eye," Perkins howled in "Honky-Tonk Gal," one of his earliest recordings, neatly encapsulating rockabilly's concerns and fears. Rockabilly, that reckless, primal thrash of honky-tonk country-and-western, was all about conflict: between rural and urban, between barroom adventure and home comfort, between the extremes Ernest Tubb described in his hit, "Saturday Satan, Sunday Saint." The honky-tonk gal Perkins adored was both his joy (hot stuff) and his pain (no longer a demure housewife); the conflict of rockabilly personified. Perkins treated this dilemma the way any self-respecting rockabilly cat would. He blazed out fiery riffs and drove through the quandary in fifth gear. He'd deal with the consequences of his rampage some other time. Even in the giddy thrill of taking his Gibson guitar for an unexpected joy ride, he knew that somewhere down the road there would be a price to pay.

Rockabilly was about release, but its release always had limits. That was the form's country birthright, and that was what made Perkins different from Presley, a rockabilly cat who expanded into straight pop and, in doing so, uprooted. A pure pop Perkins was unimaginable. This is what set him apart from Presley and what prevented him from achieving Elvis-like success. Elvis, for all his indisputable greatness, sold out in every way imaginable. Perkins, even in his most banal country-pop settings, never surrendered.

Like most of the first-generation rockabillies, Perkins started off considering himself country. His gracious, quavering tenor carried some magnificent country-and-western ballads, among them the bare-boned "Turn Around," his first Sun recording, and "Let the Jukebox Keep on Playing," as understated an expression of honky-tonk regret and paralysis as one would expect of Hank Williams himself. But Perkins's meat was his rockabilly, in which he repeatedly drove full speed to the edge of his world, leaned over the cliff to enjoy the view for a brief second, and then, as he knew he must, pulled back and carefully headed home.

Several months before his sessions featuring Jerry Lee, Perkins had recorded his greatest uptempo composition, "Dixie Fried." The song was as close as any rockabilly performer came to going over the edge and living to tell about it. His guitar flashed like the barroom-fight switchblade the tale chronicled. His voice swayed with the wobbly exuberance of his brazen, drunken protagonist, someone much more like Jerry Lee than the more mannered Perkins. "Let's all get Dixie fried," he screamed, shattering any pretension to caution, let alone civilized behavior. The violence in the lyric and the performance escalated as the song smashed into its head-on conclusion, not with the law, but with the inevitable. Perkins may have had the gleam of a honky-tonk in his eye, but his eye was fixed on home, where he prayed his honky-tonk gal had returned.

The songs Perkins had brought to Sun on December 4 were as diverse as Jerry Lee's concerns. Straight-ahead rockabilly raised its head in "Put Your Cat Clothes On" and "Your True Love." Jimmie Davis's "Sweethearts or Strangers," Wynn Stewart's "Keeper of the Key," and Fred Rose's "Be Honest with Me" were pure country. "Matchbox" was an uncredited rewrite of Blind Lemon Jefferson's blues number of the same title. Jerry Lee played the studio's upright spinet, which Clement had recently augmented by plunging thumbtacks into the string hammers. He then placed the microphone underneath the piano. Clement's alterations gave the piano a fuller, more spacious presence, making it sound more like the grand piano that Phillips still refused to buy. (There is some evidence that Clement did not install the tacks for several months to come.) It was not a new trick—ragtime pianists were familiar with the method—but for Jerry Lee it gave his chords and lead lines more bounce. He fit in well with Perkins's band: his brothers Jay Perkins on guitar and Clay Perkins on bass, and W. S. Holland on drums.

The date ran longer than Jerry Lee's had. They cut at least twenty-two versions of the six tunes. As the session began to wind down, the reception area in front of the studio gradually became more crowded. Smokey Joe Baugh, a fellow Sun performer who had released a novelty version of

"The Signifying Monkey," walked in unannounced, as did Johnny Cash and his wife, Vivian, with their eighteen-month-old baby, Rosanne. Someone opened the door between the reception area and the studio, and the session turned into more of a party. Then Elvis Presley, the most famous man in the Western world, arrived with a showgirl named Marilyn Evans, arguably the only positive aspect of his first, otherwise disastrous, appearance in Las Vegas. Johnny Cash smiled for the newspaper cameraman (Sam Phillips knew a photo opportunity when he saw one) and left to go shopping. The crowd moved into the studio and Jack Clement kept the tapes rolling.

Jerry Lee, Carl, and Elvis had all turned to a music career to avoid the dead ends they saw elsewhere—none of them wanted to relive his daddy's life—but they embraced music in the first place because it was a mystery they could love, explore, and through their pursuits find more reasons to love. All of them first discovered music in church, so it is no surprise that the common ground they found when they started harmonizing was sacred music. Jerry Lee's mother damned him for playing secular music; Carl sang about knife fights; and Elvis had just been called everything short of the antichrist because of his wild performances, but gospel music was the first thing they thought to sing together. Their connection to it was that natural. Fluid, fervent versions of songs like "When God Dips His Love in My Heart," "Just a Little Talk with Jesus," "Down by the Riverside," and "Blessed Jesus Hold My Hand" spiraled out of them in a relaxed, spontaneous rush. Perkins's band supplied the artless accompaniment, and even Marilyn Evans joined in. The song selection gradually drifted to hits of the day, among them Charlie Singleton's "Don't Forbid Me," which noted antirock singer Pat Boone had just defanged in a cover version. Elvis said that the song had been written for him, that an acetate of it had been "over my

A bizarre early promotional photograph

house for ages, man. I never did see it, so much junk lyin' around." Everyone laughed.

Jerry Lee was anxious to show off in front of Elvis and he had Phillips play an acetate of "Crazy Arms" for him. Elvis told Robert Johnson, the reporter from the local paper that Phillips had called in, "That boy can go. He has a different style, and the way he plays piano just gets inside of me." A gentleman, Elvis offered to stand up and let Jerry Lee play the piano. "I've been wanting to tell you that," Jerry Lee said, smiling, and gestured Elvis off the bench. "Scoot over!" Elvis and Carl laughed, but it was clear that Jerry Lee wanted them to be his audience.

Talk turned to Chuck Berry, their fellow performer and songwriter whose work all of them treasured. They played multiple snatches of Berry's "Too Much Monkey Business" and "Brown-Eyed Handsome Man" until they got the words right and then argued which song was better. Elvis clued in the assembled to working in Las Vegas. He spoke of seeing Billy Ward and the Dominoes in one of the show rooms. The Dominoes' lead singer was a kid named Jackie Wilson who could do a devastating Elvis impersonation, and Elvis parodied Wilson imitating him doing "Don't Be Cruel" and "Paralyzed." It was loving mimicry; Elvis had seen in Wilson a talented fan who could make him rethink his own performances of songs he had already turned into smash hits. The trio sang the rockabilly anthem "Rip It Up," Elvis enjoying an alternate version of its first line: "It's Saturday night and I just got paid, uh, laid." These were priceless moments, an opportunity for a man in the public eye to jettison the sex-symbol nonsense and just play. For a long time this session was known as the Million Dollar Quartet; but even marked down 25 percent as the result of Cash's absence (it was first thought that he had stayed and played), this was a bargain.

Elvis was cordial, but he had to move on. In singles and pairs, everyone left until only Jerry Lee remained. Unaccompanied, he replayed much of his first session: "Crazy Arms," "End of the Road," and "You're the Only Star (in My Blue Heaven)," as well as a brief instrumental with the telling title "Black Bottom Stomp." Eventually there was no one left for him to play to, so he stopped.

"How'd it go?" his cousin Myra asked him when he returned home late that night.

• • •

Clement quickly booked Jerry Lee for three more sessions over the next two weeks. Returning a favor, he accompanied Billy Lee Riley on a session that yielded "Flyin' Saucer Rock and Roll," one of the most ludicrously lovely of all rockabilly screams. Riley was the ostensible star, but Jerry Lee fought for room, ending the song with a hammering chord that he sustained after everyone else had finished playing. It was Jerry Lee's first session in which he saw Sam Phillips exert himself. A few days later, he played piano for Sun's best-selling artist, Johnny Cash; a week after that he watched Hayden Thompson huff and puff.

Jerry Lee excelled on others' recordings, but it was his own music that challenged him the most. Soon after the first of the year, Jerry Lee was allowed to record for himself again. The nonhit status of "Crazy Arms," which had entered no national chart, had not led Phillips to feel he needed to rush out a follow-up. He must not have been particularly taken by this second session, for none of it was released during Jerry Lee's tenure with Sun, but anyone with any faith in Jerry Lee could hear that he was moving toward his breakthrough.

For someone who was being encouraged to rock out, the sentimental "Silver Threads Among the Gold" was a strange choice to begin the session. Guitar interjections provided relief from Van Eaton's occasionally monotonic drumming, but Jerry Lee reached a comfortable altitude and cruised. He inserted the odd vocal and piano flourish to amuse himself; he was at ease and in control, perhaps puzzled that he was not a millionaire. The Eddy Arnold country weeper "I'm Throwing Rice (At the Girl I Love)" was even farther from rock and roll. Jerry Lee sounded older than his years (which made sense, considering his overfamiliarity with weddings). The rhythm was nearly a waltz, and Jerry Lee's solo punctured the tune's lyrics, as did the slyness with which he delivered the lines: "She was my gal/He was my pal/She liked him better somehow/I'll step aside/After I kiss the bride." It was the vocal equivalent of the sneer.

The Floyd Tillman cover, "I Love You So Much It Hurts," proceeded similarly. It took a line or two for the vocal melody to coalesce, and that vocal breathed life into the ballad's clichéd lyric. The piano solo meshed with primitive, near-martial drums; Roland Janes's guitar was unheard. Yet this sounded full. "Deep Elem Blues," a Shelton Brothers composition about the Dallas red-light district with which Jerry Lee was familiar from his Waxahachie days, was more like what Clement was after. Jerry Lee swooped into the speedy number, reminiscent of Elvis's version of "Milkcow Blues Boogie," and the drums lent this a phenomenal kick. Jerry Lee's singing was giddily all over the place; he nearly overmodulated in the style of Little Richard, whose souped-up rhythm-and-blues style the Killer greatly admired. Van Eaton's drums were more subservient, appropriately so, on the Leadbelly standard "Goodnight Irene." Janes's rhythmic style "typed" out the suicide note implied in the words, and Jerry Lee was deep into those lyrics, unless appearing deep into them when he was merely performing was part of his genius. He moved to double time halfway through and climaxed with the verse, "Sometimes I live in the country—yeah!/Sometimes I live in town/Sometimes I take a *cruel* notion/To jump in the river and drown."

Jerry Lee was driving to hell at ninety miles an hour, and Jack Clement was loving it. (A second version was more

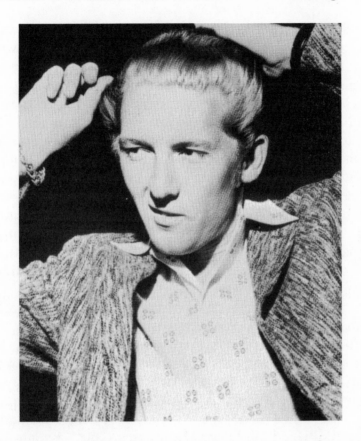

choppy, less intense, and never sped up. Phillips later dressed it up with extraneous overdubs and tacked it onto an album.) Next up was "Honey Hush," a scorching rocker in which Jerry Lee's playful voice mimicked Gene Vincent's. Janes's guitar break was a shotgun wedding of Chuck Berry to Scotty Moore, and Jerry Lee shouted as though he thought he was playing before two thousand people. A ferocious coda ended with Jerry Lee warning, "Shut up yer mouth!"

Jerry Lee was proving himself to Clement that night, demonstrating that he could take on anything. The standard "Crawdad Song" was fast, wild, and echoey. The studio was a party now, with much screaming in the background by the sidemen. Janes's one-note solos were nothing much, but Jerry Lee sang as fast as he could without running out of breath. "Dixie" was fine as source material for Jerry Lee's southernness, but otherwise it was an inconsequential instrumental. Perhaps he had some time to kill while Janes ate a hamburger; the same goes for "The Marine's Hymn," except that Janes had returned to his guitar. "That Lucky Old Sun," which was recorded either that night or soon after, was just voice and piano, and it was shocking in its naked expression of emotion. It was a tremendous ballad of defeat; the aching lyric held out heaven as an escape but expressed ambivalence as to who might inhabit it. As Jerry Lee would eventually say when he stumbled upon anything he considered remotely profound, "think about it."

Jerry Lee soon got his first taste of touring, and by the time he returned to Sun to woodshed a few weeks later, his trio—Janes, Van Eaton, and the newly dexterous J. W. Brown—were far better acquainted. This evening's work was another tour-de-force journey through whatever styles Jerry Lee could think of, with a big surprise at the end.

Jerry Lee looked back almost a century with James Bland's "Hand Me Down My Walking Cane." By now the pumping introduction was familiar, as was the echo-drenched vocal and his swift solo. He continued his attempt to walk both sides of the line with the improvised lyric, which had blues structure, gospel import, and somehow came out country-rock. A few takes of "You're the Only Star (in My Blue Heaven)" were not as fresh as the earlier version but were perhaps a bit more playfully executed.

Then he surprised Clement with a tune he had written. Except for "End of the Road," Jerry Lee was not committed to songwriting, so this was something special. "Lewis Boogie" was a tad more tentative than the released take he recorded several months later, but it was still inarguable. The self-mythologizing lyrics (which dismissed other performers, among them Elvis, whose success and showgirl companion often burned in his mind) were perfect: "Cruise on down to old Natchez town/That's where that Presley boy says 'you ain't nothin' but a hound'/But now you take my boogie/It keeps you in the groove/Until your sacroiliac begins to shiver and move/It's called the Lewis Boogie/In the Lewis way." The rappers of three decades later could take a cue from its range and specificity. Jerry Lee sang whatever came to mind, but what he was really saying over and over was "I won't be denied."

Jerry Lee was in the mood to take shots at Elvis, and one way to do that was to cover a song associated with Presley and do it better. That was the idea behind a version of Leon Payne's "I Love You Because," and it did not succeed. There could be no more echo on this vocal unless it had been recorded at the Grand Canyon, which made it distracting. Jerry Lee nodded toward Elvis's version and grabbed the song, yet he was marking time, showing off, which was not without a massive charm. Much better was a take of "I Can't Help It (If I'm Still in Love With You)," the first of Jerry Lee's many unparalleled interpretations of Hank Williams songs. Clearly this was a favorite of his; he immediately burrowed to the center of the song and gathered strength from all around him. Unlike many of his unrequited-love ballads, there was no hint of camp here. Jerry Lee knew this song mattered and let his solo skid and scrape across the drums. Not to break the mood, Jerry Lee followed it with another Williams composition, "Cold, Cold Heart," which was done just as well if a bit lighter, though Jerry Lee's full-throated singing overruled all objections.

The rest of the session, until the band arrived at the final tune, yielded nothing near that level. Spade Cooley's "Shame on You" was spry but played too quickly; Jerry Lee's timing was off. He tossed in an untamed solo right after the first chorus, but it barged in too soon to be effective. Janes's guitar solo rocked up Les Paul, but that was not much of an accomplishment. Floyd Tillman's "I'll Keep on Loving You" was acceptable uptempo country. "You Are My Sunshine" was forthright, hardened Jimmie Davis, and Jerry Lee's sprightly performance countered its death-oriented lyric. "Tomorrow Night" was dirty and not much else; several takes of the Dominoes' "Sixty Minute Man" revealed nothing save Jerry Lee's enduring ability to put across a speedy boast at whim. That out of their system, the band began to pick up some power. "It All Depends (Who Will Buy the Wine)" was a strong, resigned drinking ballad that Jerry Lee would return to for decades, and the loose "I Don't Love Nobody" was archetypal fast-country Jerry Lee. "Let me have one!" he cried, and indulged himself in a monstrous solo.

With the marathon session running near an end, Jerry Lee called for a song he remembered from his Wagon Wheel days that his group had recently begun playing onstage, "Whole Lotta Shakin' Going On." They played it as a rocker with a prominent guitar, but Jerry Lee was still figuring out what he needed to do to transform the tune into something different from what it was when he first heard it. It was energetic, but not spectacular. He ended the night promising to work on it some more.

Sessions for Carl Perkins and Ray Harris followed, as did another opportunity for Jerry Lee to figure out "Whole Lotta Shakin' Going On." They had often played it in their live shows, and by mid-February it sported a much stronger arrangement. By this time, Jane and Junior had moved out of the Brown house for good, and Myra and Senior were starting to look at each other with different intentions.

Clement was anxious to hear what the band had done with "Whole Lotta Shakin' Going On," but he was more interested in having Jerry Lee record a song he had written, a rocker called "It'll Be Me," which he was sure would be a smash. Clement said he had dreamed up the song while sitting on a toilet; by the time he presented the tune to Jerry

Lee, he had removed the original lines: "If you see a turd in your toilet bowl/It'll be me/And I'll be looking for you." The new lyrics referred to a lump in a sugar bowl.

Clement worked the quartet hard on the song, more than half a dozen full takes. The song took form over the many performances. The first take started with off-beat drums that kept the song off-kilter and a piano solo that was mostly a series of ascending and descending chords. A guitar solo spiraled around and drew back, but did not

travel far. Another version kicked off *a capella*, but deterio-
rated into a shuffle. Exploratory versions followed, Jerry
Lee gradually discovering the essence of the cleaned-up
song.

Repeated listening to multiple takes of anything can be
daunting, but take after take after take of "It'll Be Me" is
fascinating, mostly because it reveals that even if he was
trying, Jerry Lee in his Sun prime was unable to attack a
song exactly the same way twice. He slipped in a rumbling
multioctave solo here, hastened the tempo there, forgot to
take piano solos sometimes because he was enjoying Clement's words so much.

"That's a hit," Clement said. "Now what do you want
to do for the flip?" They took a pass at Gene Autry's "Ole
Pal of Yesterday," a fine example of how Jerry Lee rocked
up midtempo country, but they moved on quickly. Everyone in the band was pretty sure that "Whole Lotta Shakin'
Going On" was destined to be a hit; live, it was a killer, so to
speak.

They played it at Sun the same way they played it
onstage: intent, disquieting, unrelenting. Jerry Lee crashed
into the song as if through a bedroom window. "Come on
over baby [or was it "Come all over baby"?]/Whole lotta
shakin' going on!" he announced, and leaned hard into a
groove toward which even his hardest previous performances did not begin to hint. He rocked furiously, but the
words came out smooth and easy. The lyrics boiled down to
a demand for sexual attention, but this was not a mere plea.
Jerry Lee sang it, knowing he was beautiful, knowing he
was desirable, as if surprised that he had stumbled across
someone half as beautiful and desirable as he. Onstage,
with aching slowness he would run his fingers through his
greasy, wet blond locks as he delivered this song. He knew
he was spectacular, he knew that the woman he addressed
knew he was spectacular, and he dared her to be worthy of
him. When parents in the fifties claimed that rock and roll

was evil, they were talking about records like "Whole Lotta Shakin' Going On." "Ain't fakin'," Jerry Lee sang, and that's what worried people about him and his ilk.

When Jerry Lee barged into his piano solo, Van Eaton's drums took a bar to catch on—he was that transported by Jerry Lee's performance. Janes's guitar solo was assured; more importantly, it provided temporary relief from Lewis's lasciviousness. Jerry Lee sang, "We got kickin' in the barn/Whose barn?/What barn?/My barn!" and careered into the most frankly lecherous breakdown in fifties rock and roll (no small achievement). "Easy now," he commanded, and the band played just as hard, a little more quietly. He talked now. "Let's get real low one time," he ordered. "All you gotta do, honey, is just kinda stand in one spot. Wiggle around just a little bit. That's when you got somethin'." The mood was taut, tense. He knew he had won, so he called the band back and he swooped in for the kill, shouting the final chorus as though he knew it would be the last of his life. He knew he had conquered his listener, and the song ended with a shout of satisfaction rarely heared in public. "Whole Lotta Shakin' Going On" was about forbidden ideas coming to the surface; it was, in Jerry Lee's mind, the sound of sex.

• • •

Jerry Lee returned to the road, where "Whole Lotta Shakin' Going On" climaxed his performances as the single began its run up the three major singles charts: rhythm-and-blues, country-and-western, and pop. Soon after it was recorded, Jack Clement played the studio take of the song for Sam Phillips, who decided to gamble his company on it, pressing several hundred thousand copies of the disc before he sold a single one. Phillips was confident he had found his new Elvis. Although he told everyone who would listen that he did not for one second regret selling Elvis's contract to RCA, Sam was jealous—personally and financially—that Elvis's superstardom occurred only after leaving his tu-

telage. Not only could Jerry Lee mess around with familiar forms and yield something new, he was, like Elvis, good-looking and charismatic. Phillips cherished the Carl Perkins, Johnny Cash, and Roy Orbison records he was making, but he sensed that none of them was bold enough to grab a microphone and refuse to relinquish it no matter what. He knew that Jerry Lee had what it took; he knew that Jerry Lee was cocky enough to make it happen. Sam found Jerry Lee's craziness comforting.

Much has been said about the "crazy" or "nutty" atmosphere at Sun and how the colorful characters broke all sorts of musical and cultural rules there because they acknowledged none. All that is true, but the fact remains that this craziness or nuttiness had a significant downside, one that led many of the regulars there into fits of depression, extended substance abuse, and, in some cases, arbitrary violence. The "It" in Jerry Lee's family, and the "It" in a disproportionate number of the families that gave Sun its greatest performers, was mental illness. The music at Sun changed pop music and enlivened the lives of many listeners, but it did so at great cost to its originators.

Jerry Lee fit in at Sun because he was personally as well as musically off-kilter. Phillips saw him as someone with that magical combination of talent and senselessness. As he said of "Crazy Arms," he could sell that, if he could keep the boy from Ferriday on a leash. He might have worried a bit more if he had known the feelings Jerry Lee and his kid cousin were beginning to acknowledge for each other.

While Phillips prepared to unleash "Whole Lotta Shakin' Going On" on an unsuspecting world, Jerry Lee kept recording. Sessions in the spring and summer of 1957 yielded a wide variety of material, but not another immediately recognizable smash or even another single, except for a new version of "Lewis Boogie" that surpassed the earlier model. Jerry Lee recorded several versions of Hank Williams's "You Win Again," including a very fast take that proved that the song did not respond well to being rocked up. Jerry Lee sped through the song's drama and pathos; perhaps it was recorded at the beginning of a session, just a warm-up. Several months later he recorded a ballad version that was as slow and felt as the earlier take had been sped-up and affected. His inspiring, acute singing made it the definitive version of a top-flight song.

"Love Letters in the Sand" strutted along pleasantly,

but it was more along the lines of Pat Boone, who presently and inexplicably scored a hit with it. A similar thirties pop tune, "Little Green Valley," had a more prodding beat and was much more fun. "Pumpin' Piano Rock" arrived with an initial solemn piano chord, an effect that quickly bored Jerry Lee as he created instant boogie-woogie. The words, which he wrote, are not worth repeating, although they are a more effective stab at a statement of purpose than those he emitted throughout the seventies and eighties. However, it did feature a wonderful spinning solo that proved that Jerry Lee could not be confined by a bad song, even if it was a dud that he wrote.

Perhaps miffed that his pet song had wound up on the wrong side of Jerry Lee's next single, Jack Clement ordered up several new versions of "It'll Be Me," this time intended for inclusion on Jerry Lee's first LP. Except for a bizarre drums-and-guitar introduction that was so out of place that it worked and some tempo changes, the new versions were similar to the older takes.

If producer Clement got what he wanted out of these sessions, so did band leader Jerry Lee. In his last session before the success of "Whole Lotta Shakin' Going On" changed his life, he led Janes and Van Eaton—J. W. was out making some honest money as an electrician—into his past, calling for song after song that he had loved back in Ferriday. Once again, his childhood favorites formed the basis of the songs he chose to perform professionally. "All Night Long" was a combination of half a dozen country standards. The piano work was a prime updated Moon Mullican impersonation, and the vocal paid attention to detail à la Chuck Berry. In the end, the song was simply an excuse for Jerry Lee to push out a great new solo. "Old Time Religion" was rocked up faster than fast gospel, Jerry Lee's falsetto and the background yells, probably by Clement, making it sound somehow dirty. One listen to this solo and it is obvious what got him kicked out of Waxahachie. The New Orleans journey was "When the Saints Go

Marchin' In," another religiously oriented tune that Jerry Lee turned into a pop song with a wonderful crammed solo.

The next number, Jimmie Rodgers's "My Carolina Sunshine Girl," made it clear that in his early days Jerry Lee simply could not play a country song straight. He could only play it like himself, and that had nothing to do with what was happening in Nashville at the time. "Long Gone Lonesome Blues" was the rare Jerry Lee cover of a Hank Williams composition that did not click at all, but he ended the session with two top-rank rockers. A tumbling, ferocious "Drinkin' Wine Spo-Dee-o-Dee" brought Jerry Lee back to that Ferriday Ford dealership. "Singin' the Blues," a Marty Robbins hit, was speedy and bluesy. Jerry Lee was so excited by the number, or his performance of it, that he could not stop fully at its dramatic pauses. He stretched the song into a honky-tonk strut that suited him. As had become the rule in his recordings, he held sway over the tune.

By July, "Whole Lotta Shakin' Going On" had exploded. The antirock forces were making the usual complaints. The Alabama White Citizens Council set the agenda with the statement: "The obscenity and vulgarity of the rock-and-roll music is obviously a means by which the white man and his children can be driven down to the level with the nigger." Most critics were less honest when they expressed their fears. Jerry Lee was even worse than Elvis, many of them argued, because not only did the Ferriday Fireball move, but the songs he played while he moved left much less to overactive teen imaginations. And Jerry Lee's stage show was raucous. He would jump to his feet, leer at the audience, roll his tongue, and kick his piano stool into the wings. He would play the piano with his feet and his fists; sometimes he would jump atop the expensive grand piano a hall had rented. Usually accompanied only by J. W. on bass and Russell Smith on drums, he compensated with sheer energy and intensity the lack of additional pieces. He acknowledged no bounds.

Jerry Lee's music, his antics, and the fact that this eccentric was striking against (depending on one's viewpoint) mores or deeply held beliefs about how to behave all helped "Whole Lotta Shakin' Going On" up the charts. Trade-paper reviewers heralded the tune but noted that it did not fit into any one category, country-and-western, rhythm-and-blues, or straight pop. Aided by striking performances on "The Steve Allen Show" and "American Bandstand," the song succeeded in all categories, eventually topping two of the three *Billboard* singles charts and getting as high as Number Three on the third, a rare feat in 1957 and an unimaginable one in the genre-fractured nineties. The dif-ferences that supposedly kept country-and-western, rhythm-and-blues, and pop songs on separate radio formats never made sense to Jerry Lee. He loved any kind of music, so long as it moved him in one way or another. So it makes sense that when he figured out what he was best at on "Whole Lotta Shakin' Going On," an unclassifiable melange of all the forms he adored, fans representative of all markets responded.

Jerry Lee bought a home for his parents, a black Cad-illac for himself (in both cases, the first of many), and kept recording for Phillips. He appeared at 706 Union several times in September 1957, searching for another "Whole Lotta Shakin' Going On" that would help him sustain his newfound income of several thousand dollars a week. At least one session early in the month was so relaxed that no-body expected anything to come from it. The jump blues "Rockin' with Red" was just a messaround, with on-the-spot lyrical additions like "She rocks me to the east/She rocks me to the south/My baby, she's got a big mouth." Jerry Lee must have taken a shine to "Matchbox" while he worked it up with Perkins's band. His version was sprightly enough and featured some superior singing, but there was no place for Jerry Lee to go with the tune that Perkins hadn't already taken it. "How was that?" he asked at the

end of the take. Jerry Lee gave another Sun-identified track, Warren Smith's "Ubangi Stomp," an excellent rocking treatment, all dramatic stops and starts, although his piano was buried except for his solos; and the lyrics remain among rock and roll's most blatantly racist.

"Rock 'n' Roll Ruby" was a Warren Smith tune written (or bought) by Johnny Cash in one of that country giant's more awkward attempts to fit the rockabilly mold. Jerry

Lee had fun with it, his high-register singing sometimes wandering into falsetto, but this was not a serious attempt at a hit. He graced the Roy Orbison hit "Ooby Dooby" with the same introduction he gave to "Ubangi Stomp" and came on even harder. It was a superb version of the sweet rocker; Jerry Lee's rough voice was more appropriate for the number than Orbison's smooth tenor. "I Forgot to Remember to Forget" was an early Elvis recording of regret that Jerry Lee probably chose to prove that he could outdo Elvis, which on this song he could not. Otis Jett's stumbling drumming did not help either.

The most far-ranging Sun tune explored in these sessions was a Roy Orbison composition, "So Long I'm Gone," that had been a hit for Warren Smith. The relatively uptempo version moved fast and went nowhere. Jerry Lee was clearly not involved with the number, but the song itself exemplified much of what made the country music recorded at Sun Records different from that cut for the more established Nashville labels. At Sun, as for Jerry Lee, wild rockabilly and polite country were part of the same continuum, as surely as Saturday nights rolled into Sunday mornings. In either category, Sam Phillips invariably sought out unencumbered, passionate, plainly stated performances. He wanted a mood to establish itself the second a song began and then intensify and ignite.

Phillips's Nashville contemporaries were adding scads of strings and bus loads of backup singers to sweeten songs for the uptown crowd, but Phillips sensed that frankness was gaining an edge over forced sophistication. He arrived at this method partly by ingenuity and partly by necessity. After all, fewer musicians on a session meant fewer people to pay. Because there were less players to shift around, Phillips and his flock could experiment with different treatments of the same tune.

Warren Smith recorded two radically dissimilar

versions of "So Long I'm Gone" that go a long way toward
telling the grand story of how country spawned rockabilly.
The words were the same in both versions, but the attitudes
could not have been farther apart. Smith was best-known as
a second-tier post-Presley rocker, but his country version of
"So Long I'm Gone" foreshadowed his move into straight
country-and-western after he left Sun. On that slow version, Smith collapsed into regret, missing the occasional
guitar strum, mortified that he has to leave his philandering
lover. On his fast rockabilly variation he triumphed, a hardened man determined to beat adversity. He's out the door;
he's bound for glory. His fast "So Long I'm Gone" sounded
like freedom, nearly as much so as "Whole Lotta Shakin'
Going On."

• • •

Through autumn, Jerry Lee searched for his second
"Whole Lotta Shakin' Going On." Jack Clement thought
he had found one in "I'm Feeling Sorry." His confidence in
the sturdy country strut was justified, but it was due mostly
to his having written it. On September 10, 1957, Clement
guided Jerry Lee, J. W. Brown, Roland Janes, and Jimmy
Van Eaton through more than a dozen takes of "I'm Feelin'
Sorry," in a variety of tempos and configurations. Some
lines Jerry Lee attacked with glee, like "I know you're blue/
But, baby/I'm bluer." Listening to these endless versions
shows how many angles from which Jerry Lee could attack
a song: respectful, showboating, giddy, you name it.

Two other songs put down at the session hinted at Jerry
Lee's limits at the time. "Turn Around" was more evidence
that he could not cover Carl Perkins as definitively or easily
as he took on songs identified with some others. But "Mean
Woman Blues," an Elvis hit earlier in the year, was a rocker
as broad, though not as deep, as "Whole Lotta Shakin'
Going On." "I ain't bragging/It's understood/Everything I
do/I sure do it good," he sang, finally finding an appropri-

The Million Dollar Quartet: Jerry Lee, Carl Perkins, Elvis, and Johnny Cash (left to right)

ately overt lyrical outlet for his unending self-assurance. He started soloing virtually as soon as the song began, and his pleasure in delivering double-entendre lines like "I like a little coffee/I like a little tea/Jelly, jelly is the thing for me" was infectious. It was a worthy successor to "Whole Lotta Shakin' Going On," breakdown and all, but it was too similar to be immediately differentiable.

Sam Phillips arrived at Jerry Lee's next session with a new song he had received from a New York songwriter named Otis Blackwell, who had provided Elvis with "All Shook Up" and "Don't Be Cruel," called "Great Balls of Fire." Phillips had cut a deal for a Jerry Lee song to appear in *Jamboree*, a film about fractured love that was forgettable even before anyone had seen it. He sensed that being associated with a film—any film—might be a sure-fire and cost-effective way to launch a hit record. Blackwell had thought to offer Jerry Lee "Great Balls of Fire" after seeing the Killer shake on "The Steve Allen Show." Again it is noticeable that Phillips did not approach Blackwell. Still, Phillips knew a hit when he heard one. He quickly had Jerry Lee cut a version for *Jamboree*, which the film's producers accepted, but neither Phillips nor Jerry Lee was satisfied with that take for single release, so on October 6 they tried again (this time with tacks audibly on the piano).

It was that night, trying to tame "Great Balls of Fire," that Jerry Lee heard the voice of his mother taunting him and rebelled against the song he suddenly considered to be pure evil. Phillips was personally supervising the session; he knew he was only a few takes away from another smash on the scale of "Whole Lotta Shakin' Going On," so he pushed back. The conversation that was going on inside Jerry Lee's head turned external, and he took Mamie's part.

"You can save souls!" Sam barked deep into their dispute.

"No! No! No! No!" Jerry Lee shouted back as the argument arched toward a crescendo.

"Yes!" Phillips hollered.

"How can the devil save souls?" Jerry Lee countered at an even louder volume. "What are you talking about?"

Jerry Lee soon relented, aware that he would not be resolving this particular mystery tonight, and hurled himself into the song. Several takes later, he was much less agonized by his choice of material. "I do like to eat it," he said and made a slurping noise. "I hope you ain't puttin' that on tape. Shit, I'd give up the ship. You ready to cut? You ready to cut? You ready to cut 'Great Balls of Fire'? What am I gonna eat? I would like to eat a little pussy if I had some." At the end of the take he announced, "I'm about to gag." He had traveled the road from piety to lust in only a few minutes, and the song he was shouting provided the link.

The final take of the evening was clearly the performance worth releasing. After four staccato chords, Jerry Lee sang out of the top of his head: "You shake my nerves and you rattle my brain/ Too much love drives a man insane/ You broke my will/But what a thrill/Goodness gracious, great balls of fire!" The imagery was salacious; the delivery was even more gleefully obscene. If "Whole Lotta Shakin' Going On" was a song that promised sex, "Great Balls of Fire" delivered. Some of the lyrics and vocal interjections, like "Oooh/Feels good" and "You're kind/So fine," were as overtly sexual as Jerry Lee could get and still slip onto the radio. Roland Janes and Billy Riley must have been at the restaurant next door during this take, which featured only Lewis and drummer Van Eaton. Jerry Lee's solo started with some tossed-off sweeps and peaked with upper-key poundings that challenged Van Eaton's snare drum for the contest of Biggest Noise in the World. Many fans, critics, and performers have speculated as to who won the Lewis/ Phillips argument that night. One listen to "Great Balls of Fire" reveals that it was Jerry Lee Lewis fans who won.

Because Jerry Lee had already established himself with one multiformat smash, "Great Balls of Fire" scaled the three *Billboard* charts more quickly than its predecessor, eventually reaching Number One on the country-and-western charts, Number One on the rhythm-and-blues charts, and Number Two on the pop charts. Danny and the Juniors' extremely white doo-wop "At the Hop," with its ersatz-Killer piano, denied it the triple crown. Jerry Lee's performances of the number on three national television

Live in 1957: J. M. Van Eaton, Roland Janes, Jerry Lee, and Marvin Pepper (left to right)

shows—"The Steve Allen Show," "American Bandstand," and "Patti Page's Big Record TV Show"—hastened the advance. On radios and televisions across the land, people heard the battle between the spiritual and the secular music that raged within Jerry Lee, and it sounded to them like rock and roll.

Jerry Lee's attempt to sing pop music and not be evil suggested a similar battle being fought around the same time by the gospel-turned-country duo, Ira and Charlie Louvin, the Louvin Brothers. The brothers had recorded together for more than a decade and were at their peak in 1957. The two dived into despair like no other pair in country; it was no accident that they titled their greatest album *Tragic Songs of Life*. The bare-bones arrangements on even their hits were built around a terse string band, pared to the marrow, careful not to muscle in front of the words, which scrutinized the many intersections of religious fervor and reckless abandon.

The Louvin Brothers had grown up as poor in Alabama as Jerry Lee was in Louisiana. Gospel was their first love, but their talents were broader, and executives at their label, Capitol Records, knew it. After they scored their first major country-and-western hit in 1955 with "When I Stop Dreaming," they had to fight to get Capitol to acquiesce to even occasional sacred recordings. But, unlike Jerry Lee, their country songs were as buttoned-up and reverential as their more explicitly religious numbers. "We were hard country," Charlie Louvin said a generation later. "We never did record a dirty lyric. For my part, I don't think anyone could find a good, clean country love song offensive. If they could, they're serving somebody I haven't heard of."

For the Louvin Brothers, the transition was easy because they moved between songs of religious devotion and songs of romantic devotion. There was a precedent in country music for performers like them. For Jerry Lee, who bounced between the poles of "When the Saints Go Marching In" and "Whole Lotta Shakin' Going On," the road was more treacherous and far less frequently traveled.

Jerry Lee did not record again until after the first of the year; his touring schedule as part of various packages, Sun and otherwise, was hectic. In Memphis he was busy otherwise, finally calling it quits with Jane, in their eyes if not those of the courts. Without J. W. or Lois's knowledge or approval, on December 12, 1957, he and his cousin Myra drove south to Mississippi and were married. The family was shocked. Some said that Myra was much too young for Jerry Lee; strangely, some implied the exact opposite. Sam Phillips heard about the wedding and insisted it be kept quiet. Just to make sure that people considered Jerry Lee a good country boy, Phillips started plugging the B-side of

"Great Balls of Fire," the ballad version of "You Win Again," hard country at its most acceptable to that conservative audience.

• • •

In the first half of 1958, Jerry Lee spent most of the time either on the road or in the studio. He was living like a star, buying cars and motorcycles, spending money as if the enormous royalty checks would arrive forever with the same frequency. He brought some of his star arrogance to his January sessions, but he also brought his star talent.

Fresh from having spent a pleasant afternoon at a motorcycle shop with Roy Orbison, Jerry Lee called for "Go Go Go," one of Roy's most propulsive rockers, which the Killer redubbed "Down the Line." The first few versions were conversational, Jerry Lee feeling out the song and transporting it from Roy's world to his own. He changed some key lyrics and kept charging at it. "Wait a minute, I'm pooped out," he said between two of the eight takes. By the time he captured the song, he was putting on a show, daring the assembled to "Look-a-here!" before he bolted into a raucous solo. Billy Riley's proto-surf guitar owed more to another Orbison song, "Domino," than it did to "Go Go Go," but it still fit fine.

Another song they worked at was "I'm Sorry I'm Not Sorry," a tune identified with Carl Perkins, a strong country weeper with prominent, strutting drums and a cold-hearted attitude in its lyrics that stunned. On Hank Ballard's rhythm-and-blues hit, "Cool Cool Ways," which had been called "Sexy Ways" in its original incarnation, Jerry Lee sang extra hard to make up for the softer title. The song's breakdown section referred directly to its superior predecessor, "Whole Lotta Shakin' Going On," and the song ended with sexual taunts that insured it could not be released. Jack Hammer's "Milkshake Mademoiselle" was considered as a follow-up to "Great Balls of Fire." Its teen-oriented lyrics would have fit in well on pop radio, but Jerry

Jerry Lee and Sam Phillips, in the center of the universe, 1958

Lee's corrosive piano solo and wild singing, including a high-pitched scream, worked against the lyric and the tune was shelved after half a dozen tries.

The most successful song to emerge from the January sessions was another made-to-order contribution from Otis Blackwell, "Breathless," that yielded another multiformat hit: Number Four country-and-western, Number Three rhythm-and-blues, and Number Seven pop. The tune was less backwoodsy than what Jerry Lee usually brought to the studio, but the Killer was not about to argue with the work of the "little colored fellow" who had given him "Great Balls of Fire." Echo swirling around him, Jerry Lee's voice leaped out from the mix, howling the tale of sexual satisfaction with abandon.

One couplet in Blackwell's lyric stood out: "When you call my name/You know I burn like a wood in flame." Perhaps Jerry Lee was not paying attention to the words. If he had, he had a spectacular sacred-turned-profane image with which he could fuel another brief epistemological war with Sam. (Jerry Lee does not sing "burn" in the lyric quoted above. He sings "boin," a tossed-away syllable for Jerry Lee, but for little John Fogerty listening in northern California it was the key to a mystery of southern dialect that he would exploit in "Proud Mary" and several dozen other Creedence Clearwater Revival songs of similar caliber.)

With "Breathless" in the can, Jerry Lee flew to Australia with a package tour that included Buddy Holly, whom Jerry Lee adored, and Paul Anka, whom he terrorized. They stopped for the night in Hawaii, where Jerry Lee, guilty about neglecting Myra Gale, wrote her a rare letter that she preserved for decades and gave to Murray Silver. It read:

> How is the most beautiful girl in all the world, fine I hope. Darling I sure do miss you, because I love you so so so much. How is everybody fine to I guess. Darling please take care of your self if anything was to

happen to you I'd die and that's no joke. Oh Myra I love you with all my heart. Baby we're going to have such a beautiful life together, we're going to be so happy too. Myra if you ever done me wrong it would kill me, well I'd rather you would kill me. Well I no you woulden do me wrong would you darling. Myra I've let myself fall in love to much with you, don't break my heart. Darling this is the most beautiful place you ever seen But I can't enjoy it without you. I'll be home soon. May God watch over you, pray for me, your husband, Jerry Lee Lewis."

Jerry Lee's next Sun session was on Valentine's Day. Jerry Lee warmed up with the first songs that came to mind. The trio, consisting of Jerry Lee, J. W., and Van Eaton, turned in a barrelhouse version of Roy Brown's rhythm-and-blues smash "Good Rockin' Tonight" that featured a luxurious solo and Jerry Lee's plea that his beloved "meet me out behind the barn." He discarded as much of the original as he could, and, as was now becoming habit, evoked the breakdown of "Whole Lotta Shakin' Going On," this time with the vow, "We're gonna take it down now, little mama."

Jerry Lee probably was most familiar with "Good Rockin' Tonight" through Elvis's 1954 Sun version, and more Elvis hits spilled out. He jumped into "Jailhouse Rock" driven by alcohol, ego, and defiance. Ditto with "Hound Dog" and "Don't Be Cruel." He was showing off to himself, proving to himself that he was really the king of rock and roll, not that other guy. Other warm-up numbers included "Pink Pedal Pushers," the sort of high-school tune usually best left to its writer, Carl Perkins (except for the extremely suggestive line "she's got something her mom never had") and the Jimmie Hodges hillbilly hit of a decade before, "Someday (You'll Want Me to Want You)," a serviceable barroom ballad in which Jack Clement turned up the echo to eleven.

That out of the way, they moved to the possible-hit song in question. Sam Phillips was pleased with the way *Jamboree* had helped market "Great Balls of Fire," so he arranged for Jerry Lee to sing the theme to a juvenile-delinquent exploitation film, *High School Confidential*, starring Russ Tamblyn and Mamie Van Doren. It was a wild song, and it took Jerry Lee a few takes, of the more than a dozen in total, to get started. This gives the lie to the myth that what happened at the Memphis Recording Service was all noble-savage spontaneity and artless genius. These boys worked hard at their songs, over and over and over, until they got it right. They were professionals.

"Wait a minute," Jerry Lee said after one false start. "I screwed up, I had my mind on something else—something I shouldn't've had my mind on. Let's cut it!" They did, and out came a roaring version, from the opening double en-tendre, "Open up honey/It's your lover boy me that's knockin'," through a pure honky-tonk piano solo high-lighted by a transitional yell of, "dig dig dig dig dig hell hell," as Roland Janes's guitar took over. It was wilder than the released version, though not by much. The movie was a hit, as was the song: Number Nine country-and-western and Number Five rhythm-and-blues, although events that transpired between recording and release kept it down to Number Twenty-one on the pop charts. Also recorded around the same time, perhaps at the same session, was the ordinary rocker, "Put Me Down."

Jerry Lee hit the road again, playing some Alan Freed package shows as well as Dick Clark's "American Band-stand," where he performed live, not lip-synched, "Breathless," "You Win Again," and "Whole Lotta Shakin' Going On." At one show in New York, he was furious to learn that he was not the headliner, but rather he was second-billed behind Chuck Berry. Jerry Lee had enormous respect for Berry as a performer and songwriter, but his ego would not allow him to be second-billed to anyone. He delivered a show that was torrid even by his usual standards. One enduring rock-and-roll myth states that Jerry Lee lit his piano on fire at the conclusion of "Great Balls of Fire" and stalked off to the side of the stage to confront Berry. The story about lighting the piano on fire is all wet, but it is true that Jerry Lee stood face to face with Berry after he ended his set to thundering applause. "Follow that, nigger," he taunted and swaggered away. By Ferriday standards, Jerry Lee was not an all-out racist, but he knew the value of intimidation.

A few weeks later, Jerry Lee was much friendlier as he recorded a few more tunes for his first album. The obligatory Hank Williams compositions were the Cajun-flavored "Jambalaya," which the Louisiana boy rocked out, and "Your Cheatin' Heart," which was more scattered; in years to come Jerry Lee would record several superior versions of the latter number. Also played was another Williams-performed tune, "Lovesick Blues," on which a loose Jerry Lee had altogether too much fun. His piano was intentionally sloppy and he altered many of the lyrics.

The session did not yield much more releasable material. James Liddle's standard rocker, "Friday Night," was a poor cousin to "High School Confidential," though "Hello, Hello Baby," a Jerry Lee Lewis original, was a whooped-up blues that archivists will note as the first time he substituted his proper name for *I* in a lyric. In March 1958, that was not yet a lazy affectation. The standard "Frankie and Johnny" was never much of a song, even in the hands of Jimmie Rodgers, but Jerry Lee did perform it with some verve, and there is no Jerry Lee fan who does not get pleasure from hearing the noted philanderer sing, "My story has no moral/My story has no end/My story shows/There's no trusting none of these men."

What was by far the greatest performance recorded during the session was also by far the most unreleasable. "Big Legged Woman" was an oft-covered blues leer, and

Jerry Lee unleashed a terrific version. The performance of the song Jerry Lee had heard back in Natchez was as lecherous as Myra's parents feared he could be, all single-entendre lyrics ("I bet my bottom dollar there ain't a cherry in the house"; "When I start drilling on you, baby/You're gonna lose your nightgown") and sleazy _l_'s rolling off his tongue. This was young Jerry Lee at his most direct and terrifying, with falsetto screeches and a cry of "Don't stop me now, mama!" This was the closest Jerry Lee ever came to the Delta blues tradition of a randy rambler like Robert Johnson, and in its own way it cut just as deep as Johnson's tales of sex, death, and fear.

"It's a hit!" Jerry Lee proclaimed after the song was over. He acted as if he did not understand why his comment was greeted by laughter. Two decades later, when "Big Legged Woman" finally appeared on a reissue LP, Jerry Lee professed to be embarrassed by it.

On April 20, the usual quartet stomped through several takes of "Put Me Down," in which for someone who was supposed to sound like he was being dumped, Jerry Lee was having a ball, as well as "Fools Like Me," a slow one co-written by Jack Clement that enlivened the clichés of self-pitying country, bad rhymes and all. "Carrying On (Sexy Ways)" was fine and hard-rocking, but by now it was apparent that no one knew what to rename the Hank Ballard number. "Crazy Heart," another tune identified with Hank Williams, was executed lightly and playfully.

The next night's session was more productive, after a few run-throughs of "High School Confidential" loosened up the quartet. A cascading attack on Floyd Tillman's "Slippin' Around," another Wagon Wheel favorite, featured two lead guitars by Billy Riley and Roland James and served as a perfect double-entendre vehicle for Jerry Lee. He sang as though he knew what it meant to "live in constant fear" on a number of levels. "I'll See You in My Dreams" was a jazzy instrumental meant to mark time, a piano-roll readymade, and "Real Wild Child" was a sterling hard rocker with lines like "We'll shake until the meat comes off the bone." The session eased to a conclusion with the Louis Jordan jump-band hit "Let the Good Times Roll." Jerry Lee's idiosyncratic version suggested the sound of a New Orleans barroom just before dawn.

Jerry Lee was scheduled to fly to London on May 22 to embark on a sold-out-in-advance British tour, and Sam Phillips squeezed in one more session before the jaunt. Jerry Lee played this date solo. It was refreshing to play alone. His growth since his first solo session when he had revealed himself in front of Slim Whitman was noteworthy.

Jerry Lee started with yet another Williams track, "Settin' the Woods on Fire," later overdubbed with guitar, bass, and drums. By 1958 Jack Clement had convinced Phillips to allow him and his buddy Bill Justis to start over-dubbing strings and background choruses, but every single time this turned out to be superfluous at best and ruinsome to the original track at worst. It was comforting that not too much was overdubbed onto the released "Settin' the Woods on Fire." "Memory of You," an original Jerry Lee wrote on the flight back from Australia, was nothing special except for its sound of freedom. Solo, he had so much room to play with in the heavily echoed Sun studio that he insisted on cramming every space he could find with sound, just like his piano breaks. The same went for the Allen Toussaint scorcher, "Come What May." Alone in the studio, Jerry Lee shouted so no one's attention, including his own, lagged for even a moment.

"Break Up" was a contribution from a new singer/pianist who had impressed Jack Clement: Charlie Rich. The solo version somehow anticipated all the other instruments to be added later and in doing so rendered their addition superfluous, from Jerry Lee's uncharacteristic walking bass to his breakneck speed. A far superior Charlie Rich tune, attempted next, was the trenchant ballad "I'll Make It

Up to You." Jerry Lee zeroed in on an appropriate tempo; it was polite, but there was no way Jerry Lee's piano could sing the devotional ballad as straight as his voice could. He played "Crazy Arms" to remind himself that his previously recorded version was great, and his take on Chuck Berry's "Johnny B. Goode" reversed the typical Berry recording method by replicating Berry's guitar on the piano. As a guitarist, Berry had aped the chords of his pianist, Johnny Johnson.

One could argue that Jerry Lee was simply hunting, looking for some material to fill out his long-player. The long-delayed first album, titled *Jerry Lee Lewis*, came out later that month and featured "Don't Be Cruel," "Goodnight Irene," "Put Me Down," "It All Depends (On Who Will Buy the Wine)," "Ubangi Stomp," "Crazy Arms," "Jambalaya," "Fools Like Me," "High School Confidential," "When the Saints Go Marching In," "Matchbox," "It'll Be Me," and "Whole Lotta Shakin' Going On." Jerry Lee felt on top of the world—he had enjoyed three smash singles, and "High School Confidential" was on its way to becoming number four—and was trying to find new ways to solidify and expand his success. Like Elvis before him, he wanted his music to satisfy everyone and he knew it could.

• • •

Then the bottom fell out. Over everyone's objections, Myra accompanied Jerry Lee to London, was found out by the sensationalist Fleet Street press as the Killer's underage cousin/wife, and scandalized herself and her husband. Reporters then discovered that neither Jerry Lee's first marriage nor his second had been legally terminated, making him a bigamist and his marriage to Myra Gale illegal as well as, from their viewpoint, immoral. The resulting uproar eventually forced Jerry Lee to leave the country without performing most of the booked shows.

The tour had begun on a lighter note. Nick Tosches

reported that Jane Mitcham called Jerry Lee's hotel room and Myra answered. Jane said she wanted to wish Jerry Lee luck in his London debut and told Myra she was still in love with the Ferriday Fireball. Countered Myra, "But I'm living with him and you're not." That night Jerry Lee's show was poorly attended and booed lustily by many of those who bothered to show up.

In the center of the storm, Jerry Lee did not understand what had happened to him personally or professionally. The twenty-one-year-old's nonchalant attitude to marriage ensured that he did not think he had done anything wrong by any of his wives; his insular, innocent ideas about the record industry led him to believe that this was a small matter that would blow over by the time his flight touched down in Memphis. However, "High School Confidential" stalled on the pop chart almost immediately; and neither side of the succeeding two-sided single, the Charlie Rich pair, "Break Up" and "I'll Make It All Up to You," cracked the Top Fifty.

Phillips tried everything. He had Jerry Lee and Myra remarry publicly. He had Jack Clement cut a novelty record, under Jerry Lee's name, called "The Return of Jerry Lee," a break-in single in the style of Buchanan and Goodman's "Flying Saucer," in which an announcer dubbed Edward R. Edward asked a question and then an engineer inserted a somewhat relevant lyrical snippet from a Jerry Lee song. (Sample question: "Where did you meet your young bride?" Answer, from "High School Confidential": "Boppin' at the high school hop!")

This was supposed to solve the problem? The flip side was the great "Lewis Boogie," which no one heard. One could argue that "The Return of Jerry Lee" was recorded in the spirit of its namesake, but Phillips's decision to let Clement turn the scandal into a joke hurt everyone's already crumbling credibility. Not much more successful was the

At home with Myra, before the fall, 1957

humble open letter that Phillips placed as a full-page ad in *Billboard* and forced his charge to sign:

Dear Friends:

I have in recent weeks been the apparent center of a fantastic amount of publicity, none of which has been good.

But there must be good even in the worst people and according to the press release originating in London, I am the worst and not even deserving of one decent press release.

Now this whole thing started because I tried and did tell the truth. I told the story of my past life, as I thought it had been straightened out and that I would not hurt anybody in being man enough to tell the truth.

I confess that my life has been stormy. I confess further that since I have become a public figure, I sincerely wanted to be worthy of the decent admiration of all the people, young or old, that admired or liked what talent (if any) I have. That is, after all, all that I have in a professional way to offer.

If you don't believe that the accuracy of things can get mixed up when you are in the public eye, then I hope you never have to travel this road I'm on.

There were some legal misunderstandings in that matter that inadvertently made me look as though I invented the word indecency. I feel I, if nothing else, should be given credit for the fact that I have at least a little common sense and that if I had not thought that the legal aspects of this matter were not completely straight, I certainly would not have made a move until they were.

I did not want to hurt Jane Mitcham, nor did

I want to hurt my family and children. I went to court and did not contest Jane's divorce actions, and she was awarded seven hundred and fifty dollars a month for child support and alimony. Jane and I parted from the courtroom as friends and, as a matter of fact, chatted before, during, and after the trial with no animosity whatsoever.

In the belief that for once my life was straightened out, I invited my mother and daddy and little sister to make the trip to England. Unfortunately, Mother and Daddy felt that the trip would be too long and hard for them and didn't go, but Sister did go, along with Myra's little brother and mother.

I hope that if I am washed up as an entertainer, it won't be because of this bad publicity, because I can cry and wish all I want to, but I can't control the press or the sensationalism that these people will go to to get a scandal started to sell papers. If you don't believe me, please ask any of the other people that have been victims of the same.

Sincerely,
Jerry Lee Lewis

Less than two years after his initial appearance at 706 Union Avenue, Jerry Lee had scaled the top of the rock-and-roll ladder and fallen off. He had enjoyed the fruits of being "different," being someone whose differentness made him special; now he was learning what happened when people learned the true extent of his differentness. After a month of pouting and blaming his problems on anyone else whom he happened to meet, he returned to 706 Union Avenue, ready to redeem himself the only way he knew how.

CHAPTER 4

Sun Set

"It is far easier, I know, to criticize the failure of the South to face and solve its problems than it is to solve them."
—*W. J. Cash*, The Mind of the South

The conventional wisdom about Jerry Lee's career after the London fiasco is that it never truly recovered. The more complicated, and less romantic, truth is that although it took years for Jerry Lee to reestablish himself commercially on his records, only a few months passed before he was able to once again earn a good living on the road. Into the nineties, the road has been his home. From July 1958 to August 1963, when his elongated contract at Sun finally ran out and he graduated to Mercury's Smash subsidiary, Jerry Lee put down on tape fewer songs than he had between November 1956 and the disaster in London. Why did he record more songs in his first eighteen months than he had in the subsequent five years? Because he was on the road.

This is not to suggest that these were not years of tremendous anger for Jerry Lee. He knew he had slipped, and his disappointment in himself and those around him was exacerbated by the alcohol and pills that had been part of his life even before he arrived in Memphis. In spite of the frequent high quality of his recordings, his hits were far less

Onstage in 1957

common and had weaker legs. Sam Phillips, and the subsequent producers he assigned to Jerry Lee when he lost interest, adopted a try-anything-and-see-what-might-stick approach. They took on instrumentals and eventually resorted to putting out tracks without vocals under an assumed name, the Hawk, thinking that a new monicker might break the blacklist. Through it all, on record at least, Jerry Lee remained completely individual. One could not hear a Jerry Lee performance and not know immediately that the Killer was at the controls. His stylistic authority announced itself the moment his fingers struck the ivories; every performance was as inescapable and demanding as an unexpected lapel grab.

The sessions that were supposed to make Charlie Rich wealthy took place in July 1958, but the scandal kept the resulting double-sided single of Rich compositions, "Break Up" and "I'll Make It All Up to You," in the bottom half of the charts. Some of the takes featured Rich playing piano, clear evidence that the brain trust at Sun had become so desperate they had temporarily lost their minds. Rich was a formidable pianist, to be sure, and he was one of the few white performers who had started their careers under the Sun umbrella who were able to truly expand on those lessons when they moved to a major label. Roy Orbison was another notable exception to the rule.

Rich's talent notwithstanding, it was senseless to consider a Jerry Lee record without Jerry Lee playing piano, even if Jerry Lee's idiosyncratic style sometimes worked against a producer's tightly defined intentions. Somehow Jerry Lee shrugged off the insult; his singing on both tunes was intensely committed, at least to cutting a hit. Later in the month, Phillips crony and noted rock hater Bill Justis, whose overwrought instrumental hit of the previous year, "Raunchy," sported an inadvertently ironic title, supervised another of the backup-singer overdub extravaganzas that sank many a Jerry Lee tune by smoothing it so much that little was left to keep it afloat. As noted in a reissue, these overdubs "destroyed more Sun records at the end of the fifties than a raging warehouse fire."

Justis was at the next Jack Clement-supervised session, on November 5, 1958, and he brought his saxophone. There is some evidence that Martin Willis played sax that date and Justis just produced, but he did bring his cynicism. Jerry Lee did not care; just off the road, he was ready to rock. He announced, "I might dance to it. I might tear it to the ground," before he galloped through a "Drinkin' Wine Spo-Dee-o-Dee" that lived up to his rhetoric. "I'll Sail My Ship Alone," a Moon Mullican smash from 1950, was rollicking, although the saxophone sounded too literal, and Roland Janes's repetitive guitar lines would have been annoying had they not been buried in the pollution of a mix. "It Hurt Me So" was a polite Rich/Justis number, again with Rich on piano, and "You're the Only Star (in My Blue Heaven)" rounded out the session. Fans of pure Jerry Lee recordings were excused for wanting to stuff their laundry into Willis's saxophone. A few days later, Justis threw a wet blanket of overdubs atop "It Hurt Me So." Two hundred-odd miles east in Nashville, a producer named Jerry Kennedy took notes on Justis's method.

This was rock and roll? With background choruses out of the blandest pop and pop-country forms? Many devotees of the first explosion of rock and roll—much of it emanating from 706 Union Avenue—were disappointed to hear what had happened to the music in 1958. Everyone was getting soft. Elvis, for example, had stumbled from "Jailhouse Rock" all the way down to "A Fool Such As I." (Elvis's induction into the army solidified his move.) The first wave of rock and roll was being retaken by the crooners (Pat Boone and his ilk) and novelty performers (a big hit of 1958 was Sheb Wooley's "The Purple People Eater").

Sensing that the market for the raw sounds that had

built Sun was quickly weakening, Phillips accepted the counsel of people like Clement and Justis. There would still be a mix of teenage and adult topics in Jerry Lee's songs, teen for the pop audience and adult for country folk, but those stories would now have to be more dressed up. Compared to the strings and horns foisted upon Jerry Lee through the sixties, seventies, and eighties, the comparatively subtle backup la-la's on "You Hurt Me So" are not nearly so obstructive. But they set the pattern for what was to come; in the second phase of his tenure at Sun, it would be harder for listeners to get at Jerry Lee.

Although some of the people who overdressed Jerry Lee's Sun performances have since publicly atoned, Jack Clement in particular, Jerry Lee himself did not rebel against this treatment, even if he surely knew it was inappropriate. All the men at Sun were brought up to understand and respect southern concepts of honor. Jerry Lee was wild, but he had manners. He may have indulged in shouting matches with his boss, but he always called him Mr. Phillips. At Sun after the fall, Jerry Lee revealed his character in Sam's studio, not his office.

1958 bumped into 1959 with no reprieve for Jerry Lee from radio programmers. "I'll Sail My Ship Alone" wandered into the *Billboard* pop chart for a week, position Ninety-three, and promptly disappeared. He had the usual problems at home, too, although a bewildered Myra was about to give birth to their first child, Steve Allen Lewis. J. W. had left the group, still trying to figure out what had happened to him and his family. Mother Mamie and cousin Jimmy Lee Swaggart pressured him to absolve himself of all his worldly possessions—and give them those goodies. With all this on his mind, Jerry Lee cut loose in the studio with some performances he convinced himself could break him out of his personal and professional ruts. He was wrong on both counts, but freneticism poured out of him. Playing hard was the way he temporarily transcended his world. "Lovin' Up a Storm," consisting of just Jerry Lee, guitar, bass, and drums, was as hard and fast as any rock and roll. And the zeitgeist to the contrary, Jerry Lee still played authentic, unencumbered rock and roll. The piano solo conjured up a cyclone even more persuasively than the title image and the improvised couplet, "When we kiss/Great balls of fire," hearkened Jerry Lee back to his favorite subjects: himself and his early career. Van Eaton's outstanding demolition-derby drumming drove the number. "Big Blon' Baby" was in the spirit of "Great Balls of Fire." Instead of "Goodness gracious," he exclaimed, "Jumpin' Jehosaphat," but few heard the worthy sequel.

Clement, or whoever was running the session, sensed that these fine performances could lead to more if he got Jerry Lee into the studio again soon, and three other tunes were recorded only a few days later, this time with Jerry Lee on drums rather than piano. All three were acceptable, but none of them reached the heights of "Lovin' Up a Storm" or "Big Blon' Baby." The rhythm-and-blues "Sick and Tired," written by New Orleans stalwarts Chris Kenner and Dave Bartholomew, was sprightly and syncopated, more Little Richard than Jerry Lee in its appropriation of the former's "Lucille" riff. "(Just a Shanty in Old) Shanty Town" was a memory-driven (the child Jerry Lee had heard the song on the radio) midtempo country tune without the usual maudlin overlay. Jerry Lee forced the solo to be wilder than the song but the composition could not accept it and he ended abruptly. "Release Me" was a country standard (Ray Price and Kitty Wells both had recorded hit versions of the pained ballad in 1954) executed deftly if not brilliantly. This is a telling example of how even an uninspired Jerry Lee during this era could be spare and driving.

Jerry Lee returned to the studio on March 22, 1959, with Phillips himself apparently presiding and guessing what he could possibly do to get Jerry Lee back on the

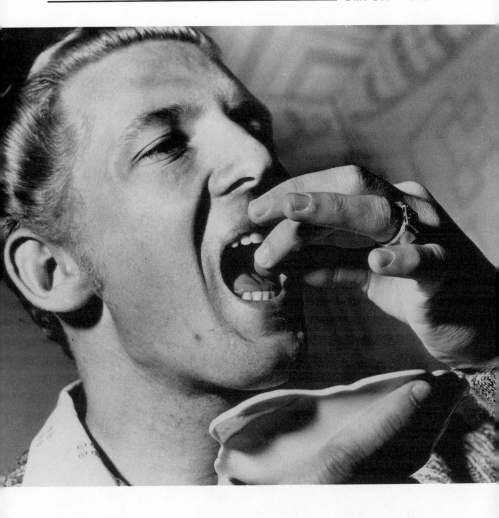

charts. Manners aside, Jerry Lee was pressuring Phillips for better answers on why he was not scoring hits anymore. He blamed Phillips for the mess, not the revelation of his marriage or the changing of public tastes. With more reason, he also resented Phillips for leading him into signing a sub-minimum-wage, five-year extension on his recording contract the year before when everyone felt like a vindicated genius. Jerry Lee and Sam were going to be stuck with each other until 1963 no matter how much either of them felt

On board Sun Records' tour bus, 1957

betrayed by the other. Unofficial blacklist or not, they had to try to make some commercial noise.

This night's session was somewhat tentative, as Jerry Lee was playing with Bill Justis's stage band rather than musicians with whom he shared a history, with the notable exception of drummer Van Eaton. Only one cut from the lengthy March 22 session was released before the dawn of the reissue age, perhaps because Sam sensed that Jerry Lee worked best with the people he knew best. By now it was nearly obligatory to include a Hank Williams song at a session, and this afternoon it was "I Could Never Be Ashamed of You." It was characterized by a prancing solo and Jerry Lee's inability or refusal to pronounce *perhaps*. He said "prehaps." A plodding rhythm kept this particular performance stuck in the starting gate. "Near You" was a slight limbering-up instrumental, not without its charms or opportunities for Jerry Lee to show off.

This was Jerry Lee's fiftieth session for his record label, and he was still intent on showing off before he did anything else. Phillips and Clement preserved these moments because they were fans, but even the dedicated must have tired of such practices after half a hundred dates. Jerry Lee showed off to amuse himself, he showed off to relieve the tension and repetitiveness of take after take of the same song, he showed off to entertain, he showed off to remind people that he was the Killer. But he showed off *all the time*. His career-long refusal to get through a session without doing this—the staff at the Memphis Recording Service the nights of the "It Was the Whiskey Talkin' (Not Me)" sessions can attest to the enduring nature of the practice—was the only part of the Killer persona that was a bluff. Bravado is what men employ to hide their insecurities. Jerry Lee showed off all the time because he was afraid that he might not be any good. He didn't need to remind everyone else that he was the Killer; he needed to remind himself.

Now that the hits were apparently over and his marriage was reduced to one hurt after another, Jerry Lee got his validation only from himself and whatever audience was starting to see him again when he played live. He was used to making do with little. Back in his childhood, horrific economic conditions had been exacerbated by the New Deal that was invented to alleviate them. The South had 28 percent of the country's population in the thirties but received less than 16 percent of dispersed federal aid.

Although the Cadillac-and-motorcycle life had been thrilling, Jerry Lee was used to making do with little. How did he make do? By entertaining himself and reassuring himself. In that way, the Killer who recorded "It Was the Whiskey Talkin' (Not Me)" in 1990 was not far removed from the kid who banged out "Silent Night" on his uncle's upright. He wanted to prove to himself that he was worthy of special treatment; he wanted deliverance from his trials. The only places Jerry Lee could roam free without fear were in the studio and onstage. There he could consistently earn approval.

Other songs recorded between show-off moves at the March 22 session were "Hillbilly Music," a spirited performance of a mediocre country-rocker that Jerry Lee elevated to a statement of purpose. It was the one song that session in which Justis's stalwarts, particularly guitarist Brad Suggs, were able to keep up with Jerry Lee. Alas, the song faded out, so listeners could not enjoy the bang with which it inevitably concluded. Many attempts were made at covering the Fats Domino hit "My Blue Heaven," in which flourish-filled piano lines were not contained by the sweet melody. After trying out several tempos, Jerry Lee suggested, "This'll be Jerry Lee Lewis style," and he rocked it out. His right hand wandered to the upper end of his eighty-eights, dancing on the edge to stop-and-start rhythms.

Sam Phillips could suffer through show-off episodes, but the prime reason he had Jerry Lee at 706 Union that

Ain't fakin', London, 1958

night was to present him with a new Otis Blackwell composition written especially for him: "Let's Talk About Us."
The teen-oriented love rocker moved along pleasantly
enough, but it needed another kick to get over the cliff.
Phillips suggested that when Jerry Lee finished his next
string of dates, he should return to complete the number.

By the time Jerry Lee next recorded at Sun in late
June, Phillips had fired Jack Clement and Bill Justis, ostensibly for insubordination. Ernie Barton supervised, and
guitarists Roland Janes and Billy Riley were back in the
fold. Again the point of the session was "Let's Talk About
Us." Six takes into it, they scored a winner. The only problem was that even though Clement and Justis were gone,
Phillips was still following their advice, heaping indifferent
backup singers onto an already bursting track. As early as
1959 it was indisputable that the prime Jerry Lee tracks
were those that were the least fussed over in post-
production. The overdubs did not help; the single failed to
enter any of the three *Billboard* singles charts.

Although few of the songs from the June sessions were
initially intended for release, many of them were strong
enough to convince Phillips otherwise. A cover of Chuck
Berry's jailbait anthem, "Little Queenie," was definitive,
the first of many Jerry Lee versions of Berry songs that
would surpass their models. The studio echo enhanced the
lecherous, conversational vocal; Jerry Lee was in control
and enjoying his power, sexual and otherwise. The only
weak spots in the mix were guitar interjections that did not
add much that Jerry Lee's lead lines did not already imply,
and the Killer's forgetting to play a piano solo. Roger Miller's "Home" was competent, bluesy country, but Jerry Lee
seemed distracted. Much better was an amazingly graceful
version of the Carter Family's "Can the Circle Be Unbroken," the archetypal God-believing country ballad.
Much worse was a rare dud by Sam's current favorite,
Charlie Rich, called "The Ballad of Billy Joe," maudlin

midtempo country sung by a man about to be executed. It showed up on the B-side of "Let's Talk About Us," fumbling through lyrics like, "I'll be hung tomorrow/Just because I had to kill that little rat." The song was much more appropriate for Johnny Cash than Jerry Lee. However, since the Man in Black had jumped ship for Columbia (and had recorded an extremely similar song called "Don't Take Your Guns to Town"), it fell on Jerry Lee's lap. Another Rich composition, "Sail Away," made more emotional sense, and Jerry Lee sang it as a duet with the writer, adding an extra overlay of resignation and yearning to an already fine tune. "Sail Away" should have replaced "The Ballad of Billy Jo" on the flip of "Let's Talk About Us."

"Am I to Be the One" was another duet, this time on a quality mild rocker. Both Jerry Lee and Rich's singing owed much to Atlantic rhythm-and-blues singers like the Coasters. On the basis of these two songs, someone should have suggested a Lewis/Rich duet album and begged Jerry Leiber and Mike Stoller to produce it. "Night Train to Memphis," a hit a generation previously for Roy Acuff, was masterfully executed as a spiritually contented rocker, an anticipatory antidote to Junior Parker's "Mystery Train" with a marvelous secular/gospel mixture, using phrases like "We're gonna sing hallelujah" and "We're gonna have a jubilee" to describe all sorts of sacred and profane activities. This was another example of Jerry Lee's mixing styles and coming up with something new and indefinable. Rounding out the session was "I'm the Guilty One," a cry-in-your-beer revenge ballad in which the revenge is on the self, tossed-off in great country style.

Cecil Scaife, Sun's promotion manager at the time, thought he knew how to get Jerry Lee out of his commercial doldrums. As he told Colin Escott, he wanted to change the Killer's image. "I wanted to get him out of typical rock-and-roll regalia," Scaife said. "Ivy League was in. I wanted him to get a crew cut. I wanted to hold a press conference

A rare sedate crowd

where Jerry would announce that he was somewhat re-
morseful. He would take on an adult image. We discussed it
for over an hour. Jerry was very polite and listened. He
would nod every once in a while, but he kept looking at his
watch. Finally, he shook it like it wasn't working, and he
looked at his buddy across the table and said, 'What time is
it?' The guy said, 'It's five before one.' Jerry said, 'Oh! The

double feature at the Strand starts in five minutes. It's
Return of the Werewolf and _The Bride of Frankenstein Meets
Godzilla_.' Then he jumped up and left the table. That was
the last time we discussed Jerry's image."

First-rate performances like those on "Night Train to
Memphis" and "I'm the Guilty One" were second nature to
Jerry Lee, not much work at all. They reflected the way he
thought. They were great, but neither was released until
long after he had left the label. His promotion manager
wanted to turn him into Pat Boone. No wonder he needed
to show off so much.

• • •

Jerry Lee, peroxided hair not within six inches of crew
cut length, did not get around to recording again until early
1960, by which time the studio at 706 Union had been
abandoned in favor of a more modern setup at 639 Madison
Avenue. It had a grand piano and a four-track recorder.
Jerry Lee's first session there, produced by Charles Underwood, was a disaster. "The Wild Side of Life" was a Hank
Thompson hit from 1952 that had become an immediate
sexist-lament, honky-tonk standard. It seemed likely that
Jerry Lee would put down a strong version, but from the
opening note it was clear that Martin Willis's saxophone
had no business being anywhere near this tune. The more
elaborate instrumentation that its presence suggested made
the song and Jerry Lee's loose performance sound more
ordinary than they really were. "Billy Boy" was a rocker
written by someone who didn't understand rock and roll,
although Jerry Lee's howdy-doody solo and lines like "I'm
a young cat/And I can't leave my mother" lifted it to bor-
derline listenable. "My Bonnie" was an intermittently spirited standard that made a little more room for the
saxophone.

A marathon session at the end of the month produced
by Sam Phillips was much more rewarding—and about ten
times as long. Neither Sam nor Jerry Lee had a clue what to

do with a newfangled four-track recorder, but they both were well lubricated and not concerned with such esoterica. Jerry Lee kept explaining "Mexicali Rose," a breezy Bing Crosby song from 1938 that was a relic of the Killer's Ferriday radio-listening years, telling Phillips over and over why it was going to be a hit. He was supercharged. Even his talking before the tune was rhythmic and intense: "It's real slow and pretty/The whole thing/Real slow and pretty/Then it changes into the beat, man." The band started it at a sluggish tempo and Jerry Lee called it off.

"It's too slow!" Jerry Lee complained.

"It's no hit," Sam complained.

"Damn right, it's a hit," Jerry Lee said. "Just wait 'til I get through with it and I'll show you it's a hit."

A few minutes later, he blazed through a turbulent rock-and-roll version of "Mexicali Rose." The session moved along as swiftly and directly as the music. "Let's do some Newport jazz," Sam suggested, searching for any fad on which to capitalize, although Jerry Lee did not want to stop insisting that "Mexicali Rose" was a hit. Sam implored, "Let's cut this instrumental just for the thrill of it," and Jerry Lee played an interpretation of the Glenn Miller hit "In the Mood" that built up steam as the band, especially guitarist Janes, caught on to Jerry Lee's most subtle asides. "I might put out an instrumental record," Sam said afterward, thinking aloud. "Maybe something else? Call it the Jerry Lee Lewis Combo featuring Roland Janes." This was the cut they released credited to "The Hawk," rather than to Jerry Lee Lewis, but no one could hear its honky-tonk version of swing and not immediately know who the perpetrator was. For all his selfless loyalty to Jerry Lee, Janes did not get his credit.

Afternoon turned to evening, and dozens of versions of many more songs were thrown at the wall. "I Get the Blues When It Rains" was either dinner music or a soporific, depending on one's tastes; "Don't Drop It" was a persuasive

Sam Phillips, Jerry Lee, Jerry Wexler, and Ahmet Ertegun (left to right), _Memphis, 1957_

barroom rocker with a weird lyrical conceit that compared love to glass; and Jerry Lee committed a pair of versions of Roy Acuff's "The Great Speckled Bird," a metaphorical tale about the steadfastness of Good against Evil that was extremely popular in Assembly of God churches. In fast and slow versions, Jerry Lee played both characters. The premier take of the song was preceded by Jerry Lee's instructions to the band, "Kinda slow, man, you know, not draggy but lively, you know, not lively but not too draggy." Whatever it sounded like, it was intended by Jerry Lee as a devout song to balance the session's frank pop.

"Bonnie B," later picked as a single, was a terrific teen-oriented rocker by Charles Underwood, although Sam should have known he could never sell many copies of a song in which Jerry Lee sang, "I would marry Bonnie B if I couid," and then went on to explain that they could not marry because they were too young. A picture sleeve featuring a pajama-clad Myra holding a teddy bear would not have been more self-defeating. "Baby, Baby Bye Bye" was a spirited complaint tune that later had backup idiots grafted on it, as did a quietly country-rocking version of Stephen Foster's "Old Black Joe," which whitewashed the pre-industrialized South. Jerry Lee's frequent readings of Foster tunes suggested that the version of the South he accepted was the romanticized one, Lost Cause and all.

A fast take of Hank Williams's "I Can't Help It (If I'm Still in Love with You)" underlined Jerry Lee's usual trouble with Hank songs at anything significantly faster than the original tempo. Still, it was a good version, even if it was sung backwards: "You can't help it if you're still in love with me." A speedy "Your Cheatin' Heart" was somewhat more effective. "As Long As I Live," written by Dorsey Burnette, bassist for the Johnny Burnette Rock 'n' Roll Trio, was a driving, optimistic rocker with a country tinge and gospel chord changes. Although Jerry Lee suspected his record audience was gone for good, he never stopped entertaining himself. "Hound Dog" had a wild solo, and Jerry Lee could do a great version of this in his sleep.

As the session tumbled deeper into the evening, an agitated Phillips taunted Jerry Lee by claiming that the Killer "couldn't cover Ray Charles for shit." An argument of "Great Balls of Fire" proportions ensued. Some say it escalated to blows. Whatever happened, it resolved in an astonishing version of "What'd I Say" that made Charles's original, fluent, uptempo gospel soul with a bang, sound tame. Sam conceded the point.

One final, wonderful performance from the session that did not see release until Ronald Reagan was president was a rock-and-roll song called, alternately, "Keep Your Hands Off of It" or "Birthday Cake." "What are you gonna do with this thing?" Jerry Lee laughed when he learned the words.

"I don't know," Sam said. "Take it out behind the barn and play it."

"Well that's the only place you're gonna be able to play it," Jerry said. "Here we go . . ." He scampered through the song as though it were a mine field, dropping chords and running, investing the double-entendre lyrics with as much slyness as his rolling tongue would allow. Thirty years later, what remains most amazing about this performance is that, even though Jerry Lee knew that there was no chance that it was ever going to see the light of day, he still played it as ferociously as all but the greatest of his Sun recordings. It was not that Jerry Lee was desperate for a hit, although he was, it was that he thought anything was possible. His unbridled optimism about himself shone through in his work. Sam listened to the playback, put the tape in its box, wrote "HELP!" on the box, and filed it.

Standouts from the next session, in June, included "Hang Up My Rock and Roll Shoes" by the late rhythm-and-blues master Chuck Willis, in which Martin Willis's finally appropriate saxophone emphasized the tune's New Orleans flavor and threw Jerry Lee's boisterous vocal into relief; a dirty excavation of W. C. Handy's gospel-blues "John Henry"; and another Chuck Willis tune, "C.C. Rider," which Jerry Lee interpreted as an emphatic, relaxed strut. A feverish instrumental called "Lewis Workout" was perfectly self-descriptive. Less worthy was a tossed-away version of Cindy Walker's "When My Blue Moon Turns to Gold Again," in which Jerry Lee's voice sounded shot; it was probably attempted at the tail end of the mostly successful session.

• • •

It has been suggested that one of the reasons Jerry Lee had trouble finding another hit in his later years with Sun was that he was not much of a songwriter. But what about Elvis Presley, who never wrote a song in his life? It has also

Jerry Lee and Sam Phillips: "He's just like me. He ain't got no sense."

been suggested that pop music had moved away from rock and roll in the early sixties, leaving Jerry Lee the artistic equivalent of homeless. Radio was soft compared to 1956, but there was still room in 1960 for Elvis's "A Mess of Blues," Wanda Jackson's "Let's Have a Party," Fats Domino's "Natural Born Lover," Ray Charles's "Let the Good Times Roll," James Brown's "You Got the Power," and many more. The blacklist was a factor, but "What'd I Say" would soon prove that it was not impenetrable. Rather, what kept Jerry Lee off the charts after the shock of his marriage to Myra faded away was one of the aspects of Sun Records that made it great: its devotion to new talent, the flip side of which was a reliance on such performers. Sun was not constructed like a major label that could nurture long-term careers. Until Motown changed the rules in 1963, regional independent labels thrived on novelty, not familiarity. The major labels treated Sun like a Triple-A baseball team; it was built for people to develop and move on to the big time. By 1960 Jerry Lee was ready for new challenges and new ideas, but his contract insured he was with Phillips for three more years. Of the greatest Sun performers, Jerry Lee stayed with Sam by far the longest. By 1960 they still had a tremendous amount of common ground stylistically and still made wonderful records together, but any disinterested observer could have seen that Jerry Lee had outgrown Sun.

An October 13 session with a large band including two guitars, three horns, and a vocal group yielded nothing useful. "When I Get Paid" and "Love Made a Fool of Me" were pulled as singles and disappeared almost immediately. Both conformed to the bland norms of Nashville country. The next session actually took place in Nashville, a distressing development for those who believed Jerry Lee did his best work away from the influence of "hillbilly heaven."

Neither Phillips nor Jerry Lee was entirely satisfied with the January 1960 version of "What'd I Say" so they went at it again at their June session. They got closer, and at the end of the take, Phillips cheered. Recording in Nashville with countrypolitan producer Billy Sherrill at the helm and crack session men at his side, Jerry Lee battled against the preconception that he would soften in such company and bested all previous versions of "What'd I Say." This time Jerry Lee was completely uninhibited, so much that even the overdubbed backup singers (brought in to remind listeners of Charles's Raelettes, who had accompanied the original hit) did not detract from his raving, shouting, and pleading. The only thing wrong with it was that it ended too soon. Jerry Lee hollered so loud he even made a dent in the blacklist: "What'd I Say" reached Number Twenty-seven country-and-western, Number Twenty-six rhythm-and-blues, and Number Thirty pop. It was not a smash, but it was a start. More important in the short run, it also helped Jerry Lee garner better bookings on the road.

Accompanying Jerry Lee on February 9, 1961, in Nashville were guitarists Hank Garland and Kelso Herston, bassist Bob Moore, and drummer Buddy Harman. They were the elite in Nashville session circles, and their other three tracks with Lewis that day showed both how sympathetic—and limiting—they could be. "Livin' Lovin' Wreck" was a teen-oriented Otis Blackwell tune, a vehicle that was starting to knock when Jerry Lee drove it. The performance was good, but it was also polite. Those looking toward the future noticed that if he wanted to, Jerry Lee could thrive in any environment, even one populated by bona fide session musicians. On Hank Williams's "Cold Cold Heart," a Number Thirty-six country hit, the problem was not so much the size of the accompaniment or the backup singers as it was the insistence of drummer Harman and bassist Moore to place repetitive, passion-free rhythms onto the tunes. Being a Hank tune guaranteed that Jerry Lee would sing "Cold Cold Heart" with passion and brains, but his piano was buried in the mix except when he was soloing, and the "clean" recording had no use for the Sun echo that served Jerry Lee's voice so well. "I Forgot to Remember to Forget" was forgettable.

Desperation being the rule, everyone at Sun and in the Lewis family was so thrilled that "What'd I Say" had hit that they insisted on repeating its recording method for Jerry Lee's next recording session on June 12. It was recorded in the same city, in the same studio, with the same players and the same producer. Again the results were artistically mixed; this time they were also commercially negligible. "C.C. Rider" was far inferior to the version of a year earlier, mostly because of the overblown accompaniment. The midtempo beat selected for Leon Payne's "I Love You Because" was nonsensical, as the song was built as a slow ballad. Again, Jerry Lee failed to top Elvis on a song they had both recorded. A take on the beautiful Drifters hit

Jud Phillips and Jerry Lee

"Save the Last Dance for Me" was better than 90 percent of what was coming out of Nashville at the time, but it seemed indifferent: Jerry Lee's approach did not have much in common with New York songwriters, even superb ones like Doc Pomus and Mort Shuman. The session's sacrificial lamb, for instance, the single, was "It Won't Happen with Me," an ego-boosting song that brought Jerry Lee's piano and vocals into the open. It was energetic in spite of drummer Harman's puzzling decision that hitting cymbals hard meant rocking out.

Two days later Jerry Lee was back in Memphis at the

Madison Avenue studio. Johnny ("Ace") Cannon's all-over-the-place saxophone ruined most of what it touched, but a few tracks survived the encounter. The whole session was bizarre. Fats Domino's "Hello Josephine (My Girl Josephine)" faded out precisely at the moment it got interesting. "High Powered Woman" by the bluesman Sonny Terry was a harshly performed woman-fearing rocker, and "Sweet Little Sixteen" was propulsive enough, but it was several rungs below Jerry Lee's finest Chuck Berry recastings.

The remaining 1961 session, on September 21 in Nashville with the same cast, including seven horns, that had botched the previous date, was slightly more successful. "Ramblin' Rose" kicked up some swamp-rock mud, and those who listened hard could ferret through the overorchestrated sound and find Jerry Lee trying to summon up blues feeling and commitment in the midst of people who did not share such interests. Barrett Strong's "Money" was a highlight of Jerry Lee's stage shows, but here the horns and vocalists stuck a pin into the song. Carl Mann's "Rockin' the Boat of Love" was a seaworthy pop exercise. It had some expansive singing by Jerry Lee, but the backup la-las annoyed as usual, though bassist Moore did a good job of anticipating and doubling Jerry Lee's left hand. "Ramblin' Rose" was the track picked for a single, and it sank. All these Nashville performances were tasty, professional, mannered. Except for "What'd I Say," none of them was wild. In 1961 Jerry Lee songs that were not wild were not worth hearing.

Jerry Lee began his penultimate year at Sun with a weirdo novelty session in Memphis under Sam Phillips's direction. Although the fine drummer Al Jackson was brought in for the date, desperation still called the shots. Chubby Checker's "The Twist" was the inescapable hit of the day, and Sam insisted on trying to cash in. Sun bluesman Junior Parker's "Feelin Good" was the basis for "I've

Been Twistin'," which featured elastic, open-air guitar by Roland Janes. The conversational shaggy-dog tale was fun no matter how opportunistic and twisted this cut was. Higher up on the psychotic scale was "Whole Lotta Twistin' Goin' On." Two other unjustly forgotten songs that emerged from this session were a Stan Kesler country ballad, "I Know What It Means," that suggested a Memphis spaghetti western (pre-Ennio Morricone), and a resilient "High Powered Woman" that crushed the Nashville attempt at the tune. A June 5 session yielded nothing except "Set My Mind at Ease," a tough blues, and a lovely take of Jimmie Rodgers's "Waiting for a Train," a defiant song of life on the grift that Jerry Lee always considered one of the Singing Brakeman's greatest.

By mid-1962, Jerry Lee's career was back on an upturn. He and his long hair returned triumphantly to England, where it seemed that everyone either idolized him or apologized to him for what had happened last time. But just as his professional life began to settle, his personal life was once again visited by tragedy. On Easter morning, Steve Allen Lewis wandered into the family pool and drowned. He was three years old. Jerry Lee told many around him that he was convinced the Lord was punishing him for not being a good enough or holy enough family man. Privately he blamed Myra, for no good reason. By the end of the year, Myra was pregnant with a daughter, Phoebe.

In the next year sessions were few, two in Memphis and one in Nashville, and not particularly productive. J. W. Brown returned for one, which may have made it easier for Jerry Lee to go through with it. In spite of everything, some of those recordings have lasted. A smoldering reinvention of "Be Bop a Lula" anticipated Stax more than it celebrated the Gene Vincent rockabilly standard; it was the rare rockabilly cut that looked forward. "Teenage Letter," familiar to Jerry Lee in a version by Big Joe Turner, a shouting bluesman, offered Jerry Lee an opportunity to invent

London, 1958

some lyrics that he could really lay into: "I need it/I gotta have it/I love you baby/I'm gonna prove it in my own way." Undoubtedly the worst of the Memphis tracks was "Seasons of My Heart," a grating duet with little sister Linda Gail.

The main reason Linda Gail was featured on a Jerry Lee Lewis record was that Sam Phillips wanted to keep making Jerry Lee records, and he figured a little nepotism might tip the scales. The Killer's contract was up on September 1, and Phillips did everything he could think of, except offer him much more money, to keep Jerry Lee, his last great performer, in his dwindling stable. But Jerry Lee had had enough, and he signed with Smash Records. So Sam did with Jerry Lee as he had with Johnny Cash half a decade before: he booked last-minute contractually obligated sessions in case the departed scored a hit on his new label. For these last Sun sessions, on August 27 and 28, 1963, Phillips decided to try something different: a string section. Big production had taken over country and pop, and Sam figured he would try to master yet another style.

None of the songs recorded in those last sessions ranked with Jerry Lee's greatest for the label, but they did suggest the future. A song like "Your Lovin' Ways" cannily anticipated what Jerry Lee would sound like five years down the road when he returned to country-and-western chart prominence. Some of the songs were weird. Hoagy Carmichael's "Hong Kong Blues" was given the new lyrics: "I'd rather be back in San Francisco/Wearing blue suede shoes." However, "One Minute Past Eternity," "Invitation to Your Party" (with its key rhyme with the title "I'm not conceited or a smartie"), "I Can't Seem to Say Goodbye," and "Carry Me Back to Old Virginia" were exemplars of how to go big-production and still keep things relatively soulful. Thanks to the backup singers, it was easy to hate some of the songs even before Jerry Lee started singing, but he sang with an adult mix of regret, assurance, and defiance. He took uptown and brought it down-home. No one knew it at the time, but he was on to something.

The world had changed drastically since Jerry Lee had recorded "Crazy Arms," and no one could argue that the 1963 versions of both Jerry Lee and rock and roll were not in important ways inferior to what they were in 1956. But on "Carry Me Back to Old Virginia," a song that mirrored Jerry Lee's own ideas of what it meant to be a Southerner, his tough solo cut through the walls of sound around it and argued, for the last time under Sam Phillips's tutelage, he would never, ever, be tamed.

CHAPTER 5

Something Has to Stick

Last night I dreamed I made it to the promised land,
I was standin' at the gate and I had the key in my
  hand.
Saint Peter said, "Come on in boy, you're finally
  home,"
I said, "No thanks Pete, I'll just be movin' along."
  —Steve Earle, "I Ain't Ever Satisfied"

Jerry Lee signed with Smash Records in September 1963, a few days after his daughter, Phoebe, was born, and he received an advance against royalties of fifty thousand dollars. He had been courted by Shelby Singleton, vice president of Mercury Records in charge of its Smash subsidiary, who had been looking for an act with marquee value; he went after Charlie Rich and Jerry Lee, and eventually he snared them both.

"He hadn't had a hit in a long time," Singleton said of the latter, "but Jerry Lee was still Jerry Lee. He still had the talent. I knew I could sell him better than Sam [Phillips] because what I had was a promotion machine. Sam had practically gotten out of the business. I had distribution, plus I had international distribution. I had major bucks behind me."

The legend of Sun is a worthy one, even if it has been

overromanticized, but Singleton had a point. A fan, he knew that Jerry Lee made some marvelous records after the hits stopped and that even if there had not been a scandal, Phillips would have had trouble working them on anything within ten steps of an equal footing with the major labels. As the pop-music market increased, major labels moved to increase market shares. Memphis independents like Sun and Goldwax did not have much of a chance to break their artists on the pop charts. Another great Memphis label, Stax, saw the writing on the wall, signed with Atlantic, and thrived.

Unaware of the final Sun recordings, Singleton had a plan to restore Jerry Lee. "The first thing I did with acts that I signed in those years who had had hit records is I immediately went into the studio and I cut a greatest hits album," he explained. "That way, because of the lack of availability of the other product in the marketplace, a greatest hits album would recoup whatever advance I gave him, plus it gave me working capital to work on new product."

Such rerecordings by former hit makers on a new label are a long-standing pop-music tradition, but the frequency of the move did not make it any less misleading, especially when the result was an album called *The Golden Rock Hits of Jerry Lee Lewis*. Still, the Sun rerecordings cut in late September with Singleton producing were overarranged, but not wholly without merit. You can't go home again, but sometimes it is pleasant to briefly visit the old neighborhood. Jerry Lee was encouraged to sing in a more mannered style than was natural for him, very different from the way he was singing those songs onstage at the time; and manners made a remake of "Whole Lotta Shakin' Going On" wholly gratuitous.

The female backing singers and the saxophone did not help matters any. The performance was acceptable but not remotely turbulent; the biggest problem was the engineer's inability to echo Jerry Lee's voice consistently. Other Sun

Onstage in 1964, deep into it

songs that got the good-but-not-inspired treatment were "Crazy Arms," "Great Balls of Fire," "High School Confidential," "I'll Make It All Up to You," "Down the Line," "Breathless," "Drinkin' Wine Spo-Dee-o-Dee," "Fools Like Me," "End of the Road," and a trio of Hank Williams cuts, "Your Cheatin' Heart," "You Win Again," and "Wedding Bells."

Even strings could not prevent Jerry Lee from flourishing when singing Hank Williams ballads. The arrangements were not significantly different from those on his eventual late-sixties hits, which made it puzzling that they were not released as singles in 1963. Even more puzzling was that they were placed on a record titled *Golden Rock Hits*. Of the Sun remakes, those that best handled the transition to the more cluttered arrangements were a speedy "Johnny B. Goode" and an unruly "Break Up" that would have come within hollering distance of the original had the backup singers been given a few minutes off. *Golden Rock Hits* was the first Jerry Lee album to squeeze onto *Billboard*'s LP charts, though not for long. It got only as high as Number 116 before it faded away.

Other recordings from the two-day session evidenced that Singleton was not sure what to do with Jerry Lee after having his new charge regurgitate past triumphs; and Jerry Lee was not providing him any clues. Unlike the try-anything approach at Sun, which was usually a result of broad interests and unfettered ambition, the catholic recordings of Jerry Lee's first Smash sessions seemed a result of random hunches. Some of the performances were very good, but they did not add up as a whole, something essential as the album market had become more lucrative. Several passes at "Hit the Road, Jack," based on Ray Charles's live version, found Jerry Lee trying to replicate his "What'd I Say," with a fine rhythmic blues-flavored solo. "Just Because," a Shelton Brothers tune recorded by Elvis at Sun, was a provocative raveup that Jerry Lee elevated to a vivid putdown.

Less vital tracks from the sessions included a truly awful song Jerry Lee wrote called "He Took It Like a Man," a not-at-all-solemn retelling of John the Baptist's beheading in which he referred to the martyr as "Ole

Johnny." Jerry Lee was not trying to be funny; for him it was natural to convey a religious icon's fate as relaxedly as he would tell that of Frankie and Johnny. The semihit from the sessions was Eddie Kilroy's "Pen and Paper," a workaday country ballad found on the flip of the nonhit "Hit the Road, Jack" single. A much better choice for a single was "The Hole He Said He'd Dig for Me," a bitter Charlie Rich-style country tune that built a worthy bridge between Jerry Lee's bare-bone Sun country and his more elaborate Smash version.

By the time Jerry Lee next recorded for Singleton, on February 14, 1964, the world had changed. A rock quartet from Liverpool, England, had forever altered how rock and roll would be assimilated, and the assassination of John Kennedy had irrevocably modified the nation's view of itself. Freedom from bland radio had arrived in the persons of John, Paul, George, and Ringo; considering what had happened in Dallas and how deeply it shook people, especially in the South and Southwest, where anger was augmented by guilt and denial, the release could not have come at a more propitious moment. Some might even claim that the miseries in the United States in early 1964 were necessary for the blitzkrieg rise of the mop-tops. Whatever the cause, the ante had been raised, and Jerry Lee had to respond to it.

And what a response it was. "I'm on Fire" only reached Number Ninety-eight on the *Billboard* pop chart before it retreated to obscurity after a week; but if radio programmers had been willing to listen, it would have enlivened the few spots on their playlists not held by Beatles tunes. "I'm on Fire" was the first time Jerry Lee's brand of elemental rock and roll made sense in this more orchestrated context, referring to Sun triumphs without merely restating them. He had finally figured out how to make a big band rock. "She Was My Baby (He Was My Friend)," recorded the same day, was an ingratiating teen-oriented pop track with a Coasters feel; "Bread and Butter Man" was uptempo country pop with an insistent vocal and a touch of blues; and "I Bet You're Gonna Like It" was a speedy big-production number about the obvious subject.

Decades later, it remains foggy whether the blacklist was a real one or just an excuse. One Mercury executive of the time said eighteen years later, "We had to blame it on something, didn't we? We couldn't say that *we* were the problem." Nonetheless, it is not hard to imagine that only a conspiracy could have kept off the radio performances this sturdy by a man with a history of million sellers.

Jerry Lee did not enter a recording studio again for another year because his touring schedule was so grueling. In that time he reconquered Europe in a tour backed by the Nashville Teens, and he recorded two of the greatest live albums in the history of American popular music.

On April 5, 1964, Jerry Lee played at the Star-Club in Reeperbahn, Hamburg, a performance preserved on a Europe-only LP entitled, imaginatively, *Live at the Star-Club*. Listening to the set for about ten seconds makes one want to send a nasty letter to Sam Phillips for not recording any onstage Jerry Lee performances during his Sun years. (In Sam's defense, live albums were not the sure-fire profit-takers they are today.) Before he began his first song Jerry Lee rolled his *l*'s; he did not wait for the opening number to start performing. The kick-off tune, "Mean Woman Blues," was leery, malicious, ferocious, frenetic, everything Jerry Lee's blues-soaked version of rock and roll offered or implied. An exhilarating "High School Confidential" climaxed in a tense piano solo, and "Money" went far beyond the recorded version. Sultry, primitive, demanding, Jerry Lee ignored the band and wrenched all he could from the ugly truths at the song's center. The breakdown before the final charge featured some defiant scatting in which Jerry Lee said everything that needed to be conveyed in wordless taunts that no one could have misunderstood. "Matchbox" was his first attempt at a Carl Perkins performance that exceeded the model. Jerry Lee defined the tune as an agreeable strut and was so taken by himself that he kept soloing through the guitar interlude and derived extra pleasure from singing, "If you don't like my peaches/Please don't shake my tree."

"What'd I Say" at the Star-Club was one of the three or four most amazing performances of Jerry Lee's career, from its far-ranging piano introduction through some screaming that took in a lifetime's worth of disappointment and frustration, into an extended coda that was at once both generous and sleazy. "Down the Line" maintained the scorching pace with a strong, rough delivery of lines like, "I'm gonna do right 'cause I was meant to do right/And you'd better believe that Jerry Lee is gonna do right."

"Jerry! Jerry!" the audience chanted; the object of their affection took up the chant; and everyone jumped into a "Great Balls of Fire" that should have set off the smoke detectors, Jerry Lee's eternal argument setting off explosions at every turn. "Good Golly Miss Molly" was a raucous Little Richard evocation, wilder even than Little Richard, and "Lewis Boogie" was an ideal, implosive pumping-piano showcase, marvelous tension implied by the band's heated attempt to keep up with the Killer. "Your Cheatin' Heart" brought the tempo down, but Jerry Lee's flexible solo and soulful singing kept the proceedings intense, as did a rough, very fast "Hound Dog." "Long Tall Sally" was another Little Richard number characterized by all sorts of yelling, both vocally and instrumentally, and Jerry Lee scorched with "Whole Lotta Shakin' Going On." *Live at the Star-Club* documented an extraordinary performance, even if only Jerry Lee's European fans had easy access to the recording.

American audiences were also extremely well served. A July 1, 1964, concert at the Municipal Auditorium in Birmingham, Alabama, was the basis for the album *The Great-*

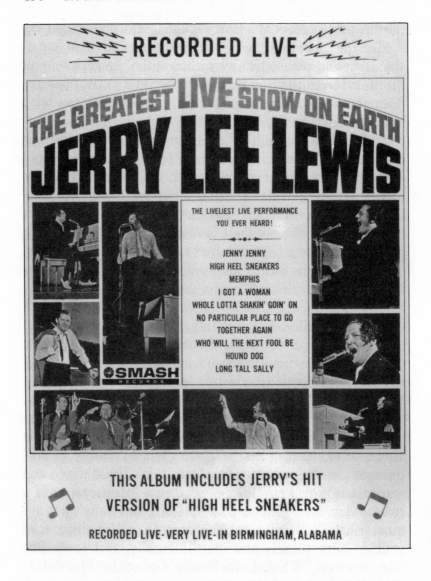

est Live Show on Earth. There was some duplication with the *Star-Club* set—four songs—but this was a wholly different act. The audience was not so boisterous as that at the Star-Club, but Jerry Lee made up for it. Little Richard's "Jenny Jenny" provided the show with a propulsive, auspicious opening salvo, and it rolled into a self-involved rap (what did Jerry Lee mean by "Talk about it one time, yeah"?) that resolved into Charlie Rich's "Who Will the Next Fool Be?" A heartbreak-country tune, it was intended to alert his audience that this show would have a wide agenda, that Jerry Lee would do everything. Chuck Berry's "Memphis" was preceded by a warning to the band, "If we can get it right this time." It moved words across verses until the story of the lyrics was overwhelmed by the story told in the ivories. On "Hound Dog" and "Mean Woman Blues," all flying hands from Jerry Lee and high-pitched screams from the audience, even those listening to the record at home could feel the set building. The single culled from the show was a bluesy take of Robert Higginbotham's "Hi-Heel Sneakers," a strut enlivened by unison clapping from the crowd and the tension between Jerry Lee's desire to take the song dirty and his responsibility to keep it radio safe. "No Particular Place to Go," prefaced by humble comments regarding writer Chuck Berry (Jerry Lee had mellowed since their confrontation), offered a fine stuttering solo and some sympathetic accompaniment from his new road band, the Memphis Beats.

"Honey, I'll tell you one thing," Jerry Lee said between breaths after the song. "It's gonna get real good in a minute. If it gets much better than this, I won't be able to stand it. Rrrrr.......I'm the kinda cat I might do a blues tune one minute then turn right around and do a country tune." After having defined himself with the precision of a haiku, he leaned into the wistful Buck Owens ballad "Together Again," a slab of hard, hard country with wry piano flourishes.

Jerry Lee was in the mood to talk. He spoke lovingly of Little Richard when introducing "a little groovy tune we hope you'll enjoy. Grrrrr. Shake it, shake it, Long Tall Sally." This soul-man version spit out even more sparks than it had at Hamburg. As expected, but still appreciated, the set climaxed with "Whole Lotta Shakin' Going On," complete with a spirited extended rap during which he directed his audience to shake "Not a whole lot/Just a little."

Some of this enthusiasm worked its way into Jerry Lee's next studio dates in January 1965, produced by Singleton and Jerry Kennedy. The first released recording from the sessions, Big John Greer's rhythm-and-blues hit "Got You on My Mind," was presented as midtempo country and was in every way less encumbered than the February 1964 sessions, perhaps because of the success of the live tapings: *The Greatest Live Show on Earth* had ventured forty-five slots higher on *Billboard*'s LP chart than *Golden Rock Hits*. "Mathilda" was a similar song executed with a similar feel, marked by an affecting, rhythmic solo. Jerry Lee breezed through a pleasant, brisk "Corrine, Corrina," a blues standard that had been resurrected by Big Joe Turner. Two songs he previously recorded at Sun, Hank Ballard's "Sexy Ways" and Hank Thompson's "The Wild Side of Life," were the equal of their predecessors; and another Joe Turner number, "Flip, Flop, and Fly," rocked hard behind wry lines like "Gimme a kiss and hold it a long, long time." "Herman the Hermit" was a peculiar rocker, chock full of wonderfully bad rhymes ("hermit"/"permit") in which Jerry Lee sounded nothing so much as bemused.

The sessions were not all grand. The Roy Hamilton soft-rhythm-and-blues hit, "Don't Let Go," a song Jerry Lee returned to many times subsequently, received the standard Nashville-session treatment; the Chuck Berry covers "Maybelline" and "Roll Over Beethoven" were time-killers; and "Baby Hold Me Close," a song written in the studio that Jerry Lee performed the next month on the television show "Shindig," was derivative, though not charmless, with a fine spoken intro and a semispoken last verse. "Skid Row" was average country with some self-pity where

regret was supposed to be. By the end of the session, the two outstanding live albums had been forgotten. Jerry Lee was not strong enough at this time in his life to wrest control of his recordings from his producers, and his producers' power was exceeded only by their indecisiveness.

• • •

Those sessions set the pattern for the next two years of studio work, until Jerry Kennedy replaced Shelby Singleton as Jerry Lee's primary producer: some rock, some blues, some country, and occasionally a whole lotta nothin' going on. Because albums had become more important, both on their own and, strangely, as marketing tools for the less expensive single records, they had to cohere better than the slapped-together early rock-and-roll LPs of the fifties. The long-player market in 1965 was only beginning to reach sophistication. It was the year of the Beatles' *Help!* and *Rubber Soul*, the Rolling Stones' *Out of Our Heads* and *December's Children (and everybody's)*, and Bob Dylan's *Bringing It All Back Home* and *Highway 61 Revisited*. Albums now existed as more than a dumping ground for collected singles and odd tracks. Jerry Lee could not compete with the new rock-and-roll leaders on their terms, although one wonders what Jerry Lee could have done with a modern song like Dylan's "Can You Please Crawl out Your Window?" or "If You Gotta Go, Go Now," and his session-man cronies did not keep up with the latest musical developments north of Nashville. Jerry Lee was never one to think about more than one song at a time, making it difficult for him to think in terms of albums. As a result, he cut tracks solely until someone told him he had succeeded. What characterized these sessions more than anything else? No advance planning, not even any that facilitated spontaneity.

The sessions, most of them in Nashville, were not exactly geared for coherence. "As far as the studio went," Singleton said, "the only thing Jerry Lee and I argued about was his bringing all his kinfolks to the sessions. He used to bring his cousins, his momma and daddy, his sisters. There'd be about thirteen of them in the control room while I was trying to make a record. He'd always ask what they thought about the record. He didn't give a damn what the musicians felt or I felt about it." Outside the studio, they

argued about everything. Singleton once had to bribe Jerry Lee with a hunting rifle to get him to play some already-booked dates in Alaska. Shelby said to use it to hunt Kodiak bears.

A rare New York City session, while Jerry Lee was in town for a TV show, yielded little more than a moderately funky attack on Huey ("Piano") Smith's second-line anthem "Rockin' Pneumonia and the Boogie Woogie Flu" and the awful "Seasons of My Heart." The latter was the song that he had recorded toward the end of this Sun period with Linda Gail and featured the spectacle of hearing Jerry Lee on harpsichord. Logistical convenience notwithstanding, it was foolish for Smash to think that Jerry Lee would thrive one thousand miles northeast of home.

Pop music is recorded for the most part in studios in and around major cities. Country music is by definition rural, although by the mid-sixties the shock felt by rural musicians and songwriters when they moved to Nashville had become country music's prime topic. By 1965, country had lost its "and western" suffix, because the idea of the frontier inherent in "and western" had disappeared. There were still many areas of the South that did not look significantly different from their pre-New Deal selves, but it was harder to find anyone who subscribed to the idea of areas of the South as rural refuges. Nearly everyone had a radio, the vast majority of white families had televisions, and interstate highways cut through even unpopulated areas. People were connected in new ways, which led to new sorts of dislocation when they had to function as usual in untested geographic areas. Jerry Lee's move from Ferriday to Memphis in 1956 was an upheaval from which he had never recovered, and the Memphis boy in him had trouble accommodating to Nashville studio rules. In big city New York without his regular players, he might as well have been on Mars.

Somewhat more rewarding was a Labor Day weekend blowout in Nashville. There were some duds, two sloppy duets with Linda Gail, an ashy "Ring of Fire" complete with a sub-mariachi band, and a drippy "Green Green Grass of Home." But the high points of the session, mostly forgotten, were the heartfelt Bill Anderson ballad "City Lights," a thrilling and involved version of Willie Nelson's "Funny How Time Slips Away," and a wise take on Roger

Miller's later oft-covered but then brand-new "King of the Road."

Jerry Lee toured extensively in the year that followed and did not want to travel two hundred miles just to record, so Smash frequently cut him at the familiar Phillips Studio at 639 Madison Avenue in Memphis. After the Labor Day 1965 dates, Jerry Lee did not record again in Nashville until August 1967. Those two years were strong ones in terms of road work; but, except for a pair of weak-charting long-players, he did not enjoy any commercial success with his recordings.

A two-day session in Memphis in January 1966 was produced by Sun's Jack Clement and featured Jerry Lee's touring band, the Memphis Beats, which should have meant that it yielded great recordings. It did not, because the material was eccentric, ill-conceived, and random. Clement should have known that he was in trouble when Jerry Lee, whose songwriting acumen was not one of his strong suits, showed up with three songs he had composed. "What a Heck of a Mess" was a fair hard-country tale about divorce. Most interesting about it was that Hank Williams, Jr., recorded it, a rare cover of a Jerry Lee-penned tune, perhaps as a thank-you gesture to Jerry Lee for recording so many songs written and/or performed by Bocephus's father. For whatever reason, the cover completed a circle. "Rockin' Jerry Lee" was a messy autobiography; Jerry Lee was more vital when he was rockin' than when he talked about rockin'.

"Lincoln Limousine" was something else, the strangest song Jerry Lee ever recorded. Smash's liner notes called it a "touching eulogy to the late President Kennedy," but this belated tribute gave no indication that Jerry Lee knew of anything JFK did before he ventured to Dallas. However, recent revelations suggest that the Killer may have had more in common with the murdered president than he realized at the time. The song was so dreadful it may have

served as a model for the Elvis tribute singles of late 1977. The lyric line, "It goes to show you never know who's your enemy or your friend," was typically baffling and is recommended to any remaining conspiracy theorists.

Other songs were less bizarre; they were also less notable. "Sticks and Stones" was a Titus Turner song that brought Jerry Lee back to Ray Charles territory. "Memphis Beat" was a moderately stimulating extrapolation of Chuck Berry's vastly superior "Memphis." "The Urge" was hefty, gnarled country-rock, and the George Jones smash ballad "She Thinks I Still Care" responded extremely well to the spare sound Clement constructed for it. When Jerry Lee was given the room he needed, he was unstoppable. On the other hand, he was also beginning to cover songs written by his longtime drinking buddies. Cecil Harrison's "Whenever You're Ready" accomplished nothing musically, although Murray Silver maintained that it did help Cecil become Linda Gail Lewis's fourth husband.

Shelby Singleton drove into Memphis for a July session that coughed up inferior versions of four songs: one mediocre ("Memphis Beat"), one a notch higher ("Twenty-four Hours a Day"), and two serviceable country performances destroyed by strings (Merle Haggard's "Swinging Doors" and Paul Selph's "If I Had It All to Do Over"). These songs, intended for the *Memphis Beat* long-player, were recorded at Roland Janes's studio. The rehearsal versions were far superior and in some cases were the takes that were used on the album.

Shelby Singleton had been extremely pleased with the relative commercial success of *The Greatest Live Show on Earth,* so he recorded an August 20, 1966, concert at Panther Hall in Fort Worth, Texas, and called the ostensible sequel *By Request: More of the Greatest Live Show on Earth.* The show was not as consistently mesmerizing as the twin 1964 triumphs in Hamburg and Birmingham, but it offered many great moments, both in song (Chuck Berry's "Little Queenie" was one long ogle) and when Jerry Lee addressed specific women in the crowd between songs ("Honey, don't worry about the blonde hair"; and "I'm the kind of guy that always likes to give the great artists what they've got coming to 'em").

Although there were many fine rock-and-roll performances in the set, Jerry Lee caused the most commotion with his deep, pleading country performances, a portent of things to come: "You Win Again," "How's My Ex Treating You?" "Crying Time" (drawn more from the Ray Charles cover version than the Buck Owens original), "I'll Sail My Ship Alone," and "Green Green Grass of Home." These songs sounded remarkable with only small-band accompaniment, and Singleton obviously had an affinity for the live shows. If he had stayed with Jerry Lee, he might have directed his charge to a sparer sound that still made commercial sense. But by the end of the year Singleton left Mercury to start his own company, and Jerry Kennedy was assigned as Jerry Lee's producer.

Jerry Lee's first two sessions under Kennedy, on May 9 and August 7, 1967, were disasters that for the most part did not serve as the logical prelude for the next year's breakthrough. "Just Dropped In (To See What Condition My Condition Was In)," a Mickey Newbury song, was later recorded by Kenny Rogers, who deserved it. Four cover versions of sizeable hits ran the gamut from pointless (Roy Orbison's uncoverable "Dream Baby (How Long Must I Dream)" and Bruce Channel's inappropriate "Hey Baby") to good and harsh (Roy Head's "Treat Her Right" and Bobby ("Blue") Bland's "Turn on Your Lovelight"). Not unexpectedly, the nadir of the sessions was the boast-bloated "Shotgun," in which nonsongwriter Cecil Harrelson struck again. The kindest evaluation of the tune was that it was not as hopeless as "Whenever You're Ready." But the truth was that the next song Jerry Lee recorded, a radio commercial for Coca-Cola, sported better lyrics.

By January 1968 Eddie Kilroy and Jerry Kennedy had decided that contemporary country was the only way Jerry Lee could return to a prominence befitting his talent. They said he was too old to be a rock-and-roll star. (To place matters in perspective, some industry professionals were worry-

A Smash promotional photograph, featuring an unusual instrument

ing whether the Beatles and the Rolling Stones were too old to rock.) Jerry Lee and the music industry were different enough in 1968 from what they had been a decade before that country seemed a likely gambit. As Shelby Singleton put it, "Country radio changed. Country acts used to try to cross over into the pop field. Now the opposite was happening. The disc jockeys were ex-rock-and-roll disc jockeys. Charlie Rich, who everybody thought of as a rockabilly, had started to get country play. Conway Twitty was another one. He was a rock act who all of a sudden was classified country even though the music was basically the same. It was time for a change. Jerry [Kennedy] cut Jerry Lee on more country than I did. I wanted to cut him pop. I wanted to sell him a million records, not a hundred thousand." Kennedy's sights were lower than Singleton's, but he was to score far more direct hits.

Many aging rockers from the South ("aging" usually meant pushing thirty) turned to country music as their appearance and interests had less and less in common with pop's teen audience. The trick was to say something like, "Forget that rock and roll. This is what I wanted to do all along. Really. Please take me back." Often the gambit worked; occasionally it was also sincere.

More than any other form of American pop music, country music is about family and community. The country audience expects its favored performers to be family members, and most families have a prodigal son or daughter. By accepting performers, country fans make their collective family whole. Kilroy and Kennedy knew that for Jerry Lee to make a dent in the country charts, he had only to ask to become part of the family again. All would be forgiven.

Three songs were recorded at that January session, with participants disagreeing whether Kilroy or Kennedy helmed the date. Nevertheless, they were all soaked in country genius in every stage, from song selection to mixing. Something significant had changed: the backing vocals

were more controlled and Jerry Lee's voice, comfortable
with echo, sounded more at ease and lived-in. Three top-
drawer dissections of fractured romance, "All the Good Is
Gone," Jerry Chesnut's "Another Place, Another Time,"
and Ernest Tubb's "Walking the Floor Over You," brought
Jerry Lee back up-to-date in country as surely as Elvis
Presley's NBC–TV special the same year made the long-lost
Hillbilly Cat relevant again. Jerry Lee's singing was as pure
as George Jones's, as direct as Buck Owens's, and as deep as
Merle Haggard's. For the first extended time in a studio
since he left Sun, Jerry Lee was completely in control and
in his element. The chosen market responded. The single
"Another Place, Another Time" reached Number Four on
the *Billboard* country charts, his highest-charting country-
and-western single in a full decade. It crossed over to the
bottom half of the pop chart, where it was his highest-
charting entry since "What'd I Say" in 1961. Jerry Lee
knew all along that he was a star; now at least the country-
music establishment finally agreed with him again.

In a typical move, the first thing Jerry Lee did after he
had salvaged his country career was to do something completely different, in this case Shakespeare. Jack Good, producer of the TV pop show "Shindig" that had featured the
Killer during his early-sixties shuffle through the wilder-
ness, imagined a rock-and-roll version of *Othello* and had
long ago talked Jerry Lee into playing the lead heavy, Iago,
in the Centre Theatre Group production. Jerry Lee grew an
evil-looking moustache and goatee and took the gig very
seriously. He learned his part by taping himself reading the
entire play, minus Iago's lines, and listening and responding
to the tape incessantly while on tour.

"Iago really puts out some words in this thing," Jerry
Lee told *Calendar* reporter Pete Johnson. "I never knew
there were so many words. Shakespeare was really something. I wonder what he would have thought of my
records."

With a microphone before him a few days before the show opened, Jerry Lee knew what to do. "I think," he announced, "the generation today who don't know much about stage plays will come here and enjoy it. They'd be out of their minds if they didn't. It has everything—rhythm and blues, rock and roll, country and western, serious acting, comedy, drama, everything."

The show ran six weeks and took in half a million dollars from people who were curious to hear Jerry Lee deliver lines like "Shake it and break it and wrap it up and take it!" and, upon seeing the corpse of a buddy, "Great balls of fire! My friend, Roderigo!" Most critics responded kindly to Jerry Lee and almost as warmly to the entire production. But *Catch My Soul* was not all camp. The audio tapes of the event that have survived indicate that Jerry Lee was truly committed to his part, trying to wrench decay and degeneration out of most lines. In typical Jerry Lee fashion, he tried something new, excelled at it, and then went back to what he felt like doing. For the first time in a long time, his artistic restlessness served him well.

• • •

Jerry Kennedy, thrilled that his interest in Jerry Lee had been justified, ordered six more sessions that year in Columbia's Nashville studios. Many of them mined gold. A double-length date on April 16, 1968, featured Jerry Lee regal, comfortable, and confident in his new role. He sang with ease and unquestionable authority songs like Merle Haggard's "I'm a Lonesome Fugitive," John Loudermilk's "Break My Mind," and Jerry Chesnut's "Play Me a Song I Can Cry To." The only disappointing tracks recorded that day were Don Chapel's "All Night Long," which made the exciting new method seem dull and formulaic, and Roy Acuff's "We Live in Two Different Worlds," a duet with Linda Gail. By far the strongest cut of the day was Glenn Sutton's "What Made Milwaukee Famous," an archetypal honky-tonk ballad. Jerry Lee contributed an incredibly in-

Ready to play Iago

volved vocal, drawing emotion out of the punch line ("What made Milwaukee famous/Has made a loser out of me") without falling to the prime vice of honky-tonk ballads, self-pity. Again, the mixture of up-to-date production and time-worn lyrical concerns could not miss. Again, matching an unparalleled stylist with commercial material worthy of him paid immediate dividends: "What Made Milwaukee Famous" charged all the way to Number Two on the country-and-western charts and made a bit of noise on the pop list.

Jerry Lee still toured a great deal, although by the next royalty period he would be able to cut down from six nights a week to five. That summer, he recorded yet another friendly, jazzy version of Floyd Tillman's signature number "Slippin' Around," as well as another custom-made tune by "What Made Milwaukee Famous" writer Glenn Sutton, called "She Still Comes Around to Love What's Left of Me." Jerry Lee burrowed into the song, another wet-eyed ballad that hovered on the edge of self-pity, and pushed it all the way to Number Two on the country chart. The powers at Smash may have been disappointed that "She Still Comes Around to Love What's Left of Me" did not cross over to pop, but fans were pleased because the lack of pop action proved that the song was true hard country. As Loretta Lynn once said, "I think country will keep on growing as long as country stays different from pop. To keep it true, you have to leave it hanging on the fence."

Three fall sessions were hit-or-miss affairs. On the down side, Jerry Lee returned to the Sun well for Otis Blackwell's "Let's Talk About Us" but he wasn't rocking in the studio just then. "Out of My Mind" showed that Jerry Lee's fiddler and guitarist Kenny Lovelace, destined to be the fifth Mr. Linda Gail Lewis, was an extraordinary picker but not much of a songwriter. Cecil Harrison and Linda Gail, still an item, co-wrote "Echoes," which, aside from an overwrought opening, was not as pitiful as the title might lead one to expect. As was becoming the norm, the highlights of the sessions were well-chosen ballads. The Merle Haggard composition "Today I Started Loving You Again" received an understated, smoldering performance, and the fifteen-year-old Webb Pierce smash "There Stands the

Glass" was, in Jerry Lee's orbit, a terrific self-pitying drinking ballad.

As also was becoming the welcome norm, the saddest and most intense of the performances was the one that became a monster country hit, in this case Glenn Sutton and Jerry Kennedy's "To Make Love Sweeter for You." A cynic might argue that these country-ballad hits were coming too easily to Jerry Lee, that these performances were merely facile. But cynics do not note that these ballads are tense, not easy; and the emotion that these ostensibly sweet ballads spat out was terror.

"To Make Love Sweeter for You" surpassed the other comeback singles, finally topping the country-and-western chart. It was Jerry Lee's first country Number One since "Great Balls of Fire." He celebrated New Year's Day 1969 by playing a show of mostly country songs that ended with a swirl of ferocious rock and roll. It was as if he was saying, yes, I have redeemed myself in your eyes. But I am still the Killer.

CHAPTER 6

Another Chance

It's good to see you back again
In the land of salvation and sin.
You know sometimes I get so lonely.
    —Dan Baird, "I Dunno"

By the time Jerry Lee's country comeback was assured, his former shepherd at Smash, Shelby Singleton, had purchased the Sun Records catalog from Sam Phillips, who was retiring on money he had made, not from rock and roll but from being an early investor in the Holiday Inn chain of motels. Digging through the vaults, Shelby chanced across Jerry Lee's last Sun sessions, immediately recognized them as the blueprint for the Ferriday Fireball's current Smash recordings, released them as quickly as possible, and scored big. Jerry Lee enjoyed five Top Ten country hits in 1969, and two of them, "Invitation to Your Party," and "One Minute Past Eternity," were long-forgotten Sun performances that Singleton had exhumed. In a roundabout way, Singleton finally had gotten Jerry Lee into the Top Ten. Everybody welcomed back the apparently contrite Jerry Lee, including performers like Bob Dylan, who wrote "To Be Alone with You" for Jerry Lee but eventually recorded it himself.

The return of fame and fortune did not ease Jerry

Lee's perpetually worried mind. Substance abuse had become more of a problem outside the studio, and it affected his concentration in the studio. In 1970 Myra finally divorced him, alleging some truly horrific behavior; in April of the next year, his beloved mother, Mamie, died, leaving him without his prime counsel in his religious struggles. Elmo, who had turned even more passive in the sixties, remained. Jerry Lee married again, this time to a sheriff's secretary named Jaren Pate. She gave birth to a daughter, Lori Leigh, in the spring of 1972. Jerry Lee had hits; Jerry Lee had problems. It was in this period that he made his most conspicuous attempt to resolve his inner conflicts. He also scored what will most likely be his last Number One single. He was growing older and more bitter, and age crept into his records.

Jerry Lee spent most of February 1969 in Nashville, working through six sessions that concentrated on country-and-western classics. Most of them came out on the LPs *Jerry Lee Lewis Sings the Country Music Hall of Fame Hits, Volumes 1 and 2*. There were also some contemporary choices squeezed in, as well as the occasional sacred concern. By now this was the usual blend. Even when he was supposed to be doing only one thing, Jerry Lee wanted to do it all.

As evidence that Jerry Lee spent much of his life avoiding responsibility are six failed marriages, several disowned children, and stormy, unsteady relationships with most of the family members who remained in his inner circle after he hit the big time. Yet he burned to change. When he submitted to duet sessions with his twenty-one-year-old sister, Linda Gail, he was more than anything trying to do right by his family. Their three duets in February—"Don't Let Me Cross Over," "Jackson," and "Sweet Thang"— were not at all embarrassing. Jerry Lee's singing in these duets was always superb, possibly because he felt he had to compensate. His comeback was secure enough that Smash

did not balk at releasing "Don't Let Me Cross Over" as a single, and his audience did not hesitate to buy it. It reached Number Nine, Jerry Lee's fifth consecutive Top Ten country-and-western hit.

The country-icon standards recorded for the *Hall of Fame* hits were as a rule safer than the recent Jerry Lee hits that preceded them. Songs like "Another Place, Another Time" and its successors were hard country in the style of Hank Williams and early George Jones, an indirect affront to the saccharine stylings coming out of Nashville studios at the time. The *Hall of Fame* sessions were a step backward toward his mid-sixties overproductions and a hint of what was to come. It was as if the idea was to slicken tradition.

By now Jerry Kennedy's hit method had turned into a paint-by-numbers procedure. For example, in almost every song the backing singers did not show up until the second chorus. This started as a means of letting a song gradually gain power, but it had quickly become a gimmick. On songs like the Don Gibson hit "Oh Lonesome Me," a reasonable cover choice, Jerry Lee was too tame to energize the song. The Killer was not at the controls; an extremely careful Jerry Kennedy was, and Kennedy was most interested in making the record sound sophisticated, dressed-up. The Hank Williams covers—"Cold Cold Heart," "Why Don't You Love Me (Like You Used to Do)," "I'm So Lonesome I Could Cry," and "Jambalaya"—had no kick. Only the most probing fans could tell that Jerry Lee loved these songs, as he put them across so indifferently. Maybe it was an off-session, maybe Jerry Lee's mind was on other troubles, maybe he was stoned. For whatever reason, he did not electrify when the "record" light was switched on. Only Don Gibson's "I Can't Stop Loving You," Lefty Frizzell's "Mom and Dad's Waltz," and Jim Reeves's "He'll Have to Go" involved the artist. Of the new songs, only "One Has My Name (The Other Has My Heart)" came close to the new standard. It was sung well but too straightforward professionally; Jerry Lee came across as a more than adequate male country crooner but did not do much more. Overjoyed to have him back in preferred form, his fans did not care. The song went Number Three country.

On April 14 Jerry Lee appeared on the Monkee's television special "33 Revolutions per Monkee." Instead of using his growing store of country hits, he opted to play "Whole Lotta Shakin' Going On" and "Down the Line." To that young audience, he was still the Killer of 1957. On

June 13 he recorded seven duets with Linda Gail. One of them, a shrill "Roll Over Beethoven," inexplicably became a minor country hit. Most amusing was "Secret Places," an adultery tale that Linda Gail wrote with two of her husbands, Cecil Harrison and Kenneth Lovelace. Soon after Jerry Lee and Kenneth appeared on "Hee Haw," playing strong, elemental versions of "Walking the Floor Over You" and "Another Place, Another Time."

An August 4 session without Linda Gail generated much more interest on everyone's part. "Waitin' for a Train" was a straightforward Jimmie Rodgers cover that probably would have climbed higher than Number Eleven if Jerry Lee's piano had not been buried under a steel guitar. Mickey Newbury's "She Even Woke Me Up to Say Goodbye" was stirring stuff, a devastating ballad highlighted by an absorbing vocal ("It's not her heart, Lord/It's her mind") that made the superfluous strings and backup singers much less grating. Still, there was an assembly-line quality about this session. No one explored, no one experimented, no one cared. Everyone there knew what the ingredients were for a late-sixties Jerry Lee country hit, and they all did what was expected. It was very professional and a little boring.

Much wilder was a September 13 appearance at John Lennon's "Rock and Roll Revival" concert in Toronto, Canada. Jerry Lee put across great rock-and-roll songs and played an electric guitar for "Mystery Train." Whether he articulated it or not, he had mapped out for himself a fruitful double career: country in the studio and rock and roll onstage. He could do everything he wanted and still satisfy everyone part of the time. But his rock-and-roll success was not based on anything current. Like Chuck Berry, Bo Diddley, and Little Richard, Jerry Lee's earliest hits were being discovered by a new generation of rock-and-roll kids who had no use for or awareness of his more recent Nashville recordings, which were made for adults. His country suc-

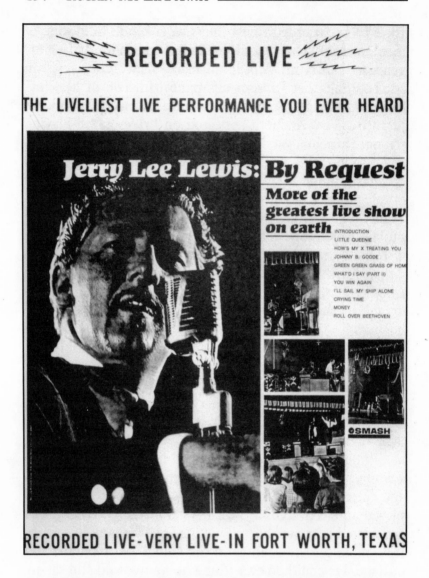

cess was in present tense; in rock and roll he was usually considered a dinosaur. He was not a threat anymore. By 1969, "Whole Lotta Shakin' Going On" was considered by much of the rock audience as benign as "The Twist."

Jerry Lee concentrated on his recording career, which at least was built on ongoing achievements, and sessions in

October and November were intermittently rewarding artistically and extremely rewarding commercially. Don Chapel's "When the Grass Grows Over Me" gave Jerry Lee an opportunity to affect his Buck Owens tenor, and his voice moved to useful agitation by the end of the tune. Faron Young's "Wine Me Up" was workable midtempo country with a touch of western swing. Also worth hearing was Ivory Joe Hunter's "Since I Met You Baby," which featured one of Lovelace's most stirring fiddle breaks and a fun, all-over-the-place vocal by the Killer. "Workin' Man Blues" was an uptempo honky-tonk Merle Haggard cover which Jerry Lee tried hard to personalize, but his piano was secluded and the whole arrangement tried too hard to please. Also, Haggard's original was definitive. Kris Kristofferson and Shel Silverstein's "Once More with Feeling," recorded several times, showed that a good lyric could make Jerry Lee the singer sound far more trenchant emotionally than Jerry Lee the man, and the repeated versions gave him enough time to fully think out the song, all the way to Number Two.

The truest cut from these sessions was a fine take of Chuck Berry's "Brown Eyed Handsome Man," a song long in Jerry Lee's repertoire. Jerry Lee's agenda in the performance was to remind those in the studio that his rock and roll was definitive, and if he wanted to he could still rock out, even with airhead backup singers swirling around him. All he had to do was want to, which was precisely the burgeoning problem.

Three days of Nashville sessions in March 1970 were troubling for a variety of reasons, most notably because the overdubs Jerry Kennedy grafted onto the tracks suffocated the tunes more than usual. This was Kennedy's solution to a difficult problem. As Jerry Lee became more erratic, recording less frequently and more arbitrarily, Kennedy felt he had to salvage each date. He was on Mercury's payroll, and part of his job was to ensure that the sessions were cost effective. As Felton Jarvis was doing with Elvis Presley, Kennedy used massive overdubs like makeup, to hide flaws and round out performances he felt were incomplete. Yet the overdubs only served to distract attention from Jerry Lee, the only reason people were listening to the records in the first place. Kennedy did not trust Jerry Lee to consistently assert himself in the studio anymore, so he was going to make sure that somebody was in charge.

Instrument and vocal-group overdubs were one thing, but fans devoted to pure Jerry Lee could have sensed the beginning of the end when two of the songs from the March sessions—Cecil Harrison and Linda Gail's punchy "Woman, Woman (Get Out of Our Way)" and the overrated country standard "Reuben James"—were subjected to vocal overdubs by the Ferriday Fireball himself. Overdubbing for Jerry Lee meant work and only work: no interacting with the band members, no involvement with the song, no incentive to be passionate. Jerry Lee was a musician who excelled in live performances, even those with indifferent session musicians. The farther away he got from such settings, the less interested he and his records became.

One distinctive number recorded during the March sessions was a sly version of "Sweet Georgia Brown," highlighted by Jerry Lee's vow, "I don't lie/Not much," and a superb fiddle break. Another was "There Must Be More to Love Than This," which would be heard as a strong, pained ballad beneath the overdubs and was another smash hit. A problematic element of the session, aside from Kennedy's heavy-handed approach to touching up the tunes, was "Gather 'Round Children," a mediocre and extremely morbid country-death ballad by Cecil and Linda Gail. Also, the Jerry Lee original, "Alvin," left unreleased for almost twenty years, was one of the least propulsive songs ever written about teen angst. He was a stylist, not a songwriter.

Enjoying a renegotiated contract, Jerry Lee presently had a technical change in his recording status. He was no longer a Smash performer, the imprint having been folded into the main Mercury label. After more than fourteen years as a recording artist, he was finally on a true major label.

Although he was clearly having less fun than ever in his studio incarnation, Jerry Lee was still anxious to scorch onstage. Six shows in May were edited down for the album *Live at the International Hotel, Las Vegas,* the latest in his series of fine in-concert sets. But the released album only hinted at the breadth of Jerry Lee's performances that week in Las Vegas. For obvious commercial reasons, nine of the ten cuts on the released LP were explicitly country tunes, many of them recapitulations of recent Jerry Lee-in-the-studio hits, with more sympathetic accompaniment built around fiddler Lovelace and drummer Morris Tarrant. "She Even Woke Me Up to Say Goodbye" came across as the first-rate country ballad it was, and those few in the Las Vegas crowd who were familiar with Jerry Lee only through his country hits must have been taken aback by how much harder he played outside of a Nashville studio, fronting a relatively small, five-piece band. "Jambalaya" and "She Still Comes Around (To Love What's Left of Me")" exceeded their studio incarnations, and on Bill Mack Smith's self-descriptive "Drinkin' Champagne," Jerry Lee's voice was pained and believable, yet his performance was remarkably effortless.

Jerry Lee introduced "Once More with Feeling" by saying, "This was Number One for us in the country field of music, which I think is the main field of music right now." Such a statement was Jerry Lee's way of acting the part of the rocker who has returned to his country roots, although a few minutes later he was tearing through "Rip It Up," "Great Balls of Fire," and "Whole Lotta Shakin' Going On." The lone noncountry number on the released LP, though, was a riveting, purposeful "Flip, Flop and Fly" with which Jerry Lee had opened some of the shows. Stuck on the end of *Live at the International*, it provided a glimmer of a more expansive world.

Of the unreleased material from these Las Vegas shows, sixty-eight additional numbers ranging from long-time favorite Jimmie Davis's "You Are My Sunshine" to John Fogerty's Killer-inflected "Proud Mary," there was enough for at least two more LPs of comparable quality. Las Vegas has never been an ideal site for rocking out—neither Elvis nor his music got out of that city alive—but, except for his New York foray several years previously, location meant nothing to an energized Jerry Lee so long as he had a piano to bang. On a fierce "Great Balls of Fire" he altered the lyrics to proclaim "Too much love drives a *stud* insane." He commenced "Oh Lonesome Me" by claiming that country music was all he ever cared about. Then he played a totally rock-and-roll version of the Don Gibson tune. "Blue Suede Shoes" came complete with pokes at Elvis and Tom Parker, and Elvis got it again in "Whole Lotta Shakin' Going On." During the extended break-down, the Ferriday Fireball said of Presley, "Him and Tom Jones couldn't shine my big toe." Chuck Berry got off better. A version of "Sweet Little Sixteen" did not kick up much dirt, but Jerry Lee did say of Berry, "I think he's the Stephen Foster of the rock-and-roll era," a tremendous compliment considering the source. The defining moment came in the third show, when Jerry Lee explained himself. "This is the only rock and roll/rhythm and blues/country and western/Grand Ol' Opry in existence," he said. "That's the way I do it, all wrapped up in one. Hang it in, all right."

The pick of the Las Vegas numbers screamed with life, but, by the time Jerry Lee returned to Nashville, he had temporarily lost interest in unleashing that side of himself. In Nashville, he conformed. With the dissolution of his longest marriage eating at him, he sounded miserable and performed miserably. He recorded more frequently now with Linda Gail, hoping to find some solace in family. A two-day

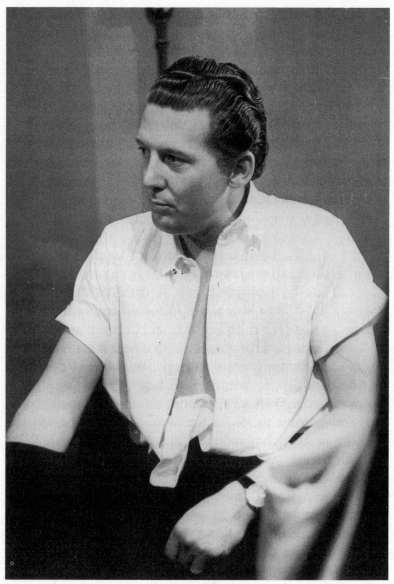

London, 1962

session in October 1970, half duets, emphasized songs of divine praise. Mamie was very ill at the time with cancer, and Jerry Lee dived into gospel as if it could heal. "The Old Rugged Cross" was deeply convincing, and "The Lily of the Valley" and "I Know That Jesus Will Be There" were as open-hearted and searching as anything Jerry Lee ever performed. "I'll Fly Away" and "My God's Not Dead" were loose-limbed, adventurous attempts to capture the thrill of ritual on vinyl. Jerry Lee's sprightly piano was too loose to some ears and was probably very similar to what shortened his tenure in Waxahachie, even though his vocals were very committed ("My God's not dead/Sorry 'bout yours, my friend").

Several secular tunes were worked up during the October session, and they ran the gamut from profound ("One More Time") through tunes as weak as their titles ("Foolaid," "Too Much to Gain to Lose") to "Black Mama," a tasteless, raised-by-wolves tale, as hilariously bad as "Alvin" and so wrongheaded about race it made the concerns of "Ubangi Stomp" sound like those of Paul McCartney and Stevie Wonder's "Ebony and Ivory." Jokey songs regarding race were a long, though not noble, tradition among some people in the South, so it was no surprise that the Ferriday boy indulged himself in some of it. What was surprising was that he did so in the midst of a self-produced gospel session organized because Jerry Lee felt guilty that Mamie's desire for him to become a solely religious purveyor had so far gone unfulfilled.

Jerry Lee insisted to his confidantes that he believed Mamie contracted cancer because he was still drinking and drugging, because he had turned his back on the Assemblies of God of his youth. He informed Mercury executives that he would be recording only religious music or pure-minded country in the future. Three sessions from December 1970 to January 1971 suggested that he was serious. Two of those dates Jerry Lee produced himself in two different studios, and they focused on Carter Family songs and newer compositions that evoked the first family of country music.

Led by A. P. Carter, the Carter Family were discovered at the same time as Jimmie Rodgers. Their obsessive tales of family, God, and death were the flip side of the Singing Brakeman's anthems of physical and spiritual dislocation. The influence of the Carter Family on country music has been as enduring as Rodgers's. His celebrations of wildness and their paeans to family and community, established in the twenties, are the two extremes of pure country-and-western that still set the outer limits. Jerry Lee's singing on the two studio sessions was alert and dedicated, but, except for the one genuine A. P. Carter number in the set, the songs were not worth the trouble.

On December 10 Jerry Lee announced that his reign as the Killer was over. Reeling from the one-two punch of the divorce from Myra and the imminent death of Mamie, the loss of the two most important women in his life, he decided to abdicate, make a clean break. He gave up booze and pills. A few days later he ensconced himself and his core band in a Memphis church and began preaching again. But he was still the Killer, even in a house of God. He introduced "I'm Longing for Home" by offering to sell copies of it after the service was over. A changed man, he wanted to testify, "I got saved! I'm gonna stay saved! I'm no hypocrite!" Musically the songs were strong if somewhat samey, thwarted only by the rudimentary drumming of Jerry Lee, Jr. "A lot of folks think I've gone crazy!" Jerry Lee, Sr., acknowledged. But the twenty-one songs, including a "My God Is Real" with a boogie-woogie bass line (his revenge on Waxahachie), were among Jerry Lee's most deeply felt recordings.

When most pop performers who claim to be pious record what they say is a religious disc, they usually play some Christmas songs and some obviously secular love ballads with *Jesus* replacing *baby* and *God* replacing *you* in the interchangeable lyrics. Jerry Lee went much deeper. Although his born-again phase ended before he placed Mamie in the ground, hastened by his own restlessness and the extremely poor chart showings of his holy-minded recordings, it was ardent while it lasted. Jerry Lee did try to come to terms with his religious responsibility, and for a time he had escaped some of the hellhounds on his trail. The only other performer in rock-and-roll history who got away with that was Aretha Franklin, another stylist of the highest order who grew up in church. Her 1972 double album, *Amazing Grace*, gathered the strength of her matchless soul recordings and brought them back to their original concept. But there was also one major difference: *Amazing Grace* rose as high as Number Seven on the *Billboard* pop album charts and sold more than half a million copies. Jerry Lee could not convince Mercury to release a single one of his in-church recordings.

•   •   •

Jerry Lee returned to the Jerry Kennedy Nashville factory and (without a hint remaining of the sort of inspirational recordings he had put down a few months earlier) resumed cranking out what was expected. Aside from the overwhelming "Touching Home," one of the most affecting of Jerry Lee's greatest ballad performances, nothing lasting emerged from a February 3 session. Two March sessions were similarly inconsistent. For every marvelous ballad like Kris Kristofferson's "Help Me Make It Through the Night," the Dallas Frazier/Doodle Owens composition "When He Walks on You (Like You Have Walked on Me)," or the wrenching "Another Hand Shakin' Goodbye," there were many indifferent tunes like "Time Changes Everything," "Hearts Were Made for Beating," and "Foolish Kind of Man," the last a Lovelace/Linda Gail composition. Higher up on the weird psychodrama scale was Jimmie Rodgers's "Mother, the Queen of My Heart," which can be read as either insanely devotional or incestuous, recorded as

Mamie was dying. The single wonderful uptempo number in the sessions was the gate-jumping "Please Don't Talk About Me When I'm Gone," an extraordinarily approachable western swing number in which stalwart Lovelace contributes a wild fiddle break and Jerry Lee introduces the band members, including himself, with nothing but admiration and fraternity in his well-worn voice. It was the friendliest moment he ever allowed himself on record.

The summer of 1971 was treacherous for Jerry Lee. The divorce from Myra had become final in May, and

Junior's behavior was becoming increasingly dependent on what happened to be flowing in his veins. However, Jerry Lee was able to gain enough strength for a handful of remarkable recordings to add to the still-growing list. Off the wagon, he was not yet teetering. Jimmie Hodges's "Someday You'll Want Me to Want You" was a concentrated love-revenge ballad most notable for being one of the first Jerry Lee recordings that included his "Think about it" warning/suggestion. "Big Blon' Baby," the Cajun thumper from his Sun days, kept the rocker in Jerry Lee happy, while "Thirteen at the Table" satisfied the man newly returned to secular music who still wanted to feel saved. "Thirteen at the Table" was a midtempo retelling of the Last Supper, built around clumsy lines like "He was a carpenter who mended broken bodies." That summer Jerry Lee tried to mend his ways by buying the film rights to *The Carpenter*, a life of Jesus; he intended to play the title role. As with Jerry Lee's other moves toward sacred-minded work, the deal fell through.

Jerry Kennedy's production formula was now stifling, but sometimes its familiarity allowed Jerry Lee to soar. A few days before a session, the Killer was able to hear most of the tunes that he did not himself suggest recording. Mercury's Roy Dea, who had recorded the Las Vegas shows, went to Jerry Lee's house. "I played acetates for him," Dea said. "I got there about three in the evening, just when he was waking up. Usually it was a title or a line that caught his attention. A lot of it had to do with what he was going through personally. 'Would You Take Another Chance on Me,' for example, fit what was going on in his personal life at the time." Indeed, it was a concept and a composition with which Jerry Lee immediately connected. Strings and backing singers aside, "Would You Take Another Chance on Me" was a marvelous hard-country ballad sung with tremendous intensity, and it was yet another song that ended with the ominous "Think about it, darlin'." It shot to Number One on the country-and-western singles chart; its flip side, a spirited "Me and Bobby McGee," became Jerry Lee's first Top 40 pop hit since "High School Confidential," way back in 1958.

As far as recordings were concerned, 1972 began wonderfully for Jerry Lee. He was loose in the studio, and for a change Jerry Kennedy did not immediately call for a leash. "Think About It, Darlin'"—this title had to come—moved well, although with each year it seemed that more and more people were stuffed in the studio with Jerry Lee, inching him further and further into the background of his own records. The Killer sang as if he knew that he was close to self-parody, but he was too amused to care. Also recorded in this session was a dripping cover of the Big Bopper's "Chantilly Lace," a fine reconstructed second-generation rock-and-roll take with a very strong vocal, in spite of there being what seemed like fifty too many people on the cut.

Roy Dea, who was at the session, tells the story best:

> I didn't like the heavy production. I didn't think it was Jerry Lee Lewis. I had been to Memphis, and we had picked four songs. We were going to add strings. We cut a couple tracks. There were fifteen string players and an arranger. Out of nowhere Jerry said, "Let's do 'Chantilly Lace'." The arranger said he didn't have charts, and Jerry said, "We're just running it down. Don't worry about the mules. Just load the wagon." The string arranger just about had a heart attack. Jerry Lee cut it once, took off his turtleneck sweater, played it back, and then played it again. He said, "That turtleneck was chokin' me." It was Jerry Lee's biggest record [Number One country for three weeks]. It proved Sam Phillips was right in the first place. Everything with Jerry Lee Lewis that works is spontaneous. It's not in the lyrics or the melody written by the writer. It's how Jerry Lee does it.

The remarkable success of a frank rock-and-roll song like "Chantilly Lace" set the stage for _The "Killer" Rocks_

On, an album intended to draw in both the rock-and-roll fans who attended his shows and the loyal country fans, many of them aging along with Jerry Lee, who did not mind being reminded what this Killer did in a previous incarnation. It seemed like a great idea, except Jerry Kennedy was even less helpful in creating rock-and-roll settings than Shelby Singleton had been during the *Golden Rock Hits* sessions of nearly a decade earlier.

Virtually all the rock oldies Jerry Lee recorded for the new album were conveyed with gusto and attitude, but Kennedy's insufferable string and chorus overdubs all but ruined everything they touched. Kennedy's method of cutting country made no sense in a rock-and-roll context. Few classic rockers were able to withstand such treatment. However, the Charlie Rich number, "Lonely Weekends," jumped out of the speakers with an unshackled piano solo, and William Bell's soul-driving "You Don't Miss Your Water" was one of Jerry Lee's saddest cuts. These two triumphs must have been enough for many listeners. *The "Killer" Rocks On* became its namesake's highest-charting pop LP since *The Greatest Live Show on Earth.*

The rest of 1972 flew by in a blur. Five more sessions did not yield a single stellar track. Everyone was distracted. Marriage number four was beginning to crumble, Mercury seemed more interested in renewing Jerry Lee's contract than in securing him top-rank songs, and the big-production numbers that were Jerry Kennedy's specialty had become so successful commercially that no one thought to return Jerry Lee to more lanky settings in which he could excel. Regarding the music, everyone was complacent.

CHAPTER 7

Last Stand

Sometimes I blame it on a woman,
The one that made my poor heart bleed.
Sometimes I blame it on the money,
Sometimes I blame it all on me.
—*Dave Alvin, "Long White Cadillac"*

The last five years of Jerry Lee's association with Smash/
Mercury started with two of his most lasting studio albums
and ended in ashes. Outside the studio, his life deteriori-
ated terribly. Jerry Lee, Jr., an acid casualty, died in a car
crash; Jaren filed for divorce; the Killer "accidentally" shot
his bassist, Butch Owens, in the chest (Owens survived to
take legal action); Jerry Lee overturned his Rolls Royce; he
was hospitalized for respiratory distress and a "nasal problem"; he was arrested waving a gun in front of Graceland
demanding to see Elvis; and he had his gallbladder removed. By 1978, there was not much Jerry Lee left. Getting yelled at by Mercury executives for skipping sessions
was the least of his problems.

At first, all was well. In the early seventies, rich British
rock stars paid homage to their less fortunate American
forebears by cutting tribute sessions, in which the aging
influence was accompanied by the new stars whose names
on the record cover would aid sales. The Chess blues perfor-

mers profited the most from this with a series of *London Sessions* LPs by Chuck Berry, Bo Diddley, Muddy Waters, and Sun alumnus Howlin' Wolf, all of which sold more copies than these artists usually managed. Artistically, however, only *The London Howlin' Wolf Sessions* was a triumph. In January 1973 Jerry Lee, Kenny Lovelace, and too many hangers-on to list traveled to London to indulge the new stars and cut hits.

The Session, as the album was called, worked in spite of everything and everyone; there was much additional worthy material that did not make it onto the double album. In chronological age, only a few years separated the Killer and the British. For instance, Jerry Lee is only thirteen months older than Rolling Stones bassist Bill Wyman. However, there were many generational and geographical differences between Jerry Lee's entourage and British rock stars like Albert Lee and Peter Frampton. For all the rules his music broke, Jerry Lee was fundamentally conservative on issues like how long a man's hair should be. British rock stars in the early seventies were uptight as well, but regarding different matters. That, combined with chemicals in the air and the arrogance one would expect of young millionaires, insured that no one asked for anyone else's phone number after the four days of sessions concluded.

Nevertheless, with the noted Head, Hands, and Feet rhythm section playing the essential rhythm parts to which the superstars would not stoop, *The Session* rocked, often hard. Fifteen years after Jerry Lee first recorded it, he finally cut a raucous "Drinkin' Wine Spo-Dee-o-Dee" that came out as a single. A sandpapery Jerry Lee sounded as though he had drunk too much wine on the ole spo-dee-o-dee, and he did not care who was in the room with him. Directing solos, Jerry Lee said, "Take it, son." He did not bother to learn anyone's name. When he warned "think about it" at the end of almost every take, no one did.

Distance can create tension, and tension is an essential

An unlikely promotional device

ingredient in great rock and roll. Take the one song Jerry
Lee had come to London prepared to record, Charlie Rich's
dark blues "No Headstone on My Grave." Perhaps because
the song was written by a like-minded pianist, an absorbed
Jerry Lee was comfortable leading the band through its
bloody charges and changes. Because Jerry Lee did not
come to London armed with any more material and there
was only a limited amount of studio time slotted for the
supergroup, Jerry Lee and the Brits had to come to a quick
understanding regarding what songs they all knew.

They tried the Rolling Stones's "(I Can't Get No) Satisfaction," but Jerry Lee could not bring himself to sing the
verse about the girl having her period. Inevitably the lack of
planning turned the set toward early rock-and-roll songs,

like Chuck Berry's "Memphis, Tennessee" (complete with a yodel) and a steamy "Johnny B. Goode." Also rocked-up was Jerry Lee's own "High School Confidential," pointlessly done as an instrumental (listeners were forgiven for thinking they were waiting for the jam to end and the song proper to begin) and a shaky "Whole Lotta Shakin' Going On" salvaged only by Rory Gallagher's sublime slide guitar (Gallagher was the only Brit outside the rhythm section who had a consistent handle on the material) and a harsh ending worthy of the Killer.

Some other early rockers were enlivened: "Sixty Minute Man," "Down the Line," "What'd I Say," and a medley comprising "Good Golly Miss Molly," "Long Tall Sally," "Jenny, Jenny," "Tutti Frutti," and "Whole Lotta Shakin' Going On" that danced like the climax to a live show. But the pick of these remakes, one that remained unreleased for more than a decade, came from an unlikely source, Gene Vincent. His signature tune, "Be Bop a Lula," which Jerry Lee had successfully covered years previously, got the ride of its life. In Vincent's hands, "Be Bop a Lula" was a persuasive little rockabilly song, a celebration of his sweetheart led by the nonsense-syllable chorus.

Jerry Lee surpassed the Vincent version by the time he had completed his ten-second portentous piano introduction, and he stretched the song until it was unrecognizable as anything but what he had imagined at the moment. The stylist with his own ideas triumphed. He approached "Be Bop a Lula" as a dirty blues that he hung onto for a glorious seven minutes and eighteen seconds. This was a loose jam with purpose, Jerry Lee's voice howling and scatting, his fingers crawling up and down his piano. After all, the most successful Jerry Lee sessions were those in which the Killer was relaxed, but not too relaxed. "This mother must be nine years long!" he shouted. And then he went on some more. This was fabulous. Perhaps in 1973 Jerry Lee had to travel far away from Nashville to work up such a sweat in the studio.

This could have been the start of a new direction, but Jerry Lee the man sabotaged Jerry Lee the artist. His next session was produced in Memphis by percussionist Tony Colton of Head, Hands, and Feet, who also contributed a strong song, "Jack Daniels (Old Number Seven)," that was executed brilliantly by a band that featured Stax masters Steve Cropper on guitar and Duck Dunn on bass. It was raucous country that anticipated and outmatched the Willie Nelson/Waylon Jennings/Tompall Glaser/Jessi Colter Outlaw movement. Mercury never put the song on an album. It deserved a better fate than being stuck on the wrong side of a single, even if the A-side, "No Headstone on My Grave," was magnificent in its own right. Of course, the Killer being the Killer, Jerry Lee alienated Colton so completely and irrevocably in their few hours together that Colton bolted as soon as he could.

When Jerry Lee returned to the Nashville Over-production Factory for a three-day, twenty-one-song blow-out produced by Stan Kesler (Mercury executive Jerry Kennedy had started off-loading some of his production chores), he also reverted to old vices. Kesler was an important Memphis music figure, as a writer and player at Sun Records and later as the producer for the delightfully whacked-out Sam the Sham and the Pharaohs. Here, though, Kesler operated as if his job was to make Jerry Kennedy seem like a producer of uncommon subtlety. Very little of this session deserved to be preserved, although Mercury insisted. Not even a motivated Jerry Lee could have made sense of songs with titles like "The Alcohol of Fame," "Mama's Hands," and "Tomorrow's Taking Baby Away," although Jerry Lee clearly delighted in singing the last song's line, "She still gave me her young body/In a lovely, friendly way." In "I Think I Need to Pray," Jerry

Lee called out, "I think we all need to pray." What he needed to pray for was a new producer. To be fair, Jerry Lee was driving Kesler crazy, and Kesler had every excuse to unconsciously sabotage the date.

The only remotely alert new song to come out of the Kesler marathon was "Honky Tonk Wine," written by one Mack Vickery, a journeyman Alabama singer and composer who had recorded under both his name for the short-lived Playboy label and the monicker Atlanta James, neither time with much success. He had also placed a few songs with Memphis soul master James Carr. He had yet to release his definitive LP, *Live at the Alabama Women's Prison*. "Honky Tonk Wine" was a minor song, and Kesler tried to kill it with strings, but it was immediately apparent that the tune moved Jerry Lee unlike anything else he recorded that night. He was in synch with the number.

The powers at Mercury listened and knew that they had a commercial problem. After a string of smashes, Jerry Lee's last five singles had not scratched their way into the country-and-western Top Ten. The Killer still had an extremely loyal core audience that would stand by its man no matter what he recorded, but the tide of across-the-board monsters had clearly ebbed. They also had a personal problem. Bassist Bob Moore, who accompanied the Ferriday Fireball on most of his Smash/Mercury sessions, overstated the case when he said, "Jerry Lee has a heading and a bottom line of each page in his life. The heading is drugs and the bottom line is drugs," but the sad fact was that there were some days when there was nothing else written on the page. The label had trouble finding people willing to work with Jerry Lee. In a move that was one part genius and two parts recklessness, they decided to send him into the studio with someone even crazier than he.

• • •

"We fought," Huey P. Meaux told Colin Escott, "but we delivered."

Myra, Jerry Lee, and Phoebe (left to right)

Meaux was one of those colorful characters who gave southern writers prime source material and who made outsiders wonder if they were being put on. A Cajun named after Louisiana dictator Huey ("Kingfish") Long, Meaux had worked in all aspects of the record business, and in September 1973 he was glad to be in his own loud clothes instead of what he had been wearing most recently: prison garb. Upon his release he had re-established contact with Mercury. Now, after agreeing with Mercury's vice president of artists and repertoire Charlie Fach that a pure Jerry Lee album was the cure to everyone's ills, he was signed to produce such an LP.

The resulting set, *Southern Roots*, was recorded virtually nonstop over three days and nights in Memphis. Meaux enjoyed extraordinary connections, so he was able to assemble a group that was undoubtedly Jerry Lee's most sympathetic accompaniment since his 1964 tour. He recruited guitarist Steve Cropper, bassist Donald ("Duck") Dunn, and drummer Al Jackson, the essential Stax rhythm section, as the core band. Then he added other top-of-the-line musicians like organist Augie Meyers of the Sir Douglas Quintet, the original Memphis Horns, members of the Memphis Beats, and Carl Perkins. Mack Vickery contributed harmonica, vocals, and enough craziness to be allowed in the same room with Meaux and Jerry Lee.

Recording conditions were chaotic, to put it mildly. Musicians, family members, delivery men, ex-girlfriends, and people just off the street wandered around, pushed engineers out of the way, and slept on the floor. Unlike the London session earlier in the year, where producer Steve Rowland tried to tone down his charges' behavior and instead made everyone more nervous, Meaux encouraged all in his kingdom to whoop it up. The unwieldy *Southern Roots* sessions were not designed with controlled behavior in mind, but they did yield what was unquestionably the most spirited and sustained studio album of Jerry Lee's long and spirited career. The album was subtitled *Back Home to Memphis* and featured Jerry Lee's only post-Sun studio performances that consistently captured what made him special, different, and impossible to pigeonhole.

A filthy Mack Vickery tune written with Jerry Lee in mind, "Meat Man," kicked off the album and pinned itself in fifth gear. "Meat Man" was two minutes and forty seconds of vivid sexual boasts, delivered furiously and convincingly: "They call me the meat man/You oughta see me eat ma'am." He did not sing as if there were any possibility that the woman might decline his offer. Jerry Lee made listeners believe he had a "Maytag tongue with a sensitive taster." He whooped it up in an avalanche of a solo and his least practiced shouting in years. His mind wasn't in a studio; as far as he was concerned he was in the darkest, toughest roadhouse in Mississippi. "Meat Man" was the most frankly sexual song of Jerry Lee's career, no small achievement. It was the first time in the studio since his glory days at Sun that he sounded truly free. Even when the song ended, he refused to stop, shouting, "Meat man, you mother!" until Meaux shut off the tape.

"When a Man Loves a Woman" was originally a hit for Percy Sledge, and Meaux's decision to record it hinted at his agenda more than any other song on *Southern Roots*. Meaux loved Memphis music, but one of his more brilliant ideas on this session was to act as if Jerry Lee's Memphis homecoming belonged at Stax, not Sun. For a decade the soul masters at Stax (and, later, Hi) had been the groundbreaking performers in town; in the mid- and late-sixties Sun was a clearing house for second-rate talent. Stax and Sun had different sounds, but they were linked because the country-blues fusion at Sun set the stage for Stax to come up with its country-rhythm-and-blues union. So in taking Jerry Lee back to a "Memphis sound," Meaux was both returning to past glories and nudging the Killer forward.

Onstage with Carl Perkins

"When a Man Loves a Woman" was a colossal ballad with a bite, and Meaux's arrangements kept the focus on Jerry Lee's voice and piano, a logical idea that in 1973 seemed novel. The only thing wrong with "When a Man Loves a Woman" was that it faded out after only four minutes and twenty seconds. "Hold On I'm Coming," a suggestive hit for Sam and Dave, was another tune that originated in the Stax axis, and Jerry Lee recast it as a funky, soulful strut. "I made love to a lotta women in Tennessee," Jerry Lee sang as if he needed to remind himself. "I'm comin, C-o-m-i-n'. . ." An alternate version was slightly faster and much looser.

Roscoe Gordon's "Just a Little Bit" got the Sir Douglas Quintet treatment, with Augie Meyers's charmingly trashy organ fighting Jerry Lee for room until piano and organ merged in an otherworldly, bass-heavy keyboard crash. The Killer's singing on this ideal funk-rocker was as ferocious as the song's rhythms. His wild pleading danced across the studio floor until it collapsed in a heap with all the other stragglers. "Born to Be a Loser" was a strong southern ballad with lyrics that Jerry Lee obviously related to: "Ain't nobody perfect," he sang. "Think about it." By the end of the song, he was addressing his potential partner as "you good-looking wench."

The second side of *Southern Roots* erupted to life with "Haunted House," originally a novelty hit for Memphis singer Gene Simmons. (In spite of its relative obscurity, "Haunted House" has garnered quite a celebrity fan club. On Halloween night 1981 Bruce Springsteen began a concert by being carried onstage in a coffin, jumping out, and singing it.) Those listening closely could hear liquor and pills rattling through the vocal. Fats Domino's "Blueberry Hill" was a straightforward, southern-ballad performance with a touch of Dixieland horns, still on the highest level.

The album ended with three songs as weird as the participants in the session; all three featured at least one "think about it." Doug Sahm's "The Revolutionary Man" was a barnstorming rocker, piano and horns once again battling organ. One suspected that good ole boy Jerry Lee's idea of revolution was different from that of confirmed hippie Sahm, but at least Jerry Lee acted like he knew what he was singing about. The backup singers, not even remotely annoying, sang, "Jerry is a rebel," in a melody swiped from Gino Washington's obscure "Gino Is a Coward." Earl ("Kit") Carson's "Big Blue Diamond" offered an unbuttoned solo, and the album slid home with another Mack Vickery song, "That Old Bourbon Street Church." The strong ballad was also thematically useful in that the Vickery numbers that opened and closed the album defined the two Jerry Lees. In "Meat Man" he was a raving, cocksure stud; by "The Old Bourbon Street

Church" he was vanquished, drunk, nearly crying, begging for forgiveness. In Vickery, a fan as well as a professional, Jerry Lee had found someone who could articulate his troubles better than he himself ever could.

Although they did not surface until the late eighties, another album's worth of first-rank tunes were cut at the *Southern Roots* sessions. Even better, full session tapes emerged in which fans could hear Jerry Lee, Meaux, and Vickery whoop it up. Everyone at that three-day session was intoxicated by talent as well as by alcohol; unlike the typical Jerry Lee seventies session, in which a truck load of hired guns played their parts and left as soon as the clock said they could, it sounded like the *Southern Roots* musicians were in Memphis because they loved the music. They were all crazy, but they were also crazy about music. With them cheering him on, Jerry Lee scorched for the last time in a long time.

Instead of reviving Jerry Lee's career, *Southern Roots* condemned it. The album never hit the *Billboard* chart because its ridiculous cover, a drawing of the Killer that looked positively antebellum, gave the LP all the appearances of yet another reissue of old cuts. All but the most loyal fans did not know that there were any new hits because nothing from *Southern Roots* got on the radio. In a pea-brained marketing move, Mercury opted for "Meat Man" as the first single. Granted, it was a stupendous song, but part of what made it fantastic was that it was a defiant, upraised middle finger at countrypolitan record formats. Jerry Lee made a sublime album, but nobody got to hear it. He resigned himself to the inevitable.

• • •

Even Jerry Lee's faithful admitted that what came between *Southern Roots* and the end of this association with Mercury was mostly lifeless. None of his more welcome trademarks showed up: no honky-tonk chords slammed against each other until they made friends, and nothing suggested that metallic-blond locks were flopping in front of his eyes while he played. His voice frequently took on a monotonic quality, as if he could not be bothered to move his mouth and tongue to enunciate different sounds. Some fans blamed the deterioration in Jerry Lee's vocals on substance abuse; others pointed to a 4:00 A.M. fight in a night club that left his nose broken in three places and was not satisfactorily attended to for years.

For whatever reason, this was the only period in Jerry Lee's career that did not feature an official live album, mostly because his shows were too infrequent and his singing and playing veered toward the lazy and monotonic. If live shows were out of the question, so were live-in-the-studio performances. It took more takes to complete songs, unless Jerry Lee became so bored or ornery that he left the studio before anyone was happy with his performances. From now on, fans knew to expect tons of overdubs, vocal and otherwise, many of them supervised by someone who was passed-out on the floor.

Jerry Lee did not argue against this recording method, in which songs were built piece by piece, with everything "perfect" and no passion allowed. "When you're making love to a woman, you can't overdub it," he told an interviewer. "You can't phone it in." So he knew better, but he either did not want to or could not exert himself.

Right after live recordings, another idea that went out the window, at least unconsciously, was bringing up issues through songs. Through the fifties, sixties, and early seventies, fans learned about Jerry Lee's ideas on everything from sex and drugs to family and religion through the way he performed; in the late seventies he was simply too out of it to bring his performances to a level where those meanings, intentional or not, could be discerned.

Yet Jerry Lee kept playing and playing. "Jerry Lee is onstage twenty-four hours a day," said Bob Moore. "When we were on the road, we'd go right offstage into the limo to the plane. On the plane he went to his Casio immediately. He'd sing and play all the way home. He never stopped." There are hundreds of private tapes of Jerry Lee playing any keyboard he could find, just for the pleasure and release it gave him. He played piano in 1977 for the same reason he had turned to the instrument more than three decades earlier: it was an escape. Other people were in the room with him, so he could show off.

October and November 1974 sessions in Nashville were once again overseen by Jerry Kennedy. "Watch me," Jerry Lee said before a take of Troy Seals's "Boogie Woogie Country Man." "I might get hot." He never got past "might." Tom T. Hall's "I Can Still Hear the Music in the Restroom" gave Jerry Lee a reason to hold notes in his best Merle Haggard voice, but the most colorful nugget about the minor hit was its promotional campaign, which featured a copy of the single affixed to a toilet seat.

"Honey Hush" was a real rock-and-roll song, complete with ersatz-Sun echo, more speed-up than comeback, hobbled by the usual overproduction. Stuart Hamblen's "Remember Me (I'm the One Who Loves You)" was a good ballad performance without too much interference; "Forever Forgiving" was a typically appropriate Mack Vickery weeper; and "I'm Still Jealous of You" was the occasion for what was now a rare event, a committed, comprehending vocal. Everything else from those sessions resembled the sort of self-pitying country ballads that the Killer had once set out to vanquish. Only Elvis was in worse shape.

Four sessions in the first half of 1975 could squeeze out only five songs worth preserving. One of those was a ringer ("Your Cheatin' Heart"), and two of them were spontaneous readings of songs Jerry Lee loved as a child that were never intended for release, "Crawdad Song" and "The House of Blue Lights." The two new songs, both custom-written ballads for the Killer's teetering self, let Jerry Lee show his pain and his self-loathing. Mack Vickery's "That

Kind of Fool" yearned for unattainable domestic bliss: it was the tale of a rockabilly cat who grew up too late. Donnie Fritts's "A Damn Good Country Song" covered similar ground almost as comprehensively. Jerry Lee sang the song hard. It meant a great deal to him and was one of the numbers he turned to during the "It Was the Whiskey Talkin' (Not Me)" sessions. His piano sneaked higher up in the mix, which meant that either Jerry Kennedy was finally letting him play his own way or he had thrown in the towel. Either way, it was a passable performance of a more than adequate song that deserved to climb higher on the country-and-western charts than Number Sixty-eight.

Mercury's Charlie Fach, frustrated that Jerry Lee was deteriorating in every way, specifically in completing the number of albums he was contracted to deliver per year, booked sessions the week before Christmas 1975 to meet the annual quota. He should have gone shopping instead. All but three of the songs were originally unissued, and they did not include the only two worthwhile tunes from the sessions. Even "I Can't Keep My Hands Off of You," the contribution from Mack Vickery, the only reliable Jerry Lee speechwriter, was written and performed with minimal energy. But Billy Swan's rollicking "I Can Help" was recorded and performed with gusto. Jerry Lee immediately identified with the lyrics: "Your child needs a daddy/We can discuss that, too." However, by the end of the song the Ferriday Fireball had retreated to his own world, shouting "Think about it, Elvis" to someone who would never hear him. Abnormal but effective was Little Richard's "Slippin' and Slidin'," done as a cigarettes-and-coffee-style, late-night blues jam.

It took almost six months for Mercury to get Jerry Lee back in a studio, and it is unclear why they expended the energy. The Killer was in no condition to record, and the third-rate material with which he was saddled did not shake him out of his stupor. "The Fifties" was the worst song

Jerry Lee had recorded since "Lincoln Limousine," fake rock and roll with lyrics that strung together titles of early rock-and-roll classics. All that survived the most cursory inspection were "The Old Country Church," interesting only for the psychodramatics inherent in hearing a stoned Jerry Lee talk to himself, and "I Sure Miss Those Good Old Times," a Mack Vickery-penned outtake from *Southern Roots* that, by comparison, did not reflect well on Jerry Kennedy's recording methods. By now, Jerry Lee was skipping live shows as frequently as he was blowing studio dates, which cost him much money. On December 5 Jerry Lee received an early Christmas present when he turned on his television and saw his cousin Jimmy Lee Swaggart begging Jesus to save the Killer's soul.

In 1977 Jerry Lee bottomed out. His comrade and competitor, Elvis, had his misery terminated, but the Killer

was forced to rock on. His two competent vocal performances that year were on "Ivory Tears," a marrow-cutting
Mack Vickery ballad of piano-man regret, and Sonny
Throckmorton's "Middle Age Crazy," a tale of a man Jerry
Lee's age trying to pass himself off as a rock-and-roll kid.
The performance was so vivid that someone in Hollywood
expanded it into a movie, à la "Ode to Billy Joe." The song
was a natural hit, all the way to Number Four, because it felt
real. The Killer was beat; he admitted it; and he found an
appealing way to convey it.

Jerry Lee's manager, Bob Porter, and the lawyers at
Mercury spent the summer of 1978 trying to hammer out a
new contract, but nobody on either side truly cared. Jerry
Lee was estranged from all the people at Mercury who
could or would set him on the right course; the divorce was
swift and as amicable as it could be considering that one
party was disappointed and the other was too out of it to
know what was occurring. Except for overdub quickies, the
last song Jerry Lee recorded for Mercury was the anorectic-
rock "Pee Wee's Place," which, apparently, was a place
where ennui ruled. Jerry Lee left Mercury, not with a bang,
not with a whimper, but with a yawn. He tried to rock, but
he could not; and he faded before the song got around to
doing the same thing.

Listening to Jerry Lee Lewis's post-*Southern Roots*
sides for Mercury is a numbing experience, especially when
compared to detailed examination of any of his four distinct
previous periods: pre-scandal Sun, post-scandal Sun, pre-
hit Smash, post-hit Mercury. No theme but dissolution
emerges from the period; no stories worth chewing over the
next day reverberate in your head. Listening to these
records is like watching one of your favorite baseball players
three or four years after he should have retired, in poor
shape, playing only as a replacement, not particularly committed, afraid to hang up his cleats because he could not
think of anything else to do but play ball.

"I thought I was indestructible," a contrite Jerry Lee told Jim Neff around the time his Mercury contract expired. "I thought the world had finally come up with a superman. I came to find out I wasn't." He was alone now, and he had to think up something new. Soon.

CHAPTER 8

Fragments of Autumn

The thing is dead. . . . Everything is dead
Except the future.
  —Wallace Stevens
  "Mr. Burnshaw and the Statue"

"History is history. The future is perfect."
  —Orel Hershiser

By the end of 1978, Jerry Lee had found a new recording sponsor, the Nashville arm of Elektra Records. When he signed, representatives of his new label promptly told Jerry Lee that they would not be recording him in Nashville. Fans cheered. During a four-day blowout in the Filmway/Heider Recording Studio in Hollywood, California, Jerry Lee recorded what will likely be his last stable album, titled simply *Jerry Lee Lewis*, perhaps as a hopeful gesture that this was the beginning of something new. Bones Howe, who had worked with Jerry Lee's arch-enemy, Elvis Presley, assembled a tight, responsive band around James Burton, a guitarist whose terse rockabilly elaborations had enlivened work by everyone from Rick Nelson to Elvis himself. Other key players included Jerry Lee's tenacious friend and occasional in-law, Kenneth Lovelace, on fiddle and guitar, and ace West Coast session drummer Hal Blaine. Some

185

Nashville sins were repeated—background choruses, strings, and horns—but the informality of the sessions made them rock in spite of such extraneousness.

"We're going to have to do the record in four days," Howe told Jerry Lee before recording began, afraid that the Killer would go tense under the pressure of having to complete an LP so quickly.

Jerry Lee was nonchalant. "What are we going to do the other two days?" he asked.

The need to work quickly and the simple excitement of

working with new people in novel settings without the usual bevy of cronies and sycophants liberated Jerry Lee to work way beyond the monotone to which he had confined himself since 1974. Here the theory that delayed attention to his broken nose restored his voice carries some weight. "Don't Let Go," a Jesse Stone song he had recorded at Mercury, started the party, and its ebullient tempo carried Jerry Lee past even the obligatory "think about it." The backing vocalists aped the sound of early rock-and-roll choruses, and for the most part did not get in the way. Only a step below was "Number One Lovin' Man," a jumpy rocker that gave the chorus a bit too much room and James Burton not nearly enough room to maneuver his outbursts.

Part of what made the Bones Howe sessions so successful was the idiosyncratic choice of material. Howe introduced Jerry Lee to a charming uptempo tune called "Rita May," and the Killer burned his way through it in a few feverish takes. It was a fine, guileless rock-and-roll song, Jerry Lee thought, different from what he was used to hearing.

"Who wrote that song?" Jerry Lee inquired.

"Bob Dylan," Bones Howe said and smiled. He thought he had delivered a punch line, but Jerry Lee showed no recognition.

"That boy's good," Jerry Lee said. "I'll do anything by him."

The possibility that Jerry Lee was putting Howe on can not be overestimated, but it was not much of a stretch of the imagination to believe that the Ferriday Fireball's musical tastes were so insular that he had not heard of Bob Dylan.

Jerry Lee was a country-blues-rockin' Midas those four January days and nights. He recast Arthur Alexander's classic "Every Day I Have to Cry" as a mainstream country ballad, not as pure as it would have sounded twenty years previously, but not overwrought either. Chris Kenner's "I

Like It Like That" was executed with the same organ-heavy sprightly fun of "Just a Little Bit" from *Southern Roots*. Sonny Throckmorton's "I Wish I Was Eighteen Again" was the type of I'm-aging-and-nostalgic country ballad at which a committed Jerry Lee could excel.

The retro move in the session that worked most successfully was a soulful strut through Charlie Rich's "Who Will the Next Fool Be" that showed off the band, especially Burton, without turning into a mere showing-off, which Jerry Lee was still doing between takes. The key to the session was a customized Mack Vickery song, "Rockin' My Life Away," a wonderful autumnal rocker that immediately became Jerry Lee's statement of intention and all-purpose theme song. Jerry Lee had always counted on Vickery to articulate for him, and here his Cyrano outdid himself. The sparkling lyrics vacillated between the completely obscure and the completely bizarre, but the feel was right.

What did those words mean? The first line of the song was "Fourteen, twenty-five, forty, ninety-eight," and the lines rolled out of Jerry Lee's mouth as if they had some deep meaning. In fact, Vickery had conceived of the song as a Specialty-era-Little-Richard-style rocker, with the first line scooping up tension like a quarterback calling signals before a play. But in popular music how something is said is far more important than what is said, and that was why the adventure of "Rockin' My Life Away" was so intense and enjoyable. Performance was more important than composition. "Watch me now," Jerry Lee shouted before his solo, and in a few seconds he erased five years of bad memories. Artistically, *Jerry Lee Lewis* was a completely successful comeback. The combination of a Number Twenty country-and-western hit and the appearance that he was lucid again made Jerry Lee a more lucrative, that is, safer, draw on the road.

The triumph did not last long. In February agents from the Internal Revenue Service showed up at his ranch

Rockin' his life away

to claim everything there. Jerry Lee's approach to paying taxes had been extremely passive. In July his father, Elmo, died. A second session with Bones Howe was more erratic than its predecessor, with a terrible version of Bob Seger's kneejerk-nostalgic "Old Time Rock and Roll" standing beside the finest "C.C. Rider" of his career. The album was shelved and never released; one song, "(Hot Damn!) I'm a

One-Woman Man," appeared on the soundtrack LP to a film about a roadie.

Nashville sessions in 1979 and 1980 were produced by Eddie Kilroy, the former used-car salesman and promo man at Mercury whose idea a dozen years previously to cut Jerry Lee country had saved the Killer's career. The dates were not as overblown as Jerry Lee's last in hillbilly heaven, but there were still too many people on every song. The fact that none of them was James Burton hurt the record when compared to _Jerry Lee Lewis_. Two albums were culled from the sessions, _When Two Worlds Collide_ and _Killer Country_. Each was halfway successful; together they add up to one fine record. At least five terrific performances were spread over the LPs, and some of them were hits, like "When Two Worlds Collide," a deep country ballad sung with great intensity. "Alabama Jubilee" and "Toot-Toot-Tootsie Goodbye" stand as Jerry Lee's most blatant Jolson-derived vocals. Even better was "Thirty-nine and Holding," an autobiographical tale of both Jerry Lee's imagined self and the audience that stuck and aged with him. It earned its Number Four placing on the country list. "I'd Do It All Again" covered similar territory almost as well, but did not chart as highly. Jerry Lee's chart success in the eighties was as random as it had always been.

The one performance from the Kilroy Nashville sessions that cut the deepest by far was a phenomenally gorgeous excavation of the pop standard, "Over the Rainbow." There had been several hit versions of the song by the likes of Judy Garland, Bing Crosby, Larry Clinton, and Glenn Miller (all in 1939, the year _The Wizard of Oz_ came out), but they were all versions by people who sounded young, alive, and possessing the fortitude to track down the metaphorical pot of gold. In Jerry Lee's version, the narrator was an old man. His voice showed its cracks, hinted at its long-ago triumphs, sounded bitter, and searched for a reason to hope. Jerry Lee was only forty-five years old when he recorded this song, but he looked and sang at least a decade beyond that. If Jerry Lee had retired after he recorded "Over the Rainbow," one could have stated that his mission had been complete. He started at the end of the road, traveled places no one had ever seen before, and was now wise enough to accept that the rainbow was unattainable.

• • •

One of the problems with real life is that it does not provide the sense of closure that one can get from great art. Jerry Lee did not stop rocking after his inconsistent behavior led to his departure from Elektra. His two albums for MCA, *My Fingers Do the Talkin'* and *I Am What I Am*, and two subsequent ones for the independent label SCR, *Six of One, Half Dozen of the Other* and *Get Out Your Big Roll Daddy*, repeated many of the same songs and performances. They were tired, listless paydays. Other sessions, run by long-time collaborators like Roland Janes, Eddie Kilroy, and Bob Moore, were somewhat more successful, but none of them led to the goal of a major-label signing. Jerry Lee had burned too many bridges.

The Killer still had life in him, especially onstage. One night in Sweden in the middle of the breakdown of "Whole Lotta Shakin' Going On," he cautioned his paramour, "Don't have an epileptic fit or nothin'/Just stand in one place." Moments like that happened all the time. But a recorded-live album with Carl Perkins and Johnny Cash called *The Survivors* (one imagines the irony was unintentional) was a dud. Still, throughout the eighties it became clear to all that the Sun experience now meant something new to these men who knew Elvis, all the King's men.

In the years since Elvis Presley died, dozens of rock and country performers have striven either to understand what set Elvis apart or to take unto themselves part of his triumph, which cannot be shared because it's both unprecedented and unrepeatable. Some, like Buck Brody Mozingo

An outake from the I Am What I Am *cover shoot*

in novelist William Price Fox's *Dixiana Moon*, have been content to stand back as Elvis shoots by and to listen for the deafening ricochet. Some, like Bruce Springsteen in his dark update of Chuck Berry's Elvis parable, "Bye Bye Johnny," have sought to champion Presley's boldest stroke, the (temporary) destruction of nearly all American musical and cultural barriers. But most merely join in chorus to praise the King, without probing below the glittering surface that hid the ugliness and deterioriation beneath.

Class of '55, released in 1986, fit in the latter, cluttered category. It was one of the most eccentric of the Elvis tribute records, partly because it never announced that as its intention. In September 1985 Jerry Lee Lewis, Johnny Cash, Carl Perkins, and a precomeback Roy Orbison returned to the site of their earliest triumphs and attempted to rekindle some of the period's exuberance. The press releases claimed the members of the "class of 1955" were united by the Sun origins and their friendship with Elvis, but that was superficial. Orbison, for one, did his most lasting work after he left Sun, and it's safe to assume that none of these men were drinking buddies of Elvis.

Instead, what pervaded and undermined this reunion was the burning wish, on the part of each man, that it had been he who had descended from Sun and established a kingdom. *Class of '55* was subtitled *Memphis Rock & Roll Homecoming*, almost identical to the subtitle of *Southern Roots*. Like all class reunions, this was a bittersweet reflection on salad years. The awkward song titles, such as "Birth of Rock and Roll" and "We Remember the King," underlined the concept. In spite of all the we're-rockin'-tonight rhetoric in the lyrics, *Class of '55* shook down to a country album with spots of spunk and a tentative, start-and-stop mood. Producer Chips Moman's slightly overwrought settings were just cushy enough to keep the featured vets going without emphasizing the way they were propped up.

On three tracks the grizzled, marked-down quartet

emerged from its reverent opportunism, making this a worthwhile musical document as well as an inevitable historical one. Lewis's slow, leering cover of the Crests's "Sixteen Candles" was as slyly lecherous as the adolescent-marriage specialist could make it. Even he had stopped counting how many times he had said "I do." (The recent overdose death of his fifth wife had led to allegations that Jerry Lee was somehow responsible.) Orbison's light-rockabilly "Coming Home" underscored the warmth of the get-together.

The clincher was the eight-minute dive into "Big Train (From Memphis)," the John Fogerty song based on Elvis's cover of Junior Parker's "Mystery Train." Here, all the participants switched off the cruise control and floored it. They glided into the track as if it were a standard, which it may yet become, repeating verses, drawing strength from every easy breath. They were accompanied by Fogerty, June Carter Cash, Jack Clement, Sam Phillips, and, in his last recorded performance, Rick Nelson. "Big Train (From Memphis)" was a meeting ground for the members of the class, the intersection at which their differences disappeared. The song repeated its near-gospel chanting chorus like a soothing prayer: "Big train/From Memphis/Now it's gone, gone, gone/Gone, gone, gone." Fogerty's song was both a celebration of Presley's life and a tersely phrased lament for what was lost with his death. The conductor was gone, but the train kept on moving. And if there was pleasure in hearing its echo, imagine how it must have felt to have been, like the members of the class of '55, privileged passengers. Jerry Lee, of course, lightened the proceedings by yelling his name and whatever else came to mind over the fade.

The eighties were an up-and-down decade for Jerry Lee, all fits and starts, no coherence. He recorded at least half a dozen albums after he left the major labels, none of them distinguished, and he blew several deals that could

Thirty-nine and holding

have put him back on a major. His songs were used in all sorts of awful movies, like *Breathless, Tremors,* and *Loverboy,* as well as in television commercials. But some chronic problems had not been solved. As late as 1990, Jerry Lee was still a patient of Dr. George Nichopolous, best-known as Elvis's private physician and all-around procurer.

Perhaps Jerry Lee's last big chance came at the end of the decade when a movie was made of Myra Lewis and Murray Silver's *Great Balls of Fire.* He received a great deal of money, said to be in the mid-six figures, to rerecord his hits and—more important to the producers—to keep his mouth shut when people asked him why the film version bore little relation to the true life it belittled. The filmmakers were monumentally cynical. One said to Jerry Lee as he prepared to cut the soundtrack, "We know you can't match the original. That's OK. Just try to get close."

Jerry Lee snapped back, "Then why the hell did you fly me out here?"

Jerry Lee justified the airfare. He believed he could beat the original versions. Whether he did or not is immaterial. The simple fact that he thought he could, that he insisted he must, screams loud and clear in his rerecordings with a band led by usually sharp producer T Bone Burnett. And once, on a thundering "That Lucky Old Sun" that made bitterness sound like love, he managed a truly definitive version of a Sun-era standard. Challenged, the Killer delivered. Perhaps one day he will deliver again.

Today Jerry Lee does not play live much and hardly records at all. He is said to feel betrayed by the *Great Balls of Fire* film experience. He has risen and fallen many times, never in the way expected. In early 1990 he booked a British tour but blew it off, apparently as a result of a battle with sixth wife, Kerrie. His promoter sued him and bad-mouthed him to the Fleet Street press that was now in its second generation of bothering Jerry Lee. The Ferriday Fireball wanted to tell his side of the story, so he wrote a letter to the British rock-enthusiast magazine *Now Dig This*. Illusions die hard:

> I want to extend my deepest apologies for having been forced into leaving my European tour so suddenly in April of this year. Mr. Mervyn Conn canceled all of our hotel and transportation credit (which was in my contract to be paid by him), forcing us to have to leave Europe altogether. He did this because I had requested that contractual agreements that hadn't been met be taken care of immediately. I had already performed three shows and had not been paid, and still haven't received our return tickets which were promised on arrival. To make matters worse, while I was in Nice, France, I believe that Mr. Conn was responsible for sending a lady to my room wanting to be paid for services she had to offer. For reasons unknown to me as to why he did this, I promptly told the lady I didn't engage in this kind of activity and sent her on her way. I was completely shocked over this and decided to return to London where my wife and son were waiting for me. When I returned to London, I found that Mr. Conn had booked even more dates for me without even having a signed contract from me. As you can see, it was getting to be a little much to handle.
>
> As we were leaving the Grafton Hotel, the management told Kerrie that she would have to pay for the entire bill as the credit had been pulled from day one of our stay, and not since the France date as we had been previously told. When she showed them the contract as to Mr. Conn's obligations, they told her they didn't care about my contract and she would have to pay. She then proceeded to go out of the hotel to get me and to inform me as to what had taken place, and they bodily grabbed her and bent her hands and blocked the door so she couldn't get out. The band happened to see the commotion and pushed the door in. The management proceeded in taking some of the

band members' luggage, after they had already paid their incidentals.

We were already working for far less than I get for a show normally, as Mr. Conn had threatened to have us completely deported from the country if we worked for another promoter. He knew my wife had family there, and that we were wanting to stay there and work there three or four months a year. He continued on with saying that I owed him money, which I didn't, and would garnish my wages, etc. After being persuaded by my agent to do the tour, I relented.

I am very sorry that so many people got hurt in the crossfire of it all. I'm sorry that we were all subject to Mr. Conn's abuse and hope that it won't ever occur again. I just pray that Mr. Conn will never put another entertainer through such a nightmare. Kerrie is still recovering from the shock of being held against her will, and from being bruised up so badly. We hope to return to England very soon and make it up to you all. THE KILLER WILL RETURN!

God bless you all.
Jerry Lee Lewis and family
Nesbit, Mississippi, USA

The letter starts off as an apology to fans, wanders through an explanation of the events that conspired against him, and climaxes in an all-capital-letters payoff boast. Anyone cynical enough to believe that Jerry Lee is incapable of further great moments has only to read the conviction behind "THE KILLER WILL RETURN!" to become at least temporarily converted. The Killer is not at the controls all the time, but when he is you had better watch out. Think about it.

C H A P T E R   9

Let the Jukebox Keep
On Playing

Don't have the inclination to look back on any mis-
take;
Like Cain, I now behold this chain of events that I
must break.
In the fury of the moment I can see the Master's hand;
In every leaf that trembles, in every grain of sand.
—Bob Dylan, "Every Grain of Sand"

Giants sometimes rise from their slumbers invigorated. Onstage, the only place of work that consistently matters to him, Jerry Lee is still capable of virtually anything. Many of his performances verge on sleepwalks; but the Killer, even as he inches out of his fifth decade, still has few peers when it comes to live performance if one catches him on a night when he gives a damn. He can rock more ferociously than most heavy metal kids; he makes groups like Poison and Motley Crue sound like the pathetic comic book characters they are, all show and no threat. He can lay into country ballads with more intensity than Nashville's New Traditionalists; only Dwight Yoakam shares his all-encompassing dread. He can plow through intoxicating blues harder than a young practitioner like Robert Cray. If he wants to, Jerry Lee can cut anybody on anything. The problem is getting him to make an attempt. When something is at stake, he usually still delivers, as the riveting soundtrack to *Great Balls of Fire* evidences.

What makes seeing Jerry Lee perform nowadays such a frustrating experience is the knowledge in every fan's mind that if Jerry Lee happens to be inspired he will put on a great show, but the likelihood is that Jerry Lee himself will not know if he will commit to the evening's show until he is onstage. He may toss off some rockers, often the monotonic "Rockin' Jerry Lee" or a tentative version of one of his lesser Sun hits. But he will follow them with stately ballad performances, such as "Over the Rainbow" and the timeless "You Win Again," in which every syllable matters to him. Not surprisingly, ballads of emotional and spiritual devastation are the performances closest to Jerry Lee's heart. That has been the case at least as far back as "Crazy Arms." Sister Linda Gail reports that Jerry Lee recently told her, "I've done everythng. I've got nothing left to do."

Jerry Lee's original intentions were modest and honorable enough: he wanted to make a living playing piano, enough so that he could live a more comfortable life than his parents had, and he wanted to serve his Lord. On the face of it, those aspirations should have been accomplished and maintained simply and cleanly by someone of Jerry Lee's genius. But it was clear even when he was a teenager that his talents were so mammoth and so malleable that they could conquer the world if he wanted them to, and matters became wildly complicated. Jerry Lee tried to live a double life for a time—family man and preacher by day, showman and sinner by night—and to this day he still feels the pull of both sides. One night he performs a steamy, gin-soaked set at some Memphis club; the next day he may be announcing to a local paper that he has finally been saved and will devote the rest of his life to his Savior and his family. Both times his sincerity is transparent.

These are not callous flip-flops. Just as Jerry Lee has never recovered from the shock of the 1958 scandal and his subsequent fishbowl existence, he has never escaped the fierce ambivalence regarding his career choice fostered in him by his mother. Instead of perceiving the fundamental incongruities of his life as a shortcoming of other people's expectations, he seems them as representative of deficiencies within himself. So he continues to punish himself for not conforming to the morés of a hypocritical world.

The culture that Jerry Lee loves and exploits is far different from what it was when he and Elmo embarked on their first fateful trip to Memphis. Jerry Lee's boyhood dream of becoming an all-encompassing performer, one who could do anything, makes no sense to all but the most ambitious kids now growing up in the many Ferridays that dot the South. Popular culture in the United States becomes more compartmentalized each year. As the market for leisure grows, so does the gradual narrowing of what one can find at any time. As a Ferriday child, Jerry Lee could track down perhaps half a dozen stations on his uncle's radio. Now, even in Ferriday, he can turn on cable television and have access to more than one hundred channels, most of them extremely specialized. The sports channels show only sporting events, the pop-music channels show only music-videos from some limited part of the pop field, and so on. If you want something different, you usually have to change the channel. Nearly all the cable channels seek to show one small slice of the world; few of them even hint that there is anything out there beyond their provincial offerings.

Today's record company head is most likely someone who has excelled in selling or promoting product, not someone with experience in discovering or generating music.

That makes for an industry with vastly altered priorities. The narrowing of individual cultural offerings has been accompanied by a consolidation of power in the music industry among five major multinational companies. The days of someone like Sam Phillips, who was able to pump out consistent national hits without major-label support, are gone, the occasional one-shot from a rap entrepreneur notwithstanding. To be truly heard, a performer has to hook up with a major label. And these major labels have departments within themselves, such as pop, rock, country, black, and dance, that further pigeonhole music. Then there are different "boutique" sublabels with specific agendas. When someone like Michael Jackson or Prince succeeds across multiple artificial formats, it is a shock; for prime performers, it once was the rule.

These conglomerates are not geared for someone like Jerry Lee, who belongs on a label that recognizes no market-influenced limits on creativity. Jerry Lee transcended small-minded ideas like genres virtually from the moment he started performing, and that is one of the reasons why he does not have a major-label deal. These people want clinical specialists, not wide-eyed generalists. They want people who show facility at regurgitating past triumphs, either their own or those of others, which is the reason why so many films, books, and records produced nowadays end with a number. Sequels and reunions are easy money. Cultural retreads are not merely accepted by the powers that be, they are encouraged.

Pop culture has become extremely compartmentalized, perhaps irrevocably so, since Jerry Lee left Ferriday. The present boom in compact-disc reissues of classic blues, country-and-western, and early rock-and-roll records is at least partly fueled by a sophisticated audience's inability to relate to current performers who have more to do with demographic research than music. If a Ferriday kid, a potential Jerry Lee, is going to be inspired to begin a career in

HOME EDITION
Christmas 1987

music by what he or she hears on the radio, it is likely that he or she is listening to an oldies station. There is much magnificient music being recorded these days, although as the market expands, less of it gets heard by a mass audience. Some of the greatest pop music of the eighties was recorded by the Los Angeles-based punk band, X. However, none of their many unrelenting performances, among them a movie-soundtrack cover of Jerry Lee's "Breathless," spent much time on commercial radio. It is no accident that one of their most durable compositions is called "The Unheard Music."

Through all this Jerry Lee endures, even if contemporary culture has fragmented to the point that it can not produce another like Jerry Lee. Sometimes his concerts resemble dramatizations of internal monologues. He plays a dirty "Big Legged Woman" and scolds himself; he lays into a gorgeous "You Win Again" and offers up a dirty joke; he philosophizes on the dangers of drugs and sings "Drinkin' Wine Spo-Dee-o-Dee." He still exemplifies nearly all the major dilemmas that Southerners have faced in this century, and his inability to resolve them says more about the unresolved problems of the nation than the unsettled state of the man.

Yet the man cannot be the primary issue. We care about Jerry Lee for what he says through his work. That is the voice that we will care about a generation from now, just as his music from a generation ago rings true in today's world. The true spirit of Jerry Lee and what he still represents showed up most clearly in the sparkling "It Was the Whiskey Talkin' (Not Me)" session. Touchstone Pictures, the company bankrolling *Dick Tracy*, had already pumped untold millions into the film by the time Jerry Lee got his call from Andy Paley. Several of those Touchstone millions had been tossed in the direction of costar Madonna, whose preeminence as a pop star made her the Elvis of her time. If any music from *Dick Tracy* was going to get the corporate push (the soundtrack was being recorded for Madonna's record label), it was going to be that of sure-thing Madonna.

So Jerry Lee was recording a pretty-good tune that he surely must have been told would not capture the ears of the masses. He was playing second fiddle to a woman young enough to be his daughter, a bold woman who had taken up his mantle of shocking the audience into considering new ideas. But he played the song hard, as if by sheer will he could beat out the newcomer. Back at the Memphis Recording Service, looking up at a massive photograph of himself in his mid-fifties prime, he knew. And for one blessed moment, he felt vindicated.

The Records
A Selective Collection

THE BASIC COLLECTION

Sun

Classic (Bear Family 15420) reveals mystery after mystery over the course of its eight jam-packed and nearly always excellent compact discs. *Classic*, an expanded version of *The Sun Years* (Sun Box 102), a twelve-LP set, includes virtually everything Jerry Lee recorded for Sam Phillips (along with much hilarious studio chatter including the "Great Balls of Fire" argument), the major exception being the legendary December 4, 1956, session, much of which is on *The Complete Million Dollar Session* (Charly 102/RCA 2023).

Smash/Mercury

The Killer 1963–1968 (Bear Family 15210, 10 LPs)
The Killer 1969–1972 (Bear Family 15228, 11 LPs)
The Killer 1973–1977 (Bear Family 15229, 12 LPs)
Everything, including hours of outtakes and arguments, many of them revelatory. Early pressings of these three boxes sets featured bonus LPs full of interviews and other intermittently worthwhile ephemera. Colin Escott's notes are essential reading.

Elektra

Jerry Lee Lewis (Elektra 184) is the terrific comeback album with James Burton; "Over the Rainbow" can be heard on either *Killer Country* (Elektra 291) or *The Best of Jerry Lee Lewis, Featuring "39 and Holding"* (Elektra 60191). Warner Brothers, which owns the Elektra country catalog, has released a collection of Jerry Lee's Elektra best, compiled by the author.

The Eighties and Beyond

There are half a dozen performances from this period worth retaining. *Class of '55* (Smash 830 002) is the fascinating Memphis "homecoming" LP with Johnny Cash, Roy Orbison, and Carl Perkins; *Rockin' My Life Away* (Tomato 2696612) captures some fine shows at a southern California honky tonk; two versions of "It Was the Whiskey Talkin' (Not Me)" are on the *Dick Tracy* soundtrack (Sire 26236); what may be the final major charge is on the soundtrack to *Great Balls of Fire* (Polydor 839 516). Aside from the defiant *Live at the Vapors Club* (Ace 326), there are no recent live LPs that conjure up the power of which Jerry Lee is still capable on the right night. Worth seeing is the videocassette *Jerry Lee Lewis and Friends* (MCA 10252), a London show with an all-star band that explodes when one of the Killer's most unlikely disciples, the great Irish soul singer Van Morrison, joins him for duets on "Goodnight Irene" and "What'd I Say."

• • •

A mere listening of Jerry Lee Lewis's recordings would fill a book by itself. (Killer scholar Ari Bass is well on his way to producing such a volume.) Alas, a listing of his worthwhile original LPs still in print wouldn't fill this page.

This doesn't mean that the vast majority of Jerry Lee's recordings—and much of the top-rank stuff—isn't available. Reissue geniuses on both sides of the Atlantic have performed impressive restoration jobs (though, to be fair, a lot of garbage has appeared since the release of the film _Great Balls of Fire_).

Jerry Lee was an original, but even originals have predecessors. His affinity for Al Jolson records is well-documented (especially since the Jolson influence on him is more showmanship than musical; also, some of the Jolson in Jerry Lee is filtered through Charlie Poole), but venturing into his influences on the blues side is thorny. His listening staples as a child were primarily country-and-western music, and it is through country-and-western records that he developed.

The single greatest influence on Jerry Lee was Hank Williams. For decades Williams's music was available only in poor-sounding rechanneled-stereo versions stuffed with posthumous overdubs of the worst kind. PolyGram, which now owns the MGM catalog, set the record straight in the late 1980s with a series of eight magnificent double albums that present the vast majority of Williams's recordings as they were intended to be heard. The essential collection is _The Original Singles Collection . . . Plus_ (Polydor 847 194), a three-CD set that includes nearly all his most popular performances as well as some wonderful rarities like the pre-Bocephus original version of "There's a Tear in My Beer." Those who wish to probe deeper are directed toward _Rare Demos: First to Last_ (Country Music Foundation 067), which features twenty-four solo performances, just a man and his guitar, versions substantially scarier than their released counterparts.

Nearly all of Jimmie Rodgers's recordings have been reissued in eight volumes by Rounder Records, and all the Singing Brakeman's output is worth securing. _First Sessions, 1927–1928_ (Rounder 1056) and _The Early Years, 1928–1929_ (Rounder 1057), show that Rodgers arrived full-grown; _On the Way Up, 1929_ (Rounder 1058), _Riding High, 1929–1930_ (Rounder 1059), _America's Blue Yodeler, 1930–1931_

(Rounder 1060), *Down the Old Country Road, 1931–1932* (Rounder 1061), *No Hard Times, 1932* (Rounder 1062) and *Last Sessions, 1933* (Rounder 1063) elaborate on those initial triumphs and set the pattern for the next half century of country music. Those in search of context can hear a few of Rodgers's first recorded cuts on *The Bristol Sessions* (Country Music Foundation 011), an awe-inspiring set of Ralph Peer sessions that also features the Carter Family and twenty-one other performers whose 1927 recordings were a watershed for early country-and-western practitioners. The original Carter Family on their own are best-served by *'Mid the Green Fields of Virginia* (RCA 2772), *On Border Radio* (JEMF 101), and *A Collection of Favorites* (Stetson 3022). Their standard "Can the Circle Be Unbroken" finds its most agreeable home on *Columbia Country Classics Volume 1: The Golden Age* (Columbia 46029), where it keeps company with the likes of Roy Acuff, Bob Wills, and Bill Monroe.

The only performer who taught Jerry Lee more about showstopping than Al Jolson was Moon Mullican, and Mullican's *Seven Nights to Rock: The King Years, 1946–56* (Western 2001) is the best of many good collections now available. Jerry Lee's greatest straight boogie-woogie influence was Merrill Moore, whose double-CD *Boogie My Blues Away* (Bear Family 15505) includes everything he ever recorded for Capitol Records, at least half of it worth hearing.

The Louvin Brothers anticipated Jerry Lee's sacred-secular vacillations, and their early performances most likely heard by a formative Killer are on *Songs That Tell a Story* (Rounder 1030) and *The Louvin Brothers* (Rounder 07). Their greatest recordings did not emerge until Jerry Lee showed up in Memphis; they are on the misnamed *The Best of the Early Louvin Brothers* (Capitol 9608) and the titanic *Tragic Songs of Life* (Rounder 12). Whatever proto-western swing ideas Jerry Lee did not lift from Jimmie Rodgers he first heard from Bob Wills and the Texas Playboys, whose *The Bob Wills Anthology* (CBS 32416) is defini-

tive. Jerry Lee's most fiery honky-tonk began with Jimmie
Rodgers' torch holder and genius in his own right Ernest
Tubb, whose refreshingly impolite _Honky Tonk Classics_
(Rounder 14) is stellar, as are _The Country Music Hall of
Fame_ (MCA 10086) and the massive boxed set _Let's Say
Goodbye Like We Said Hello_ (Bear Family 15498).

What Jerry Lee heard on the radio as a Ferriday wild
child is effectively recreated by _Country U.S.A._, an estima-
ble twenty-three CD set from Time–Life Music (each year
is available separately). Its first seven volumes, covering
1950 to 1956, feature the Killer's original repertoire, from
his uncle's upright all the way to Sam Phillips's spinet.
What most of all made Jerry Lee go to Memphis to insist
that Phillips hear him was hearing the work of Elvis Presley.
The Complete Sun Sessions (RCA 6414) includes nearly everything that has survived from Elvis's thirteen-month tenure as a Sun recording artist, including what seems like ten
thousand alternate versions of "I'm Left, You're Right,
She's Gone." Elvis's finest post-Sun recordings are on _Re-
consider Baby_ (RCA 5418), twelve of his toughest blues
tunes, and _The Complete Burbank Sessions, Vol. 1_ (Audifon
627968), a bootleg that captures the King live in the studio
at the precise moment in 1968 when he became relevant
again.

The amount of great music recorded in such a short
time at the Memphis Recording Service is so massive that it
is not surprising that multivolume sets are needed to tell the
grand stories, each of which is worth at least a book in itself.
Sun Records: The Blues Years (Sun Box 105), nine LPs,
peeks in on Sam Phillips coaxing great performances out of
the likes of Howlin' Wolf, Junior Parker, and dozens of performers almost as colossal; _The Sun Country Years_ (Bear
Family 15211), twelve LPs, focuses on the transition years
before rock and roll changed the rules; _Sun Records: The
Rocking Years_ (Sun Box 106) and _Sun into the Sixties_ (Sun
Box 109) are recommended only to completists.

The top rank of Sun performers have all received the

collections they have earned. Johnny Cash's *The Man in Black* (Bear Family 15517) and *The Classic Carl Perkins* (Bear Family 15494) are both five-CD collections that detail not only their complete Sun output, but how their music changed when they left the label. Roy Orbison's *The Sun Years* (Bear Family 15461), Billy Riley's *Classic Recordings* (Bear Family 15444), Howlin' Wolf's *Memphis Days* (Bear Family 15460/15500), and Charlie Rich's *Original Hits and Midnight Demos* (Charly 10) and *Don't Put No Headstone on My Grave* (Zu-Zazz 2002) state their respective performers' cases with authority.

Jerry Lee's Sun work is best heard in its entirety, something not true of his subsequent work for Smash/Mercury (although the boxed sets are there for those who want or need them). Unfortunately the current nonboxed sets available chronicling those years are incomplete: *Southern Roots* and *The Greatest Live Show on Earth* are currently out of print, and the three CDs called *The Killer* that Poly-Gram fished out of the Bear Family boxes are too idio-syncratic to be of much use. Available now are *Live at the Star-Club* (Bear Family 15467), *The Session* (Mercury 822 751), and a collection of worthwhile oddities and out-takes called *30th Anniversary Album* (Mercury 830 207).

For fans, one of the worst things about the deserved failure of the *Great Balls of Fire* film is that it has brought to a virtual halt the steady stream of worthy Jerry Lee reissues that began a decade earlier. Jerry Lee's post-Mercury cata-log remains a mess, full of indifferent repackages like Curb's must-to-avoid *Best of Jerry Lee Lewis* and some mis-erable recordings produced by Bob Moore on another set worth missing, *Rocket*.

In recent years, Jerry Lee has often been best heard as an influence on other performers. Many try simply to re-produce the Killer's licks and mannerisms, but a few have actually expanded on them. In the mid-seventies, Gary Stewart mixed Jerry Lee's honky-tonk ethics with a more

modern perspective and shot out two magnificent albums—
Out of Hand (Hightone 8026) and _Your Place or Mine_ (RCA
4169)—before he was condemned to repeat Jerry Lee's fate.
More recently Dwight Yoakam has proven himself a worthy
inheritor of Jerry Lee's honky tonk side on _Just Lookin' for
a Hit_ (Reprise 25989) and _If There Was a Way_ (Reprise
26344). Two now-disbanded rock-and-roll groups enlivened
Jerry Lee's spirit. Jason and the Scorchers were a Nashville-
based quartet whose Hank Williams-meets-the-Clash
major-label debut, _Fervor_ (EMI 19008), was steeped in the
contradictions that envelop Jerry Lee; the Georgia Satel-
lites's last and greatest album, _In the Land of Salvation and
Sin_ (Elektra 60887), probed the riddles that still earn the
warning "Think about it." They play their guitars like Jerry Lee played his piano. The tradition continues; the circle
remains unbroken.

Index

Meteor Records, 49
"Mexicali Rose," 110
Meyers, Augie, 176
"Middle Age Crazy," 13, 23, 183
"Milkcow Blues Boogie," 60
"Milkshake Mademoiselle," 81
Miller, Glenn, 110, 191
Miller, Roger, 106, 137
Mitcham, Jane, 43, 45, 53, 64, 90
Mitcham, Jewell, 49
"Mom and Dad's Waltz," 152
Moman, Chips, 194
"Money," 118, 128
Monkees, 152
Moore, Bob, 116, 173, 179, 192
Moore, Merrill, 43
Moore, Scotty, 51, 52, 61
Morricone, Ennio, 119
"Mother, the Queen of My Heart," 162
Motley Crue, 201
Motown Records, 114
"Move It On Over," 38
Muddy Waters, 168
Mullican, Aubrey ("Moon"), 36–7, 44, 50, 70, 98
"My Blue Heaven," 104
"My Bonnie," 109
"My Carolina Sunshine Girl," 71
"My God Is Real," 41, 161
"My God's Not Dead," 160
"My Rough and Rowdy Ways," 31
"Mystery Train," 107, 153, 195

Nashville Teens, 128
"Natural Born Lover," 114
Neff, Jim, 183
Nelson, Rick, 185, 195
Nelson, Willie, 136
Nettles, Bill, 39
Newbury, Mickey, 140, 153
Nichopolous, Dr. George, 197
"Night Train to Memphis," 107, 109
"No Headstone on My Grave," 169, 171
"No Particular Place to Go," 131
"Number One Lovin' Man," 187

O'Connor, Flannery, 32
"Ode to Billy Joe," 183
"Oh Lonesome Me," 152, 158
"The Old Country Church," 182
"The Old Rugged Cross," 160
"Old Time Religion," 70
"Old Time Rock and Roll," 190
"Ole Pal of Yesterday," 66
"Once More with Feeling," 155, 157
"One Has My Name (The Other Has My Heart)," 152
"One Minute Past Eternity," 121, 149
"One More Time," 160
"Ooby Dooby," 74
Orbison, Roy, 48, 51, 68, 74, 81, 97, 140, 194–95
"Out of My Mind," 146
"Over the Rainbow," 191–92, 202
Owens, Buck, 131, 140, 143, 155
Owens, Doodle, 162

Paley, Andy, 14–6, 19, 21, 23–6
"Paralyzed," 58
Parker, Junior. See *Little Junior's Blue Flames*.
Pate, Jaren, 150
Patton, Charley, 37
Paul, Les, 52, 63
Payne, Leon, 63, 116
Peer, Ralph, 48
"Pen and Paper," 127
Pepper, Marvin, **79**
Perkins, Carl, 16, 48, 53–8, 64, 68, 72, 75, 81, 84, 129, 192, 194; **76, 176**
Perkins, Clay, 55
Phillips, Jud, **117**
Phillips, Sam, 11–2, 16–7, 24, 44, 48, 50, 55–9, 61, 69, 80, 85, 88, 90, 97, 100–03, 105–06, 109–11, 114, 121–23, 128, 149, 195, 204; **82, 111, 114**
  as a talent scout, 48, 77
  belief in "Whole Lottá Shakin' Going On," 67–8
  production method, 74–5, 77, 85, 98–9, 112, 115, 118, 121
Pierce Webb, 47, 146
"Pinetop's Boogie Woogie," 35
"Pink Pedal Pushers," 84
"Play Me a Song I Can Cry To," 144
"Please Don't Talk About Me When I'm Gone," 163
Poison, 201
Pomus, Doc, 117
Porter, Bob, 183
Presley, Elvis, 12, 16, 19–20, 30, 43–5, 48–9, 51, 53–4, 56, 58, 60, 63, 67, 75, 89, 98, 113–14, 126, 185, 192–95, 206; **76**
Price, Ray, 22, 47, 100
Pride, Charley, 26
Prince, 41, 204
"Proud Mary," 83
"Pumpin' Piano Rock," 70
"Put Me Down," 85, 87, 89
"Put Your Cat Clothes On," 55
Pyle, Gomer, 14

Quaid, Dennis, 27

"Ramblin' Rose," 118
"Raunchy," 97
RCA Records, 48
Reagan, Ronald, 112
"Real Wild Child," 88
Reeves, Jim, 152
"Release Me," 100
"Remember Me (I'm the One Who Loves You)," 180
"The Return of Jerry Lee," 90
"Reuben James," 156
"Revolutionary Man," 177
Rich, Charlie, 88, 97, 106–07, 123, 127, 131, 142, 166, 169, 188
Riley, Billy Lee, 16, 50–1, 59, 78, 81, 87, 106
"Ring of Fire," 136
"Rip It Up," 58, 157
"Rita May," 187
Ritter, Tex, 21
Robbins, Marty, 71

About the Author

Jimmy Guterman is the author of *12 Days on The Road* (with Noel Monk), *Sinéad*, and *The Worst Rock and Roll Records of All Time* (with Owen O'Donnell). He has written for *Rolling Stone*, *Spy*, *The Journal of Country Music*, *PC Week*, and many other publications. He has compiled and annotated reissue records for many record companies, including a collection of Jerry Lee Lewis's Elektra recordings, released by Warner Brothers. His current projects include a study of the United States peace movement during the Gulf War, a novel about the pop-music industry, and a screenplay based on the Shusaku Endo novel *Silence*.